GLAVNOE UPRAVLENIE GIDROMETEOROLOGICHESKOI SLUZHBY
PRI SOVETE MINISTROV SSSR · INSTITUT EKSPERIMENTAL'NOI METEOROLOGII

Main Administration of the Hydrometeorological Service, Council
of Ministers of the USSR · Institute of Experimental Meteorology

Proceedings Nos. 21, 25

K. P. Makhon'ko and S. G. Malakhov, Editors

NUCLEAR METEOROLOGY

(Yadernaya meteorologiya)

Proceedings of the All-Union Conference
on Nuclear Meteorology Held at
Obninsk, 23—28 June 1969

Gidrometeoizdat
Moskva, 1971, 1972

Translated from Russian

Israel Program of Scientific Translations
Jerusalem 1974

Contents

iii

III. RADIOACTIVE PARTICLES DURING NUCLEAR BURSTS IN THE TROPOSPHERE

IV. PROCESSES OF ATMOSPHERIC SCAVENGING

V. NATURAL RADIOACTIVITY OF THE ATMOSPHERE

VI. EQUIPMENT AND METHODS FOR THE STUDY OF RADIOACTIVE CONTAMINATION IN THE ENVIRONMENT

FOREWORD

The papers in this collection were read at the All-Union Conference on Nuclear Meteorology held on 23 — 28 June 1969 at the Institute of Experimental Meteorology in the town of Obninsk. The Conference was organized by the Main Administration of the USSR Hydrometeorological Service.

The following are the main topics discussed at the Conference:
a) utilization of radioactive tracers in meteorological investigations;
b) global contamination of the atmosphere and fallout of radioactive products of nuclear blasts;
c) natural radioactivity of the atmosphere;
d) atmospheric scavenging of radioactive contaminants;
e) formation of radioactive aerosols and their properties;
f) equipment and procedures used for studying radioactive contamination of the environment.

During the sessions of the various sections, other questions relating to the accumulation of radioactive products of nuclear blasts on the earth's surface were also examined.

The collection will interest specialists of environmental pollution control, scientists in the field of nuclear geophysics, engineers specializing in the construction and operation of instruments for measuring the radioactivity of air, water and soil, workers in radiological and radiochemical laboratories, as well as postgraduate students in related fields.

I. GLOBAL POLLUTION OF THE ATMOSPHERE AND FALLOUT OF NUCLEAR BLAST PRODUCTS

UDC 551.510.7

VERTICAL DISTRIBUTION OF RADIOACTIVE AEROSOLS IN THE TROPOSPHERE OVER THE EUROPEAN USSR IN 1964–1967

L. E. Nazarov, L. A. Volokitina, Ya. I. Gaziev,
A. F. Kuzenkov, S. G. Malakhov, and A. S. Vasil'ev

Data are given on the vertical distribution of the concentration of decay products of radon and aerosol products of nuclear blasts in the troposphere over the USSR in 1964–1967. Aerosynoptic analysis of cases of considerable growth and decrease in the concentration of fission products in the ground air layer in the vicinity of Moscow established that the drift of stratospheric aerosols into the upper troposphere takes place at the tropopause discontinuity or funnel at the cyclonic periphery of the jet. At ground level the radioactive spot appears most frequently beneath the anticyclonic periphery of the jet. Examination of the simplest theoretical models of the vertical concentration distribution of fission products and short-lived decay products of radon in the troposphere yields the coefficient of vertical turbulent diffusion k_z and speed of vertical ordered motion ω, whose values are given.

The vertical distribution of the concentration of the decay products of radon and the aerosol products of nuclear blasts in the troposphere over the USSR was studied in 1964–1967 by means of samples taken by LI-2, IL-14 and IL-18 aircraft with special aerosol collectors on Petraynov filters. The dynamic head created by the aircraft motion was used as the force to drive the air through the filter. The rate of air flow was measured by a discharge washer or a Pitot tube. Samples were taken at heights between 1 and 10–11 km.

As a rule, the concentration of radioactive aerosols was determined from the total β-activity of the samples, using the calibration preparation $Sr^{90} + Y^{90}$. The concentration of short-lived decay products of radon was determined from the filter activity after 1–1.5 hours, and the concentration of the fission products several days after samples were taken. The analysis of the decay curve of the β-activity of the filter was followed in many cases by a gamma-spectral and radiochemical analysis of the aerosol samples following procedures described elsewhere /2, 9/.

§1. VERTICAL DISTRIBUTION OF THE CONCENTRATION OF DECAY PRODUCTS OF RADON AND FISSION PRODUCTS IN THE TROPOSPHERE

Three series of measurements of the vertical concentration distribution of fission products in the troposphere were conducted in all. In the first series, the concentration of the short-lived decay products of radon and the fission products were measured simultaneously in the 1–5-km layer at 1-km intervals within a radius of 300 km around Moscow during summer

TABLE 1. Measurements of concentration (10^{-12} curie/m³) of short-lived decay products of Rn and β-radioactive fission products in the atmosphere near Moscow during different periods of 1964

Sounding level, km	3 July A	8 July —	10 July D	14 July D	15 July D	16 July A	17 July —	18 July —	28 July D	20 Nov. A	2 Dec. —	2 Dec. —	3 Dec. —	25 Dec. —
5	13.0/3.0	4.0	1.6/1.4	11.0/1.3	10.0/2.3	18.0/2.6	18.0/3.5	1.5	6.5/1.5	11.0/0.3	3.0/0.3	5.0/0.5	3.0/0.7	3.0/0.4
4	7.0/1.0		0.2/1.6	9.0/0.7	7.0/1.2	11.0/1.3	3.0/0.5	0.6	4.0/1.0	6.0/0.2	7.0/0.2	8.0/0.3	7.0/0.2	6.0/0.3
3	10.0/0.7		0.6/1.4	12.0/1.3	11.0/1.0	14.0/0.1	6.0/0.7	0.6	5.0/0.8	8.0/0.2	12.0/0.1	4.0/0.1	6.0/0.2	7.0/0.2
2	13.0/0.8	1.0	1.1/1.1	31.0/1.2	6.0/0.6	12.0/0.4	7.0/0.4	2.3	10.0/0.6	15.0/0.2	5.0/0.3		26.0/0.1	10.0/0.2
1	28.0/1.1		2.6/0.9	48.0/1.2	52.0/1.6	9.5/0.3	6.0/1.5	2.0	21.4/0.5	12.0/0.1	8.0	16.0/0.2	42.0/0.1	12.0/0.1

Note. D denotes descending and A ascending air motions; Rn values are given in the numerator and β in the denominator.

2

and autumn of 1964. In the course of this series fourteen vertical concentration profiles of radioactive aerosols were obtained in the lower troposphere. The results are presented in Table 1, where the volume concentration is given without correction for changes in air density with altitude.

The second series of measurements were conducted from November 1964 to April 1965, also in the vicinity of Moscow. The samples were taken in the middle and upper troposphere and in the lower stratosphere at altitudes of $6-7$, $8-9$, and $10-12$ km. In this case the concentration of the fission products only was measured. During the measurements, 18 samples were taken at $6-7$ km, 61 at $8-9$ km, and 34 at $11-12$ km. The concentration of sums of β-active fission products was measured simultaneously in the ground air layer, as well as the fallout of these products from the atmosphere. The procedure of such measurements was described in /7/. This allowed one to estimate the rate of cleansing of the atmosphere (km/day) in the form of the ratio of the daily fallout to the ground concentration of fission products. The results of the second series of observations are shown in Table 2. All the data are given in relative units, the unit being the concentration of fission products in 1 kg air at the surface. Besides, the vertical profiles of the concentration were averaged over periods of 1—2 weeks.

TABLE 2. Vertical distribution of the concentrations of fission products in the atmosphere in the vicinity of Moscow

Date	Concentration per unit air mass at various levels, km			Rate of atmospheric cleansing, km/day	Mean precipitation, mm/day
	6.5	9	11.5		
1964					
11 — 13 November	6.0	6.5	41	2.0	0.8
17 — 20 November	13	240	520	3.2	2.3
23 — 24 November	16	70	116	1.4	0.7
8 — 11 December	5.6	5.4	49	1.0	1.2
17 — 29 December	39	172	234	2.1	1.6
1965					
25 — 30 January	4.0	13	119	0.6	0.0
1 — 11 February	22	113	415	1.45	0.8
11 — 31 March	—	65	415	0.5	0.3
6 — 13 April	—	7.8	26	0.5	0.0

Note. Here and below, a dash indicates that no measurements were taken.

In the third measurement series, the concentrations of fission products and of short-lived decay byproducts of radon were determined at heights of 1—10 km during 1966—1967 (Table 3). The measurements were conducted sporadically over the eastern part of Ukraine and in the Moscow region in different tropospheric layers. Of great interest in this series are data on the concentration of short-lived decay byproducts of radon in the middle and upper troposphere. As known, there are practically no data in the literature about the concentration of radon in the troposphere above 5—6 km.

TABLE 3. Concentration of short-lived decay products of radon (10^{-12} curie/kg) in the troposphere over European USSR

Date	Average height, km				
	1—2	2—4	4—6	6—8	8—10
1966					
7 July	—	—	17	15	15
22 July	56	19	10	—	—
24 July	—	17	11	12	16
27 July	24	27	13	7	2
28 July	13	3	—	2	2
1967					
29 January	45	20	—	16	4
9 February	—	—	8	3	4

In all cases of the first series of observations and in most cases of the third series the measurements were conducted within the troposphere, i. e., the tropopause lay above the sampling region. In the second series of observations the tropopause frequently lay between the sampling levels. This made it possible to investigate the influence of the tropopause on the vertical distribution of the concentration of fission products. All the data obtained during the second series were split into two groups. The first group consisted of cases in which the tropopause lay between 7 and 9 km in the sampling period. The second group consisted of cases in which the tropopause level was between 9 and 11 km. The third group consisted of cases when the tropopause was situated above the sampling level. The results of such experimental data processing are presented in Table 4. It follows that the height of the tropopause plays an important part in the formation of the vertical concentration profile of fission products in the atmosphere. As a rule, the largest concentration growth is observed between the levels within which the tropopause lies. It was also found that, on the average, a lower tropopause is accompanied by a higher cleansing rate of the troposphere for the same levels of atmospheric precipitation (measurement groups 1 and 3).

TABLE 4. Vertical distribution of fission product concentration in the atmosphere in the Moscow region as a function of tropospheric height

Group	Level, km			Rate of atmospheric cleansing, km/day	Average precipitation, mm/day
	6.5	9	11.5		
1	9.5	117	182	2.0	1.4
2	11	20.2	152	2.1	0.7
3	6.2	7.24	13.6	0.8	1.6

Note. The concentration per unit air mass at ground level is taken as unity.

Analysis of the vertical distributions of the concentrations of fission products and byproducts of radon decay in the troposphere (the first and third series of observations) established that in roughly more than half of the cases this distribution can be approximated by an exponential function. The concentration of the decay products of radon decreases monotonically with altitude, while the concentration of fission products increases monotonically. Examples of such an approximation can be seen on Figure 1, plotted on a logarithmic scale.

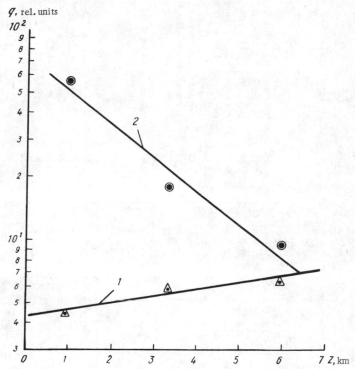

FIGURE 1. Examples of evaluation of a and b from vertical profiles of Rn and fission products:

1) Rn, $b = + 0.08 \text{ km}^{-1}$; 2) fission products, $a = - 0.35 \text{ km}^{-1}$.

TABLE 5. Evaluation of a and b (km^{-1}) for the vertical distribution of the concentration of decay products of radon and fission products in the lower troposphere (1964)

Date	Height, km	a	b	Date	Height, km	a	b
3 July	1—4	−0.55		28 July	1—4	−0.69	
	2—5		0.69*		1—4		0.20
8 July	2—5	.	0.46	20 Nov.	1—4	−0.15	
10 July	1—4	−0.92			1—5		0.34*
	1—5		0.20	3 Dec.	1—5	−0.69	
14 July	1—4	−0.62	0.45	25 Dec.	1—5		0.46
15 July	1—4	−1.4*			1—5	−0.28	
	2—5		0.46		1—5		0.31

* A considerable scatter of points is observed.

5

TABLE 6. Exponents a and b (km^{-1}) for the vertical distribution of the concentrations of the decay products of radon and the fission products in the troposphere over European USSR in 1966−1967

Region of observations	Date	Sampling altitude, km	Tropopause altitude, km	a	b	Data of GMTs of GUGMS on the vertical motions in the 1−5-km layer
Eastern Ukraine	1966					
	9 July	1 — 6	11.5 16.4	−0.25	+0.25	Weak ascending − (5−15) mbar/12 hr
	9 July	6 — 9		−	0.13	The same
	22 July	1 — 6	11.0	−0.35	0.08	Descending +(20−55) mbar/12 hr
	27 July	2 — 6	10.8 15.2	−0.23	0.05	Descending +(10−25) mbar/12 hr
	28 July	1 — 5	10.8	−0.60	0.0	Descending +(30−60) mbar/12 hr
	28 July	5 — 10	11.0	0.09	0.35	The same
	30 July	2 — 6		−0.13	0.17	Descending (1.5-km level) +20 mbar/12 hr
	30 July	6 — 9		−0.53	0.17	The same (5.0-km level) +0 mbar/12 hr
	3 August	3.5 — 8.5	10.5	0.23	0.05	Descending +(15−25) mbar/12 hr
	28 August	7.0 — 9.0	11.6	−0.23	0.46	
	30 August	3.5 — 8.0	12.8	−0.34	0.07	Descending +(20—30) mbar/12 hr
Vicinity of Moscow	1967					
	25 July	2.5 — 8.5	10.6	−0.07	0.17	Ascending − (13−28) mbar/12 hr
	27 July	2.5 — 9.0	10.4	−0.23	0.13	Weak ascending − (0.7 − 0.4) mbar/12 hr
	31 July	1.0 — 9.0	10.3	−0.23	0.23	Ascending − (25−49) mbar/12 hr
	9 February	4.5 — 10.0	10.1	−0.14	0.23	Ascending − (24−40) mbar/12 hr
	29 January	1.0 — 6.0	10.6	−0.15	0.23	3 km − 30 mbar/12 hr; 5 km − 0.0 mbar/12 hr
	29 January	8.0 — 10.0		−1.0	+2.0	The same
Eastern Ukraine	9 July	2.0 — 6.0	11.0	−0.34	+0.19	Descending + 20 mbar/12 hr

Table 5 gives values of the exponents for the decay products of radon (*b*) and for the fission products (*a*). It must be kept in mind that these quantities correspond to volume concentrations of the radioactive aerosols, obtained without allowing for changes in air density with altitude. The exponents in Table 6 correspond to allowance for changes in mass concentration of radioactive aerosols with height. The series of vertical distributions of radioactive aerosol concentrations in the troposphere, obtained in the third series of observations, is approximated by two exponents, which differ for the different altitude ranges.

The second half of the vertical concentration profiles of fission products and decay products of radon in the troposphere has a more complex character.

The concentrations of radioactive aerosols in the different layers of the troposphere can be very different, and the vertical distribution itself can be nonmonotonic. Concentration maxima or minima are noted at different altitudes and in some cases an opposite change in concentration with altitude is observed, i.e., the radon concentration increases with height, while the fission product concentration decreases. We cite as an example the cases observed on 16 and 17 July 1964.

Such vertical profiles indicate a stratified structure of the toposphere; each layer has specific features in its prehistory, and in the given case the part played by the advection of the various air masses at different altitudes in the troposphere is large.

TABLE 7. Concentration of isotopes q $(10^{-5}$ curie/kg) in the troposphere in the vicinity of Moscow (averaged values)

Isotope	Height, km	q
Summer 1966—1968		
Pb^{210}	0	7
	1.0	5.7
	5.0	4.7
	7.0	1.5
	8.5	3.5
Summer 1966		
Ce^{144}	1	7.0
	5	33
	6.5	36
	8.0	28
	9.5	98
Summer 1966		
Cs^{137}	1.0	9
	5.0	18
	6.5	12
	8.0	20
	9.5	47

Table 7 gives the results of the gamma-spectral and radiochemical analysis of the aerosol samples. The results, averaged over a considerable period of time for different altitudes, indicate that the nature of the vertical distribution of isotope concentrations has much in common with similar distributions obtained from the total beta-activity of the samples.

§2. AEROSYNOPTIC ANALYSIS OF CASES OF CONSIDERABLE GROWTH AND DECREASE IN FISSION PRODUCT CONCENTRATION IN THE GROUND AIR LAYER NEAR MOSCOW

Time fluctuations in the concentration of fission products in the atmosphere at 6.5, 9 and 11.5 km, obtained during the second series of observations, were used in the aerosynoptic analysis of the causes of the vertical growth and decrease in the concentration of these products.
The cases for analysis were selected visually from the data presented on Figure 2.

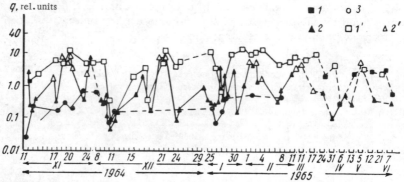

FIGURE 2. Concentration fluctuations of fission products as a function of the height and time of measurements:

1) 11—12 km; 2) 7—9 km; 3) 6 km; 1', 2') measurements in the tropopause region and above.

A considerable increase in concentration at some level of the atmosphere occurred in the periods 17—18 November and 21—22 December 1964, 1—2 and 10—11 February 1965; a considerable decrease in concentration was observed in the periods 10—11 November and 23—24 December 1964. From 17 to 18 November 1964 over Moscow there was observed an intense increase in the concentration of artificial radioactivity, simultaneously at all measurement levels. The tropopause height on 18 November over Moscow dropped from 286 to 367 mbar, whence it follows that the 11.5-km level lay in the lower stratosphere, the 9-km layer in the tropopause layer, and the 6.5-km level in the troposphere. Thus, in the period 17 to 18 November 1964 there occurred a simultaneous increase in concentration in the lower stratosphere, and in the upper and middle troposphere. The analysis of baric topography charts showed that on 18 November the tropopause dropped sharply owing to the advection of cold air on the cyclonic periphery of the tropospheric jet stream approaching Moscow.

At 1500 hrs on 18 November, a high frontal zone (HFZ) adjoining the tropopause in the jet zone passed over Moscow. These aerosynoptic conditions probably contributed to the penetration of radioactive aerosols of stratospheric origin into the troposphere /4/ and to the simultaneous concentration increase in both the lower stratosphere and the upper and middle troposphere.

In the course of the four days 19 to 22 December 1964, a considerable increase in the concentration of the activity occurred in the lower stratosphere (11.5 km) over Moscow, accompanied by a simultaneous increase in concentration at the 9-km level. The tropopause height over Moscow in these days dropped continuously from 234 mbar at 0300 hrs on 19 December to 366 mbar at 1500 hrs on 22 December. As a result the 9-km (300-mbar) level lay in the tropopause layer, which contributed to the rapid penetration of stratospheric radioactive aerosols at that level. The lowering of the tropopause occurred, as in the preceding case, owing to the advection of cold, caused by the approach to Moscow of a powerful HFZ and the passage of a current with wind speeds at the axis attaining 60 m/sec.

Similar situations were also observed in many other instances of rapid growth of concentration levels of fission products in the troposphere. This corroborates the known mechanism /4, 10/ of rapid transfer of stratospheric air masses to the troposphere during a sharp lowering of the tropopause associated with the passage of baroclinic perturbations in the troposphere. These phenomena take place when the cyclonic periphery of the jet stream passes over the measurement region.

This conclusion agrees with data on ozone. It was shown /1, 3/ that the total amount of ozone in the atmosphere over the observation point increases to above its normal level at the cyclonic periphery of the jet stream and decreases below its normal level at the anticyclonic side of the stream.

In periods of low concentration of radioactive fission products in the troposphere from 10 to 11 November 1964, the tropopause height increased owing to the advection of heat. This occurred in the zone of the anticyclonic periphery of a powerful jet stream moving toward Moscow at up to 90 m/sec at the axis. The anticyclonic periphery, unlike the cyclonic periphery of the jet, is characterized by lower turbulence and lower vertical mixing. The rise of the tropopause and weakening of the vertical exchange in the anticyclonic periphery of the jet were probably responsible for the decreased concentration in the troposphere at a height of 9 km over Moscow.

The investigations conducted above were supplemented by an analysis of time fluctuations in our ground-level concentrations of fission products in the vicinity of Moscow in 1965 — 1966. In order to eliminate the seasonal effect we used not the absolute values of the concentration, but the deviations in the daily concentration from the average monthly values ($\Delta q = q_{\mathrm{d}} - Q_{\mathrm{av.m}}$ curie/m^3). The fluctuations in concentration were compared with the passage of the jet streams through the measurement region.

The jet streams were found from the daily baric topography charts: the extratropical streams from the 500- and 300-mbar absolute-topography charts, and the subtropical ones from the 200-mbar charts. It was established that the passage of jet streams is accompanied in only 20 — 40% of

9

cases by a substantial growth in the ground-level concentration of fission products (by a factor larger than 1.5) in the first three days. In other cases the passage of the stream can be accompanied either by very weak growth in concentration or even by a drop. According to Koptsevich /6/, the growth in ground concentrations usually takes place under the anticyclonic periphery of the jet.

One cause for the low concentration of fission products at ground level during the passage of the jet is possibly the location of the measurement region below the cyclonic periphery of the jet stream. Radioactive fission products entering the upper troposphere under the cyclonic periphery of the jet penetrate the ground layer only under the anticyclonic periphery of the jet, together with the descending currents /6/. If we start from this assumption, we must seek a linear correlation between the increase in fission product concentration at ground level and the passage of the anticyclonic periphery of the jet above the measurement region.

The approach of the anticyclonic periphery of the jet can be determined from the increased geopotential height and the temperature of the 300-mbar surface. This surface was selected, since the extratropical and subtropical streams at this surface will be necessarily observed. For control purposes all the calculations were conducted in parallel for the 100-mb surface as well (Table 8). The correlation coefficients were calculated for two seasons of the year for daily changes in the concentration of the sum of β-active substances in the air at ground level (Δq_d) as a function of daily changes in geopotential height and the temperature of the 300-mb isobaric surface, expressed as deviations from the mean monthly values ($\Delta H_{gp.m}$ and $\Delta t\,°C$).

TABLE 8. Correlation coefficients between the daily changes in the geopotential height ($\Delta H_{gp.m}$) and temperature ($\Delta t\,°C$) of the 300-mbar surface and the daily changes in concentration of the total β-activity (Δq_d)

Season	$\Delta H_{gp.m}$ and Δq_d	Number of cases	$\Delta t\,°C$ and Δq_d	Number of cases
Summer, 1966	0.68	24	0.67	23
Winter, 1965	0.71	17	0.72	15

The fairly high correlation coefficients corroborate the existence of a linear correlation between the growth in concentration of β-activity of the fission products at ground level and the increase in the height and temperature at the 300-mb surface during the passage of the stream. However, these coefficients should be considered as approximate due to the limited amount of data. A similar relationship was not detected for the 100-mb isobaric surface. The correlation between these values was also checked separately for those days on which no streams passed over Moscow, to ensure that the effect of growth of activity at ground level cannot be attributed solely to the increase in the pressure and temperature at the 300-mb level. It was found that no linear correlation exists in this case.

To sum up, the transfer of stratospheric aerosols into the upper troposphere occurs at the discontinuity or funnel of the tropopause at the cyclonic periphery of the jet. At ground level the radioactive spot occurs most frequently under the anticyclonic periphery of the jet, characterized by an

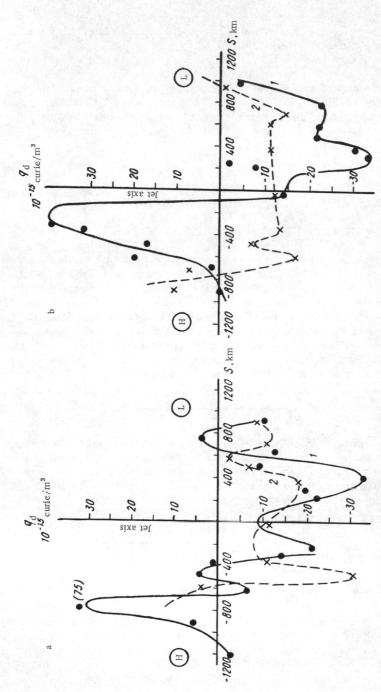

FIGURE 3. Concentration fluctuations in fission products in the ground air level at different distances from the jet stream (JS) axis:

a) spring; b) summer; H) anticyclone; L) cyclone; 1) extratropical JS; 2) subtropical JS.

11

increased geopotential height of the 300-mb surface and of the temperature at that surface.

The transfer in the stratosphere to the ground level evidently takes place from the cyclonic to the anticyclonic periphery, where descending air currents bring them to the ground.

To illustrate this important conclusion, we give on Figure 3 horizontal sections of the fields of ground concentration directed perpendicular to the jet axis for the extratropical and subtropical jets, separately for the spring and summer of 1965 and 1966. It is clear from Figure 3 that the largest increase in radioactivity at ground level takes place under the anticyclonic periphery of the jet at a distance of 300—800 km from the jet axis.

§3. SIMPLEST THEORETICAL MODELS OF THE
VERTICAL DISTRIBUTION OF THE CONCENTRATIONS
OF FISSION PRODUCTS AND SHORT-LIVED DECAY
PRODUCTS OF RADON IN THE TROPOSPHERE

Consider now the simplest theoretical model, a one-dimensional steady-state model, of the vertical distribution in the troposphere of radon and fission products, which would allow for the influence of vertical turbulent exchange and the speed of vertical ordered motion in the lower troposphere.

We shall assume that the coefficient of vertical turbulent diffusion k_z is independent of height, and the speed of vertical ordered motion $w = $ const. The variation in air density with height is approximated by an exponential law with exponent $C = -0.12\,\text{km}^{-1}$. The equation of vertical transfer of radioactive substances in the atmosphere is then expressible in the form

$$k_z \frac{d^2q}{dz^2} - (w + k_z C)\frac{dq}{dz} - (\lambda + \sigma)q = 0. \qquad (1)$$

Here q is the concentration of radioactive admixtures per unit air mass; λ is the radioactive decay constant; $\sigma = 1/\tau$, where τ is the average time of residence of radioactive isotopes in the lower troposphere. The general solution to equation (1) is

$$q = A \exp \frac{1}{2}\left[C + \frac{w}{k_z} + \sqrt{\left(C + \frac{w}{k_z}\right)^2 + \frac{4(\lambda + \sigma)}{k_z}}\right]z +$$
$$+ B \exp \frac{1}{2}\left[C + \frac{w}{k_z} - \sqrt{\left(C + \frac{w}{k_z}\right)^2 + \frac{4(\lambda + \sigma)}{k_z}}\right]z. \qquad (2)$$

For radon, $\lambda = 2.1 \times 10^{-6}\,\text{sec}^{-1}$ and $\sigma = 0$. For the fission products we set $\lambda = 0$.

Since the concentration of radon decreases with height and tends to zero at high altitudes, its vertical distribution can be described by restricting ourselves to the second term in (2) ($q \to 0$ for $z \to \infty$). The following simplifications are introduced to simplify calculations. Since the concentration of fission products increases with height, when describing the vertical distribution of fission products in the troposphere we restrict ourselves to the first term in formula (2) ($B = 0$). This simplifies considerably all our calculations, although it obviously introduces some errors, which are neglected in view of the tentative character of the calculations.

For the decay products of radon we then obtain

$$-2a = C + \frac{w}{k_z} - \sqrt{\left(C + \frac{w}{k_z}\right)^2 + \frac{4\lambda}{k_z}} \qquad (3)$$

and for the fission products in the washout layer

$$2b = C + \frac{w}{k_z} + \sqrt{\left(C + \frac{w}{k_z}\right)^2 + \frac{4\lambda}{k_z}}. \qquad (4)$$

In the atmosphere above the washout layer, $\sigma = 0$ and

$$b = C + \frac{w}{k_z}. \qquad (5)$$

Expressions (3)—(5) can be used to evaluate k_z and w in the troposphere. Use is made of Tables 5 and 6, since the mean lifetime of radioactive fission products in the washout layer is several days /5, 8/, i.e., σ is of the same order as λ and we can set $\sigma = \lambda$. Then, for the washout layer,

$$\frac{w}{k_z} = a + b, \quad k_z = \frac{\sigma}{-ab}. \qquad (6)$$

In the troposphere above the washout layer w/k_z is easily evaluated by formula (5), after which k_z, and therefore w, can be determined from formula (3).

TABLE 9. Evaluation of w and k_z in the lower troposphere in the vicinity of Moscow (1964)

Date	w, cm/sec	k_z, m²/sec	k_z, m²/sec for $w = 0$
1	2	3	4
3 July	+ 0.1	5.5	7
10 July	− 0.3	11.4	2.5
14 July	− 0.1	7.5	5.5
15 July	− 0.3	3.2	1.0
28 July	− 0.4	10.0	4.3
20 November	+ 0.5	53.0	100
3 December	− 0.2	6.5	4.3
25 December	0	23.0	27.0

Note. The + sign indicates ascending motions and the − sign descending motions.

Evaluations of w and k_z for the first and third measurement series are given in Tables 9 and 10 (the second and third columns in Table 9, the fourth and fifth in Table 10). In establishing Table 9 we took C as zero, since

13

in that case the change in air density with altitude was disregarded in the measurements. When the vertical concentration profile was approximated by two exponents, solutions (3) — (6) were applied to each layer separately and independently. This is associated with the fact that our solution is one-dimensional and it makes no sense to equate streams at the boundary of two layers with different values of w, due to the impossibility of allowing for the advection.

TABLE 10. Values of w and k_z for measurements of the third series (1966— 1967, European USSR)

Measurement region	Date	Height, km	w, cm/sec	k_z, m^2/sec	w, cm/sec, from meteo-data (1—5-km layer)	k_z, m^2/sec for $w = 0$
	1966					
Eastern Ukraine	9 July	1—6	0	23	+0.2	23
	22 July	1—6	—3.0	75	—0.7	16
	27 July	2—6	—3.7	130	—0.4	26
		6—10	+0.4	9	—	—
	28 July	1—5*	—	—	—1.1	5.0
		5—10	+1.0	50	—	—
	30 July	2—6	—0.8	100	—0.2	68
		6—9	0	5.5	—	—
	3 August	3.5—8.5	—0.2	33	—0.4	—
	30 August	3.5—8.0	—0.1	15	—0.4	—
	27 August	7.0—9.0	+0.5	16	—	—
	1967					
Moscow region	9 July	2.0—6.0	—0.9	32	—0.4	14
	25 July	2.5—8.5	+1.0	200	+0.4	200
	27 July	2.5—9.0	0	25	0	—
	31 July	1.0—9.0	+0.2**	21	+0.7	—
	29 January	1.0—6.0	+0.7	60	+0.3	50
	9 February	4.5—10.0	+0.20	23	+0.6	—

* The determination of w and k_z is impossible, since $b = 0$.
** If we compute separately for the washout layer (1—6 km) we obtain descending currents.

We selected as washout layer the layer extending up to 5—6 km. This was dictated by the conditions and frequency of our measurements at different heights. An interesting conclusion follows from the data of Tables 9 and 10. In a large majority of cases the signs of the calculated vertical air speed coincide with the directions of vertical speeds determined by the USSR Hydrometeorological Center.

Attempts at a quantitative comparison of the calculated vertical air speeds with the data of the Center (Table 10, columns 4 and 6) yield discrepancies of several orders of magnitude. It is true that the transition from speed expressed in mbar/12 hr to speed in cm/sec was approximate, since the air density value was taken in all cases for the standard atmosphere. The following fact can be advanced as regards the first series of measurements. According to the map of vertical motions of the USSR Hydrometeorological Center, on 10 July 1964 there were observed at the 700-mb level descending motions of magnitude 132 mbar/12 hr, or roughly 1.7 cm/sec. This is approximately twice the value given in Table 3. Subsequently, i. e., on 14 — 15 July, the speeds of the descending motions decreased. The trend to a decrease during this period is also evident from Table 3.

All these facts point to the considerable sensitivity of the vertical concentration distributions of fission products in the troposphere as regards the sign and magnitude of ordered vertical motions. As a rule, in descending motions the vertical gradient of the concentration of decay products of radon increases, while the vertical gradient of the concentration of fission products decreases. The concentration of decay products of radon is much more sensitive to vertical currents than the concentration of fission products.

In the literature, the vertical concentration profiles of radon in the lower troposphere are frequently used for estimating the value of k_z. The vertical ordered motions are neglected, i. e., it is assumed that $w = 0$. To test this assumption, we cite in Tables 9 and 10 the results of evaluating k_z with the aid of formula (3) for $w = 0$. In all cases of descending motions the corresponding value of k_z is somewhat lower than the value determined taking into account that $w \neq 0$. These differences increase as a rule with increase in descending motions. An opposite, but less clearcut relationship is observed in the case of ascending motions.

We also attempted to use equations (3) and (4) to evaluate σ, assuming that $w = 0$. In all cases of considerable descending motions the values of σ were very low, and hardly corresponded to real cases ($\tau = 40 - 80$ days), probably due to the erroneous assumption $w = 0$. When the values of w did not exceed ± 0.2 cm/sec, the values differed little from each other and were equal on the average to $1.9 - 0.9 \cdot 10^{-6}$ sec^{-1} (five cases). This is near to the value of λ for the decay products of radon and corroborates the truth of our assumption ($\sigma = \lambda$).

Note in conclusion that the refinement of the theoretical model of the vertical distribution of radioactive substances in the atmosphere can lead to satisfactory agreement with measured values not only as regards the sign of the vertical speed, but also as regard its magnitude. This will also be of great importance for meteorology. In particular, it is better to use to that end the decay products of thoron, and not the fission products, especially for the lower troposphere.

BIBLIOGRAPHY

1. Vasin, E. F. and K. N. Vorob'ev. K voprosu raspredeleniya obshchego soderzhaniya ozona v struinykh techeniyakh (Concerning the Distribution of the Total Ozone Content in Jet Streams). — Trudy GGO, No. 184. 1966.
2. Vilenskii, V. D. and V. I. Baranov. Opredelenie dolgozhivushchikh β-izluchatelei v atmosfernykh vypadeniyakh (Determination of Long-lived β-Emitters in Atmospheric Fallout). — Radiokhimiya, Vol. 4, No. 4. 1962.

3. Gushchin, G. P. and I. A. Shatunov. Atmosfernyi ozon i struinye techeniya (Atmospheric Ozone and Jet Streams). — Trudy GGO, No. 154. 1964.

4. Dmitrieva, G. V. and V. N. Kasatkina. Aerosinopticheskie usloviya poyavleniya u poverkhnosti zemli oblastei povyshennykh kontsentratsii stratosfernykh vypadenii radioaktivnykh produktov (Aerosynoptic Conditions Governing the Appearance at the Earth's Surface of Regions of Increased Concentration of Stratospheric Fallout of Radioactive Products). — In: "Radioaktivnye izotopy v atmosfere i ikh ispol'zovanie v meteorologii" ("Radioactive Isotopes in the Atmosphere and their Utilization in Meteorology"). Moskva, Atomizdat. 1965.

5. Karol', I. L. and V. D. Vilenskii. Otsenki parametrov vertikal'nogo obmena i srednei skorosti udaleniya aerozolei oblakami i osadkami v nizhnei chasti troposfery po dannym o estestvennoi radioaktivnosti prizemnogo vozdukha (Evaluation of Vertical Exchange Parameters and the Mean Rate of Aerosol Removal by Clouds and Precipitation in the Lower Troposphere on the Basis of Data about the Natural Radioactivity of Ground Level Air). — In: "Radioaktivnye izotopy v atmosfere i ikh ispol'zovanie v meteorologii" ("Radioactive Isotopes in the Atmosphere and their Utilization in Meteorology"). Moskva, Atomizdat. 1965.

6. Koptsevich, I. Large-Scale Space-Time Variations in Atmospheric Contamination of the Lower Troposphere by Stratospheric Radioactive Substances). — In: Atmospheric Scavenging of Radio-isotopes. Israel Program for Scientific Translations, Jerusalem. 1970.

7. Malakhov, S. G., E. N. Davydov, and M. P. Nekhorosheva. Vremennye kolebaniya kontsentratsii produktov deleniya v prizemnom sloe atmosfery v Podmoskov'e i na ostrove Kheisa Zemli Frantsa-Iosifa (Time Fluctuations in the Concentration of Fission Products in the Ground Layer of the Atmosphere in the Vicinity of Moscow and on Hayes Island in Franz Josef Land). — In: "Radioaktivnye izotopy v atmosfere i ikh ispol'zovanie v meteorologii ("Radioactive Isotopes in the Atmosphere and their Utilization in Meteorology"). Moskva, Atomizdat. 1965.

8. Makhon'ko, K. P. Samoochishchenie nizhnei troposfery ot radioaktivnoi pyli (Radioactive Dust Scavenging in the Lower Troposphere). — Izvestiya AN SSSR, Fizika Atmosfery i Okeana, Vol. 2, No. 5. 1966.

9. Sbornik metodik po opredeleniyu radioaktivnosti vneshnei sredy (Collection of Procedures for Determining the Radioactivity of the Environment). Parts III—IV. — Moskva, Gidrometeoizdat. 1968.

10. Staley, D. Evaluation of Potential Vorticity Changes near the Tropopause and the Related Vertical Motion, Vertical Advection of Vorticity and Transfer of Radioactive Debris from Stratosphere to Troposphere. — J. Met., Vol. 17, No. 6. 1960.

UDC 551.72 : 551.15.5

DISTRIBUTION OF FISSION PRODUCTS OVER OCEANS IN THE TROPICAL ZONE AND THEIR RELATION TO ATMOSPHERIC PROCESSES

G. V. Dmitrieva, Yu. V. Krasnopevtsev, and S. G. Malakhov

New data (for the period 1967—1968) are examined regarding the latitudinal distribution of the concentration of fission products over oceans in different regions of the tropical zone. The data show that the air at sea level in the tropical zone over the Indian Ocean and the West Pacific in the considered period is very inhomogeneous as regards the content of radioactive products. This inhomogeneity was caused by the influx in the tropical zone of air with higher radioactivity from subtropical or moderate latitudes (winter hemisphere) after the passage in these latitudes of quasi-meridional cold fronts. These incursions possibly contribute sometimes also to the formation of separate zones of convergence lines in the equatorial region. Under certain synoptic conditions, the air entering the equatorial region from extratropical latitudes at times crossed the equator and could be included in the circulation of the other hemisphere. The assumption is made that, after their transformation into deep wide cyclones, Pacific typhoons can contribute to the transport of air from the southern to the northern hemisphere.

This paper examines a number of latitudinal distributions of air radioactivity in the tropical zone over water areas of various oceans. Attention is paid to the different characteristics of the distributions, which are illustrated by corresponding synoptic charts.

Comprehensive analysis of several distributions of air radioactivity and synoptic processes over the surrounding territory led to a number of conclusions regarding the structure of the tropical zone, the factors leading to some features of the radioactivity distribution, and possible mechanisms of air transport from one hemisphere to the other.

The distributions of air radioactivity over oceans presented in this paper are based on observations conducted from Soviet research vessels. The concentrations of the sum of β-active fission products in sea-level air obtained by daily or twice-daily samplings were used. Satellite cloudiness data were used to analyze the synoptic situation.

The right of Figure 1 presents two latitudinal distributions of radioactive fission product concentrations in sea-level air of the tropical zone of the eastern part of the Indian Ocean and the West Pacific in the northern hemisphere. The solid curve corresponds to July—August 1968 and characterizes the change in concentration along the ship path: from the south of the Sea of Japan southwest up to Singapore, then through the Strait of Malacca into the Indian Ocean, further southwest to the point 10°S, 65°E, and then south to 35°S. This journey is illustrated to the left of Figure 1 by the solid line.

The dashed curve on the right of Figure 1 represents the change in the concentration of fission products when the same journey (the dashed line to the left of Figure 1) is undertaken in the opposite direction (from south to north) in the period 16 September to 17 October 1968.

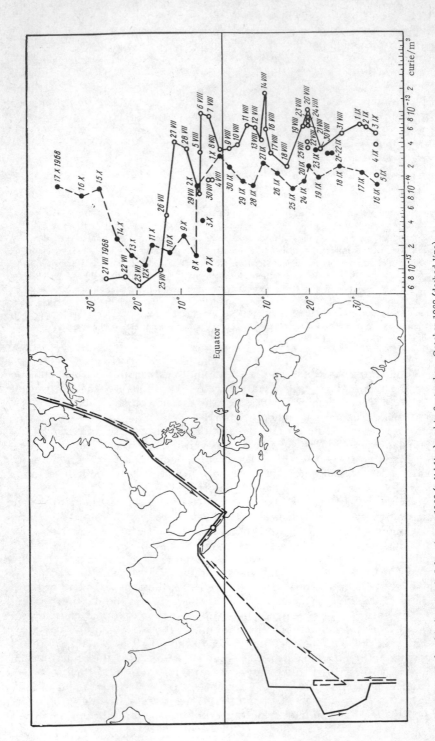

FIGURE 1. Left — ship journeys in July — August 1968 (solid line) and in September — October 1968 (dashed line).

Right — two latitudinal distributions of total β-activity of air in the tropical zone, corresponding to the journeys mapped on the left.

The distribution of the concentration of fission products, represented by the solid line, is characterized by:

1) a sharp increase in concentration (by almost two orders of magnitude) after the ship crossed 14—12°N (25 — 27 July 1968);

2) high values of fission product concentration even after the ship had moved farther south, including the equatorial region;

3) very large concentration fluctuations in the tropical zone to the south of 12°N both during ship motion and when it is at rest or drifts.

The examined distribution of sea-level air indicates that the air of the southern hemisphere, polluted in the first half of July 1968 by nuclear blasts over the Pacific of the southern hemisphere /5/, propagated by 26 July to the sea-level layer over the West Pacific up to 14°N. Besides, the sea-level air of the tropical zone of the considered region was substantially inhomogeneous as regards content of radioactive fission products.

The propagation in summer or autumn in the northern hemisphere of air from the southern hemisphere at sea level up to 10—15°N over the West Pacific was also noted /2, 7/; also examined were latitudinal distributions of fission product concentration at sea level during the August 1960 and September 1961 voyages. It was shown /2, 7/ that the northern boundary of air propagation over the southern hemisphere in the sea-level layer over the West Pacific was the intratropical convergence zone. However, in August 1960 /2/ this was its northern boundary, lying at about 20°N. In September 1961 the air of the southern hemisphere in the same region did not reach the northern boundary of the zone of intratropical convergence /7/, located at about 15°N. The northern boundary of air propagation over the southern hemisphere was a second boundary, weakly expressed by meteorological elements and lying somewhat to the south (at roughly 10°N). This was possibly the southern boundary of the intratropical convergence zone. The lowest concentrations of fission products were observed in September 1961 between these two boundaries.

The development of atmospheric processes at the end of July 1968 at the southeastern shores of Asia can be determined from the four synoptic charts comprising Figure 2 (the ship position on each is marked by a triangle). Three typhoons developed at the southeastern shores of Asia over the Pacific in the period under consideration. The most intense typhoon, "Mary," started on 20—21 July in the region of the island of Guam, after which "Nadine" and "Olive" appeared to the west. At the end of this period all three typhoons combined into one wide deep cyclonic region. The ship in its southward motion passed between the two western typhoons during their initial development. When the ship crossed the cyclonic region combining the typhoons, the concentration of radioactive fission products (the right of Figure 1) remained low, and only when it exited into its southwestern part at latitude 12—14°N did their concentration increase sharply.

The intratropical convergence zone was not marked on synoptic charts during this period over the southwestern part of the Pacific, since it is very difficult to insert under conditions of typhoon development. However, the sharp jump in radioactivity when the ship left the cyclonic region, indicating passage of the ship from air masses of the northern hemisphere into air masses of the southern hemisphere, means that in the given case, over the southwest of the Pacific in the 12—15°N zone, there existed a clearcut boundary between the air of the northern and southern hemispheres which passed to the south of the developing typhoons, i. e., the typhoons started to develop in air masses of the northern hemisphere. On Figure 2a, the supposed location of this boundary is represented by a dashed line.

It is very probable that with the development of the typhoons and their transformation into a powerful cyclone, when large air volumes started to penetrate its circulation system from the ground layer, air lying to the south of the intratropical convergence zone, and possibly directly from the southern hemisphere, was drawn into the cyclone. This assumption is corroborated by 1) the extensive system of satellite-recorded cumuli at the eastern and southeastern periphery of the cyclone and extending almost from the equator to the north along the 140°E meridian (Figure 2c), 2) the winds to the south of the cyclone, and 3) the high-pressure nucleus located on 28 July somewhat to the north of the equator. The nucleus arose from a ridge directed on preceding days to this region from the southern hemisphere.

The air from the equatorial region, drawn to the earth's surface in the tropical cyclone, can be transported rapidly into the upper layers, and then propagated into the northen hemisphere in line with the circulation conditions of the upper layers, dropping to the ground layer behind the cyclones.

This process is possibly one of the mechanisms governing the entry of southern-hemisphere air into the circulation system of the northern hemisphere. This mechanism of air transport from the southern to the northern hemisphere must function most actively at the end of summer and autumn in the northern hemisphere, i. e., during the development of typhoons in the southwestern part of the Pacific.

Examination of the development of radioactivity (the solid line of Figure 1) when the ship had left the cyclonic region and approached the equator, and then crossed the equator and subsequently journeyed southward, shows that radioactivity values constantly underwent considerable fluctuations, with maxima every 3—5 days on the average.

The concentration of fission products in sea-level air changed over a similar period during the return voyage (the path is represented by the dashed line to the left of Figure 1, and the radioactivity by the dashed curve to the right of Figure 1). Figure 1 shows that the concentration level of fission products in the southern hemisphere over the Indian Ocean in September 1968 decreased somewhat, compared with August of the same year. In subtropical latitudes of the northern hemisphere over the West Pacific the concentration level by October 1968 increased by an order, compared with the end of July 1968.

Synoptic analysis of the causes of radioactivity fluctuations in the tropical zone, based on the results of many voyages, showed that the increase in radioactivity is generally associated with the same synoptic processes: the passage of quasi-meridional cold fronts in subtropical latitudes. We have in mind here the voyages shown on Figure 1 (their synoptic charts are given on Figures 2—5). The voyage in 1967—1968, represented on Figure 6 by two latitudinal distributions (the corresponding synoptic charts are shown on Figure 7), and also the voyages of previous years, were studied elsewhere /2, 3, 7/. The concentration of fission products in ground-level

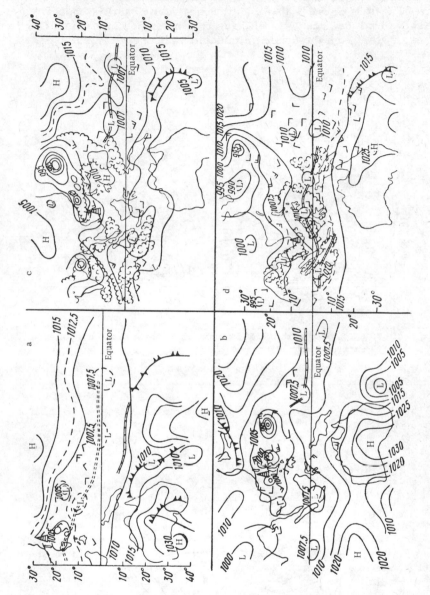

FIGURE 2. Weather charts for the ship positions, indicated by a triangle.

air always increases immediately behind the cold front in the region of the ridge of the forward part of the anticyclone. These increases in concentration at moderate latitudes are associated with rapid quasi-horizontal penetration of the ground-level layer by radioactive air from the stratosphere /3/. It is possible that under these synoptic conditions, air entering from above into the ground-level layer originates not only from the stratosphere, but also from the upper or middle troposphere.

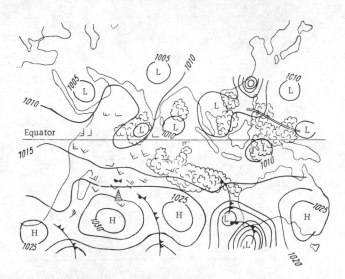

FIGURE 3. Weather chart of 22 September 1968. The ship position is marked by a triangle. Period of increased radioactivity.

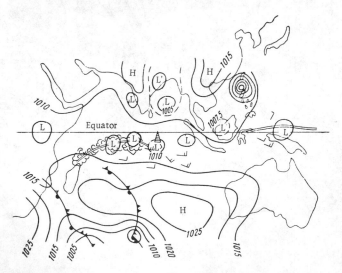

FIGURE 4. Weather chart of 29 September 1968. Decreased radioactivity.

The mechanism governing the entry of stratospheric air into the troposphere in moderate latitudes was investigated elsewhere /6, 8, 9/. This
transport mechanism is evidently also realized in lower latitudes of the
northern and southern hemispheres if, in the troposphere, cold air penetrates
far into low latitudes. Simultaneously, the ridge at ground level is intensified behind the cold front, weakly expressed in low latitudes. Higher up,
a depression propagates from moderate latitudes, in which a cyclonic
center is frequently formed. This process, accompanied by a sharp increase
in the radioactivity of sea-level air, was frequently observed by one of the
authors of this paper in the tropics up to 7° over the Atlantic at the northwestern shores of Africa, over the Pacific at the southeastern shores of
Asia and in the region of the Hawaii islands, and over the Indian Ocean at
the southwestern shores of Australia. *

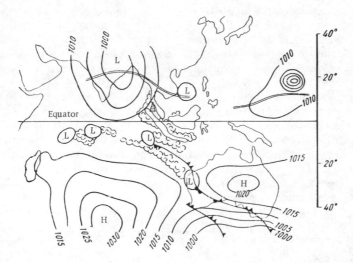

FIGURE 5. Weather chart of 3 October. Onset of decreased radioactivity.

For the indicated synoptic conditions, the parcels of radioactive air
entering the ground layer from above then propagate slowly over the periphery of the anticyclones either toward the equator or toward the west.
They then extend parallel to the equator at a large or small distance from
it (but within the latitudes of 5—25°), depending on the season, configuration
and size of the anticyclone. For this reason, passage through these latitudes
is frequently accompanied by radioactivity maxima.

Thus the entry of radioactive air from subtropical latitudes into lower
ones takes place in parcels. This leads to an inhomogeneous content of
radioactive fission products in the sea-level air both in space and in time
(the inhomogeneity of the tropical air apparently extends not only to the
content of radioactivity). The frequency of penetration of air parcels with

---

* Such a process has been described elsewhere for the tropics of the Atlantic /1/.

a high concentration of radioactive products in the tropics depends on the frequency of the passage of cold quasi-meridional fronts in subtropical latitudes. In the southern hemisphere it is evidently higher than in the northern hemisphere. In some regions it is higher than elsewhere at the same latitude, and depends also on the season. In some cases one parcel of radioactive air in the tropics overtakes another one, so causing wider radioactivity peaks.

We shall illustrate this process by several examples. Consider first Figure 6, which illustrates the ship path from the Atlantic, through the Indian Ocean and into the Pacific, from December 1967 to February 1968. The center of Figure 6 shows a plot of two latitudinal distributions of fission product concentrations corresponding to this path. The solid line on the figure represents the concentration of fission products along the path shown by a solid line to the left of the figure. The dashed line characterizes the concentration along the path to the left of Figure 6.

It is seen from the solid line that the largest radioactivity maximum lies between 10 and 20°N, over the Atlantic. A similar peak exists at the same latitudes over the Pacific (the dashed line). Note further that minimum radioactivity was observed in the equatorial region over the Atlantic, and maximum radioactivity over the east of the Indian Ocean.

Figure 7 shows some synoptic charts corresponding to the given path (the ship position for the chart date is denoted on each chart by a triangle). The charts for 1 January and 16 February 1968, i. e., those days on which the highest concentrations were recorded at 10°–20°N over the Atlantic and Pacific, show that maximum radioactivity was observed in both cases at the southern periphery of the anticyclones at the ridges behind the cold fronts. The cold fronts over both the Atlantic and Pacific oceans attained 5°N at the time under consideration. However, over the West Pacific the processes of cold air influx into the equatorial region are more active in winter than over the East Atlantic.

The high concentration of radioactivity (Figure 6) observed over the Indian Ocean in the equatorial region (the source in the winter of 1968 comprised the upper troposphere and the stratosphere at moderate latitudes of the northern hemisphere) indicates that during previous cold influxes over the Pacific the air of the northern hemisphere, moving at ground level to the southwest, crossed the equator over the Indian Ocean. The weather chart of 27 January 1968 (Figure 7) indicates that the southern boundary of its propagation was the convergence zone lying (according to synoptic analysis data) over the Indian Ocean to the south of the equator.

Over the Atlantic the convergence zone passed to the north of the equator, and minimum radioactivity was observed as the ship crossed the equator.

The weather chart of 16 January 1968 shows the ship position in the Indian Ocean in the southern hemisphere to lie ahead of the cold front during decreased concentration.

The material presented in this article yields one more synoptic situation favorable to the ground-level transport of air from the southern to the northern hemisphere.

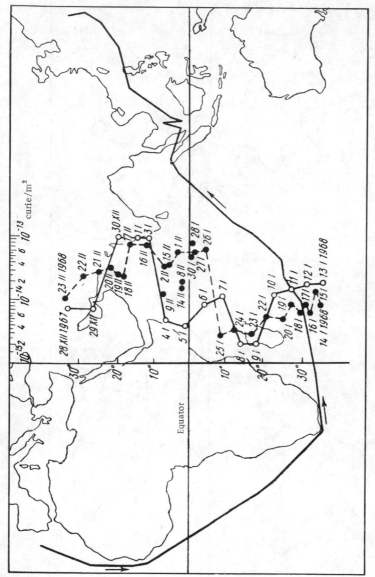

FIGURE 6. Left: ship route in the Atlantic in December 1967 and January 1968. Right: ship route in the Indian and Pacific oceans in January—February 1968. Center: two latitudinal distributions of total β-activity of the air.

The solid line corresponds to the route illustrated on the left, and the dashed line to the route on the right.

25

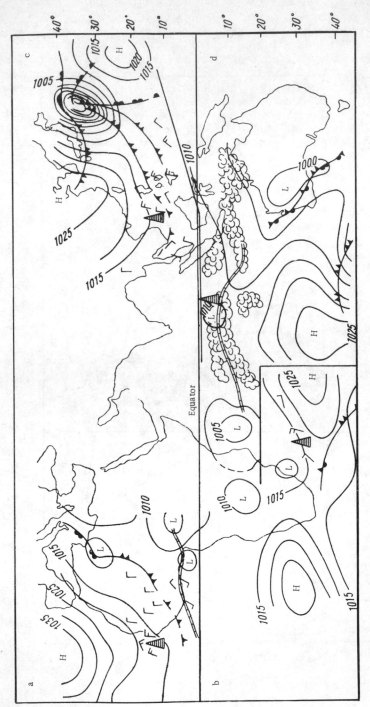

FIGURE 7. Weather charts for ship positions, indicated by a triangle.

Figures 3—5 present synoptic charts corresponding to the latitudinal distribution of fission product concentration over the Indian Ocean (dashed line on Figure 1). During the period of increased concentration on 22 September (Figure 3) the ship was situated at about 25°S, at the northeast periphery of the anticyclone near a hardly-moving front, which was the continuation of the cold front passing along the 80°E meridian. In the given case it is also of interest to note that the southeastern winds observed in the ship's region extended further to the northwest, intersecting the isobars, up to the equator at the eastern shores of Africa. Here the winds veered south and preserved their southerly direction also to the north of the equator, roughly up to 5—10°N. The observed wind distribution indicates that in the western part of the Indian Ocean, in the sea-level layer, there existed conditions favorable to the passage of air from the southern to the northern hemisphere with subsequent transport to the east. Such airflows from the southern to the northern hemisphere at the end of summer and autumn of 1968 can cause considerable peaks in the latitudinal distribution of radio-activity somewhat to the north of the equator, since the source of large concentrations of radioactive fission products in this period was the southern hemisphere.

A radioactivity peak was in fact observed (Figure 1) when the ship crossed the equator above the East Indian Ocean to the north of the intra-tropical convergence zone at the end of September 1968. The ship moved in September 1968 from the southwest to the northeast. A drop in radio-activity was observed after passing through the intratropical convergence zone at latitude 10—5° of the southern hemisphere on 29 September (Figure 4). An increase in radioactivity to values characteristic of southern hemisphere air was observed in the region and to the north of the equator.

It is possible that the development of a similar situation was also due to increased radioactivity over the East Indian Ocean and the southwest of the Pacific north of the equator at the end of July 1968.

The material presented in this article indicates the considerable inhomo-geneity of air in the tropical zone as regards its content of fission products. This inhomogeneity, as seen from the synoptic analysis of specific distribu-tions of radioactivity, was caused by the influx in the tropical zone of parcels of more radioactive air from subtropical or moderate latitudes after passing quasi-meridional cold fronts in these latitudes. The air entering from extratropical latitudes into the sea-level layer of the equatorial region can, under specific synoptic conditions, cross the equator and participate in the circulation of the other hemisphere.

In conclusion, we turn our attention to the following. Analysis of synoptic charts of the tropical zone of the Indian Ocean in the southern hemisphere, on which are also marked satellite data on cloudiness, shows that the cold fronts, which are clearly seen in subtropical latitudes up to about 20°S, extend further in the tropics in the form of wide cloud banks, recorded by satellites. These banks are elongated in accordance with the wind direction from southeast to northwest, sometimes reaching the equator and at times parallel to it. On the weather chart of 22 September 1968 (Figure 3) such a bank is seen near the front passing the western shores of Australia. In roughly the same region, a similar bank near the cold front can be seen on the weather chart of 3 October 1968 (Figure 5).

A similar pattern can be observed on many other synoptic charts plotted from satellite data. This cloudiness is relatively stable in time and, in accordance with the winds, propagates slowly westward, detaching itself from the front with which it was linked at the beginning. Different portions of the intratropical convergence zone are apparently sometimes associated with the position of such cloud banks near the equator on synoptic charts.

The connection between these cloud banks and the cold fronts is so far hypothetical and requires further corroboration. But if the appearance of a cloud bank is associated with the same synoptic processes which cause the entry of different parcels of radioactive air in the tropics, the combined analysis of radiometric, satellite and standard meteorological data will help to explain the very complex structure of the tropical zone, the processes taking place within it, and the exchange mechanism between the hemispheres.

BIBLIOGRAPHY

1. Artemov, V.M., G.V. Dmitrieva, E.D. Stukin, and E.I. Yushkan. Radioaktivnoe zagryaznenie privodnogo sloya atmosfery v vostochnoi Atlantike v mae 1968 g. (Radioactive Pollution of the Sea-Level Layer of the Atmosphere in the East Atlantic in May 1968).— Synopses of Reports to the All-Union Conference on Nuclear Meteorology (23—28 June 1969). Obninsk, Rotaprint IEM. 1969.
2. Vilenskii, V.D., G.V. Dmitrieva, and Yu.V. Krasnopevtsev. Estestvennaya i iskusstvennaya radioaktivnost' atmosfery nad okeanami i ee svyaz' s meteorologicheskimi faktorami (Natural and Artificial Radioactivity of the Atmosphere over Oceans and its Relation to Meteorological Factors).— In: "Radioaktivnye izotopy v atmosfere i ikh ispol'zovanie v meteorologii" ("Radio-active Isotopes in the Atmosphere and their Utilization in Meteorology"). Moskva, Atomizdat. 1965.
3. Dmitrieva, G.V. et al. Radioaktivnost' vozdukha nad okeanami Yuzhnogo polushariya i Antarktidoi i ee svyaz' s meteorologicheskimi faktorami (Air Radioactivity over Oceans of the Southern Hemisphere and Antarctica and its Relation to Meteorological Factors).— Trudy IEM, No. 5. 1969.
4. Dmitrieva, G.V. and V.I. Kasatkina. Aerosinopticheskie usloviya poyavleniya u poverkhnosti zemli oblastei povyshennoi kontsentratsii stratosfernykh radioaktivnykh produktov (Aerosynoptic Conditions Governing the Appearance at the Earth's Surface of Regions of Increased Concentration of Stratospheric Radioactive Products). — In: "Radioaktivnye izotopy v atmosfere i ikh ispol'zovanie v meteorologii" ("Radioactive Isotopes in the Atmosphere and their Utilization in Meteorology"). Moskva, Atomizdat. 1965.
5. Cambray, R.S. et al. Radioactive Fallout in Air and Rain. Results to the Middle of 1968.— AERE Report 5899. 1968.
6. Danielsen, E.F. Project "Springfield Report."—DASA-1567, Washington. July 1964.
7. Dmitrieva, G.V., Yu.V. Krasnopevtsev, V.V. Lukjanov, and S.G. Malakhov. Investigation of the Radioactive Aerosol Distribution over Oceans and Some Problems of the Latitudinal Exchange in the Tropical Zone.— Tellus, Vol. 18, No. 2, pp. 407—415. 1966.
8. Reiter, E.R. and J.D. Mahlman. Heavy Radioactive Fallout over the Southern United States, November, 1962.—J. Geophys. Res., Vol. 70, No. 18. 1965.
9. Staley, D. On the Mechanism of Mass and Radioactivity Transport from Stratosphere to Troposphere.— J. Atmos. Sci., Vol. 19, No. 6. 1962.

UDC 551.577.7

DETERMINATION OF RADIOISOTOPE FALLOUT
FROM ITS CONTENT IN CHRONOLOGICAL LAYERS
OF HIGH-ALTITUDE GLACIERS

E. N. Davydov, K. P. Makhon'ko, M. A. Tsevelev, and
Z. S. Shulepko

The contents of Sr^{90}, Cs^{137}, Ce^{144}, Mn^{54}, Ru^{106}, and Pb^{210} are determined in chronological layers of neve and ice in high-altitude glaciers of the Caucasus and Tyan-Shan. The annual fallout of Cs^{137} determined by means of a cuvette-type collector is found to agree satisfactorily with the fallout determined from the Cs^{137} content in the chronological layers of the glacier in the period 1963−1967. A similar comparison for Sr^{90} in the period 1956−1967 showed that the proportion of Sr^{90} contained in the chronological layers of these glaciers is about 10% of the atmospheric fallout of the isotope, which corresponds roughly to the proportion of Sr existing in indissoluble form.

It is shown that about 90% of Sr^{90} and roughly 40% of Pb^{210}, falling on the glacier surface from the atmosphere, are eliminated together with the melted snow, while Cs^{137} hardly migrates at all.

The time variation in the fallout of different isotopes, determined from their content in chronological layers of the glaciers, led to the following value for the half-removal period of isotopes of fission products from the atmosphere: $T_{1/2} \sim 11$ months. The figure for Mn^{54} is $T_{1/2} \sim 28$ months.

The determination of the content of radioactive isotopes in chronological layers of neve and ice in icecaps and glaciers enables one to find the radioactive fallout in regions where work with standard fallout collectors is difficult, due to their inaccessibility or to frequent snowfalls and snowstorms /3/. Moreover, when initiating observations in various regions, sampling of chronological layers of neve and ice establishes the pattern of radioactive fallout in previous years, and this is very important. However, it must be kept in mind that whereas for polar regions with their severe climate it is probably possible to neglect summer melting of snow in zones of glacier accumulation and at the summits of icecaps and the removal of isotopes by melting snow /3/, for glaciers in middle latitudes this question is in need of preliminary study. The known properties of chemical elements whose radioactive isotopes are present in the products of nuclear blasts indicate that Sr^{90} will migrate most easily with melted snow. Other isotopes, such as Cs^{137}, Ce^{144} and Mn^{54}, exist mainly in the form of hardly soluble compounds and in practice do not migrate.

Expeditions were conducted in summer 1961, 1962 and 1967 to the high-altitude glaciers of the Caucasus and Tyan-Shan in order to test the possibility of determining radioactive atmospheric fallout from the isotope content in the chronological layers of glaciers in middle latitudes. In 1962, samples of neve and ice were taken by Davydov from the Terskol glacier, descending from El'brus (Central Caucasus) between the Ledovaya Baza and Priyut Odinnadtsati points at approximately 4,000 m above sea level.

Samples were taken in the Tyan-Shan mountains at a height of 3,600 m above sea level, in 1961 from the Srednii Barkrak glacier (Davydov) and in 1967 from the Kara-Batkak glacier, from the northern slopes of Terskei Ala-Tau (Davydov and Tsevelev). At that altitude snow does not melt completely in summer, and isotopes deposited from the atmosphere remain in this layer without mixing with the radioactive fallout of previous years. The chronological layers of the previous four or five years are usually distinguished visually from the seasonal ice strata, without special glaciological investigations.

The sampling locations were selected in the zone of glacier accumulation at the flattest and most level portions of the neve field, far from avalanches and from zones where displaced snow could accumulate. Fifty blocks of neve and ice were excavated layer by layer. The samples (weighing between 15 and 30 kg) were melted on site in a specially designed gas snow-melter after first introducing isotopic carriers. The water was then channeled through an ion-exchange column with KU-2 and EDE-10P ionites, in which the isotopes were retained. The water content in chronological layers of the glacier was measured simultaneously.

Subsequent sample processing was performed in the laboratory: the ion-exchange resin was incinerated in a muffle furnace, and a gamma-spectral determination of Cs^{137}, Ce^{144}, Ru^{106}, Mn^{54} (Polyakov) and a radiochemical determination of Sr^{90} and Pb^{210} (Shulepko) were conducted.

TABLE 1. Comparison of strontium-90 fallout with its content in chronological layers of glaciers

Period	Fallout of Sr^{90}, mcurie/km$^2 \cdot$ year			Fraction of Sr^{90} in the glacier, %	Glacier
	Glacier	USA, 40—43°N	Kirgiz SSR (Frunze)		
1956—1957	0.30	4.17	—	7.2	Terskol
1957—1958	0.41	4.20	—	9.8	"
1958—1959	0.48	8.83	—	5.4	"
1959—1960	0.80	2.44	—	33	"
1959—1960	1.20	2.44	—	49	Srednii Barkrak
1960—1961	0.63	1.59	—	40	Terskol
1960—1961	0.36	1.59	—	23	Srednii Barkrak
1961—1962	3.53*	9.37	3.60	98*	Terskol
1962—1963	—	15.70	14.9	—	
1963—1964	2.24	19.74	14.5	15	Kara-Batkak
1964—1965	0.73	6.50	15.0	4.9	"
1965—1966	0.36	3.59	3.41	11	"
1966—1967	0.51*	1.64	0.81	63*	"

* The data correspond to the upper layer of neve and snow during sampling.

The determined contents of Sr^{90} in chronological layers of glaciers are given in Table 1. For comparison we give there the values of the annual atmospheric fallout of Sr^{90} over the territory of Kirgiz SSR (our measurements) and over the territory of the USA, averaged on the basis of data from the Argon, New York, Pittsburg, Vermillion and Salt Lake City stations, located roughly at the same latitude /9/. The monthly fallout was collected in tanks and averaged over the period from July to June of the following year. A correction allowing for radioactive decay was introduced when calculating fallout from the content of Sr^{90} in the chronological layers of the glacier. It is seen that the fraction of Sr^{90} contained in these layers is of the order of ten per cent of the atmospheric fallout of the isotope. However, in the upper layer of the neve this proportion is much larger, since during sampling this layer was soaked with melted snow containing dissolved Sr^{90}. In most mountain glaciers, melting inside the glacier is so small that it can be neglected /4/. The advective melting embraces only the surface of the snow: 70—80% of solar radiation penetrating the snow is absorbed by a 5—10 cm thick layer, and a depth of 20 cm is attained only by 3—5% of the entire radiation incident on the snow cover.

Thus, direct determination of the fallout of Sr^{90} from its content in the chronological layers of glaciers of moderate latitudes leads to underestimated values unless corrections are introduced.

TABLE 2. Content of radioactive isotopes in chronological layers of the Kara-Batkak glacier: P (mcurie/km^2) and P_0 (mcurie/km$^2 \cdot$ mm)

	Isotope	Dating of the layer				Accumulation for 1963—1967
		1963—1964	1964—1965	1965—1966	1966—1967	
P	Strontium-90	2.24	0.73	0.36	0.51	3.6
P_0		2.6	1.06	0.38	0.54	1.05
P	Cesium-137	20.0	11.5	11.5	1.65	42.8
P_0		23.3	16.7	12.0	1.75	12.4
P	Cerium-144	133	51.7	23.7	2.65	19.5
P_0		155	75.0	24.8	2.82	2.9
P	Manganese-54	16.4	7.50	2.84	0.51	3.1
P_0		19.0	10.9	2.98	0.54	0.9
P	Ruthenium-106	—	610	185	86.4	236
P_0		—	885	194	91.8	69
P	Lead-210	0.76	0.59	0.35	0.37	1.98
P_0		0.89	0.86	0.37	0.39	0.58
Precipitation, mm		859	689	955	941	3444
Fallout of Cs^{137} in Frunze		15.7	13.4	3.30	1.97	34.4

The determination of the content of other isotopes in the samples are now examined. Table 2 contains the fallout P of isotopes on the Kara-Batkak glacier, calculated from their content in chronological glacier layers, and also P_0, the fallout per mm atmospheric precipitation. All the data are corrected for the decay and reduced to the middle of the time interval. For comparison, we give also the fallout of Cs^{137} in the nearby town of Frunze, determined by gathering atmospheric fallout in a cuvette with distilled water.

The values of the atmospheric fallout of Cs^{137} in Frunze and on the Kara-Batkak glacier are seen to be very similar. The somewhat greater fallout of Cs^{137} on the glacier is explained by the usual increase in the levels of radioactive contamination of the atmosphere /11/ and of fallout /7/ with altitude. Thus, the method of determining the annual fallout of Cs^{137} and other isotopes possessing a weak migration capacity, from their content in the chronological layers of glaciers of moderate latitudes, is quite satisfactory.

An examination of Table 2 shows that since 1963 the fallout of isotopes of nuclear blast products dropped continually, pointing to the absence of any new substantial penetration of radioactive products of nuclear blasts in the atmosphere after 1962. At the same time, the fallout of Pb^{210} (an isotope of natural origin) remained at roughly the same level. Existing fluctuations in the annual levels of Pb^{210} fallout can be explained by the fluctuations in climatic conditions.

TABLE 3. Isotope ratios in the chronological layers of the Kara-Batkak glacier

Dating of the layer	$\dfrac{Cs^{137}}{Sr^{90}}$	$\dfrac{Ce^{144}}{Cs^{137}}$	$\dfrac{Mn^{54}}{Cs^{137}}$	$\dfrac{Ru^{106}}{Cs^{137}}$	$\dfrac{Cs^{137}}{Pb^{210}}$
1966—1967	3.24	1.61	0.31	52.3	4.47
1965—1966	32.0	2.06	0.25	16.1	32.9
1964—1965	15.8	4.50	0.65	53.0	19.5
1963—1964	8.93	6.66	0.82	—	26.4
1963—1967	11.9	0.46	0.07	5.52	21.6
Melted snow 1967	0.27	—	—	—	0.32

Table 3 presents the ratios of isotope fallout in different years, calculated from the data of Table 2. Starting with 1963, the Mn^{54}/Cs^{137} and Ce^{144}/Cs^{137} ratios decreased systematically. This is due both to the radioactive decay of Mn^{54} and Ce^{144} discharged into the atmosphere up to that time, and to the absence of new noticeable fluxes of these isotopes in the atmosphere. We observe anomalously high values of the ratio Cs^{137}/Sr^{90}. While this ratio is usually equal to $a = 1.7$ /6/ for atmospheric samples, in glacier samples for the period 1963—1967 it is $Cs^{137}/Sr^{90} = 11.9$, and in samples of melted snow taken in the summer of 1967 it is equal to 0.27. Thus, a deficit of Sr^{90} is formed in the glacier ice and a surplus (compared with Cs^{137}) in the melted snow. This is quite understandable, since a considerable proportion of the Sr^{90} deposited from the atmosphere is in an easily soluble form /5/.

In summer, during the period of glacier thawing (very important under the conditions of southern USSR), Sr^{90} is carried away by melted snow to a much greater extent than Cs^{137}, which occurs in practically indissoluble forms. We shall find the migration coefficient of Sr^{90}, defined as the ratio of the amount of Sr^{90} isotope migrating with the melted snow to the total amount received by the glacier through fallout:

$$\delta = \frac{\Delta Sr^{90}}{Sr^{90} + \Delta Sr^{90}}. \tag{1}$$

If the fallout of isotopes on the glacier satisfies the ratio

$$\frac{Cs^{137}}{Sr^{90} + \Delta Sr^{90}} = a = 1.7, \tag{2}$$

it is clear, using (1) and (2), that for the period 1963—1967 the migration coefficient of Sr^{90} was

$$\delta = 1 - \frac{a}{Cs^{137}/Sr^{90}} = 86\%. \qquad (3)$$

The migration coefficient of Sr^{90} can also be estimated in another manner, by comparing the content of Sr^{90} in the glacier with the fallout from the atmosphere measured in adjacent regions, i. e., directly by formula (1). Using the data of Tables 1 and 2 for the period 1963—1967, we obtain according to (1) $\delta = 89\%$, which agrees satisfactorily with the above figure. A similar result has been obtained for the Kesselwandferner glacier, located at the same latitude in the Austrian Alps /12/.

The concentrations of Sr^{90} in the glacier neve and in precipitation at Vienna and Klagenfurt were compared /12/. A deficit of approximately 90% Sr^{90} was obtained, i. e., about 10% of Sr^{90} is in an indissoluble form and remains in the neve after the melted snow has flowed away.

The migration of Sr^{90} from the upper layer of the Kara-Batkak glacier (1966—1967), estimated by formula (3), was the smallest and represented in all 47%; the figures from deeper layers are roughly the same: 95% (1965—1966), 89% (1964—1965), and 81% (1963—1964). This can be explained by the fact that the samples were collected in the summer period, when the upper layer of snow and   impervious stratum, contained a
                            n, before the onset of snow, the
                            d carries with it dissolved Sr^{90}.
                            is possible even in lower strata of
                            ous ice strata. The existence of
                            growth of neve grains in the lower
                            uantitatively, this effect is negligible.
                            the melted snow as well as a
                            r isotopes (Ce^{144}, Ru^{106} and Mn^{54})
                            sents isotope concentrations in
                            acier (Q) in the period 1966—1967,

June 1967, Kara-Batkak glacier)

S, curie/km^2	ΣP, mcurie/km^2	δS, %
3.14	3.6	87
0.83	43	2

Coefficient δ_s was calculated as the ratio of the runoff S to the amount of isotopes accumulated in the glacier ΣP. In Table 4, $\delta_s = 87\%$ was obtained for Sr^{90} which is near the values given above, while $\delta_s = 2\%$ was obtained for Cs^{137}, i. e., hardly any Cs^{137} migrates.

We can conclude that the annual fallout of all isotopes listed above, except Sr^{90}, can be determined from their content in the chronological layers of glaciers in moderate latitudes.

In view of the fact that the natural isotope Pb^{210} is used widely for determining the age of ice in glaciers of high latitudes (see /8/), we determined the content of that isotope in samples of the Kara-Batkak glacier. It was found that the mean Pb^{210} concentration in samples of neve and ice is $2 \cdot 10^{-12}$ curie/liter, which agrees satisfactorily with its concentration in precipitation falling in the northern hemisphere, and in neve samples from the Kesselwandferner glacier /12/.

Roughly the same concentration of Pb^{210} was observed in melted snow in 1967, which indicates that the amount of migrating Pb^{210} corresponds roughly to the amount of melted snow flowing down from the glacier. Since the total precipitation for the period 1963—1967 was 3,444 mm, and the water content of this neve layer is 2,066 mm, the water runoff from the neve field is 40%, on the average. Therefore, roughly half the Pb^{210} deposited on the glacier is removed with the melted snow. The existence of Pb^{210} migration with the melted snow is also corroborated by the proximity in magnitude of the Cs^{137}/Sr^{90} and Cs^{137}/Pb^{210} ratios (Table 3). The conclusion drawn must be regarded at this stage as tentative, due to the relatively small number of samples analyzed for Pb^{210}, but in the light of our data the method of dating glaciers from the content of Pb^{210} seems questionable.

TABLE 5. Drop in the strontium-90 concentration in melted snow of the Srednii Barkrak glacier along its runoff path

Sampling location	Sr^{90}, 10^{-12} curie/liter	Sorption, %
Puddle on the neve field	2.6	0
Brook at the moraine	0.65	75
Aiging River	0.33	87

Melted snow flowing down from glaciers carries at first a fairly large amount of Sr^{90}, but its concentration in the water drops rather sharply as a result of isotope sorption by the stream bed. We give as an example (Table 5) the decrease of Sr^{90} concentration in water flowing down from the Srednii Barkrak glacier on its way from the neve field into a brook flowing down from the glacier, and later into a river. It is seen that in the river the Sr^{90} concentration is already an order of magnitude lower than in the melted puddle on the neve field.

Our data on the isotope content in chronological layers of glaciers enable us to evaluate the radioactive contamination scavenging rate in the atmosphere. If we assume that the process of removing isotopes from the atmosphere after the 1962 tests is steady, which seems correct when averaging over a year, it can be assumed that the annual radioactive fallout is proportional to the reserves of the corresponding isotope in the atmosphere. Then the variation with time of the radioactive fallout will correspond to the changes in the atmospheric reserves of the radioisotope. Such a change in atmospheric fallout with time, calculated from the isotope content in chronological layers of the Kara-Batkak glacier and reduced to the sampling time, is presented on Figure 1. For comparison, we give there the annual atmospheric fallout corrected for the decay (represented by circles). The decrease in Cs^{137} fallout is described satisfactorily by an exponent with half-removal period $T^{1}/_{2}= 11$ months. This curve describes somewhat less satisfactorily the removal of Ce^{144} and Ru^{106}, which also formed in considerable amounts after 1963. The half-removal of Sr^{90}, in spite of its migration with melted snow, could be determined very satisfactorily from the Sr^{90} content in the chronological layers of ice in the period 1963—1966.

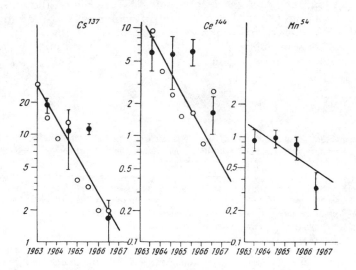

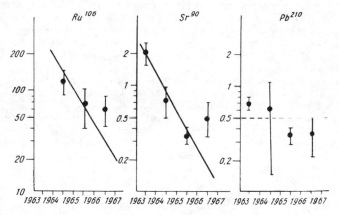

FIGURE 1. Diagram of scavenging of atmospheric radioisotopes, plotted from data on their content in chronological layers of the Kara-Batkak glacier.

The content of Sr^{90} in the 1966—1967 layer was large, because the sampling was conducted in midsummer before summer melting had ended; the corresponding point on Figure 1 does not lie on the curve corresponding to $T_{1/2} = 11$ months.

The removal of Mn^{54}, formed mainly during the 1962 test series, took place with mean half-removal period $T_{1/2} = 28$ months. This feature of Mn^{54} was also noted earlier /1/.

The above results agree in general with earlier published data on the half-removal period of isotopes in the atmosphere /10/. Thus, the half-removal period of radioisotopes of global origin in the atmosphere can be determined from their content in chronological layers of glaciers of mountain systems of southern USSR on the basis of samples taken in the lower part of the glacier in the accumulation zone.

The author is grateful to T. V. Polyakov for carrying out the gamma-spectral analysis of the samples.

BIBLIOGRAPHY

1. Avramenko, A. S. and K. P. Makhon'ko. Nekotorye voprosy vymyvaniya radioaktivnykh izotopov iz atmosfery (Some Problems of Radioisotope Washout from the Atmosphere). — Trudy IEM, No. 5. 1969.

2. Vilenskii, V. D., E. N. Davydov, and S. G. Malakhov. K voprosu o sezonnykh i geograficheskikh izmeneniyakh soderzhaniya svintsa-210 v atmosfere (Concerning Seasonal and Geographical Changes in the Content of Lead-210 in the Atmosphere). — In: "Radioaktivnye izotopy v atmosfere i ikh ispol'zovanie v meteorologii" ("Radioactive Isotopes in the Atmosphere and their Utilization in Meteorology"). Moskva, Atomizdat. 1965.

3. Davydov, E. N. and M. P. Nekhorosheva. Opyt opredeleniya godovykh vypadenii Sr^{90} v polyarnykh raionakh po soderzhaniyu ego v sezonnykh sloyakh firna i l'da na lednikakh Zemli Frantsa-Iosifa i Severnoi Zemli (Experience in the Determination of the Annual Fallout of Sr^{90} in Polar Regions from its Content in the Seasonal Layers of Neve and Ice on Franz Josef Land and Severnaya Zemlya Glaciers). — In: "Radioaktivnye izotopy v atmosfere i ikh ispol'zovanie v meteorologii" ("Radioactive Isotopes in the Atmosphere and their Utilization in Meteorology"). Moskva, Atomizdat. 1965.

4. Kotlyakov, V. M. Snezhnyi pokrov Zemli i ledniki (The Snow Cover of the Earth and Glaciers). — Leningrad, Gidrometeoizdat. 1968.

5. Pavlotskaya, F. I. and L. N. Zatsepina. Ob izuchenii form postupleniya nekotorykh produktov deleniya na zemnuyu poverkhnost' (Study of the Forms of Movement of Some Fission Products to the Earth's Surface). — Atomnaya Energiya, Vol. 20, No. 4. 1966.

6. Shvedov, V. P. and S. I. Shirokov (editors). Radioaktivnye zagryazneniya vneshnoi sredy (Radioactive Contamination of the Environment). — Moskva, Gosatomizdat. 1962.

7. Tsevelev, M. A. and K. P. Makhon'ko. Nekotorye osobennosti raspredeleniya radioaktivnykh vypadenii v gornykh usloviyakh (Some Characteristics of the Radioactive Fallout Distribution in Mountain Conditions). — Trudy IEM, No. 5. 1969.

8. Crozaz, G., E. Picciotto, and W. De Breuck. Antarctic Snow Chronology with Pb-210. — J. Geophys. Res., Vol. 69, p. 2597. 1964.

9. Fallout Program. Quarterly Summary Report. — HASL-214 (Appendix). 1969.

10. Feely, W. et al. Transport and Fallout of Stratospheric Radioactive Debris. — Tellus, Vol. 18, Nos. 2—3. 1966.

11. Keck, G. and N. Amizwi. Vergleichsmessungen der langlebigen Gesamt-beta-Aktivität der Luft in zwei verschiedenen Höhenlagen der Alpen. — Naturwissenschaften, Vol. 51, No. 14. 1964.

12. Picciotto, E. and G. Crozaz. Lead-210 and Strontium-90 in an Alpine Glacier. — Earth and Planetary Science Letters, No. 3. 1967.

UDC 539.163

RADIOACTIVE ISOTOPES OF EUROPIUM PRODUCED BY NUCLEAR BLASTS

S. V. Iokhel'son, I. M. Nazarov, F. Ya. Rovinskii,
V. P. Chirkov, and E. I. Yushkan

Nuclear blasts lead to the appearance of different radioisotopes of europium: europium-155 ($T_{1/2}$ = = 1.7 years), europium-156 ($T_{1/2}$ = 15.4 days), which are fission fragments, and europium-152 ($T_{1/2}$ = 12 years), europium-154 ($T_{1/2}$ = 16 years) — products of activation reactions.

According to data in the literature, these isotopes were detected in the epicentral region of nuclear tests conducted in Nevada (USA). On the other hand, they have not been detected in the composition of radioactive global contamination of the earth's surface.

To determine the contribution of long-lived europium radioisotopes to the global contamination of a locality, a sample of moss gathered in the Caucasus (in the vicinity of Lake Rits) was analyzed by the methods of radiochemistry and gamma-spectrometry. In the sample, in addition to other fragmentation products, the presence of europium-155 was detected and identified reliably for the first time. It was also established reliably that no europium-152 and 154 is present. The density of the global contamination of dry land by europium-155 and its contribution to the gamma-radiation dose were hence evaluated.

Nuclear blasts lead to the formation of various radioisotopes of europium: fission fragments — europium-155 ($T_{1/2}$=1.7 years) and europium-156 ($T_{1/2}$ = =15.4 days); products of activation reactions with the explosion neutrons — europium-152 ($T_{1/2}$=12 years) and europium-154 ($T_{1/2}$=16 years). Some data on the possible formation of europium-152 and 154 during the fission of nuclear fuel have appeared lately /1/.

According to published data, europium-152, 154, 155 and 156 were detected in the epicentral zone of nuclear tests conducted in Nevada, USA /4, 5, 7/. Europium-155 was found in atmospheric air /3,6/. These europium radioisotopes were not found earlier in the composition of the radioactive global contamination of the earth's surface.

A sample of forest moss was selected in October 1968 in the Lake Rits region (Caucasus) with a view to examining the presence of europium in the global contamination of a locality. The sample was taken from an area of $50 \times 50 \, m^2$. The total area of the sample was about 6 m², and the weight 50 kg. Samples of moss were taken in places possessing a uniform and thick carpet of moss. It is known /8/ that forest moss adsorbs well the products of nuclear blasts. Besides, such a sample is more convenient for subsequent chemical enrichment than a soil sample.

The representativeness of a sample of such dimensions for the specified area can be considered satisfactory. The sample was incinerated at a temperature of the order of 200°C and then subjected to gamma-spectrometric and radiochemical analysis. The gamma-spectrometric methods were used to determine quantitatively antimony-125 ($T_{1/2}$=2 years) and cesium-137 ($T_{1/2}$=30 years). For identification and a quantitative analysis of the radioisotopes of europium, the fraction of rare-earth elements, purified of cerium by threefold precipitation of Ce $(IO_3)_4$, was isolated radiochemically.

The gamma-spectrometry of the rare-earth fraction established that of the europium radioisotopes listed, only europium-155 is present at a concentration of about $1.4 \cdot 10^{-11}$ curie/g per sample. Europium-152 and 154 were not found in measurable quantities. Taking into account the sensitivity of the analytical methods used, we can conclude that their amount cannot exceed $6 \cdot 10^{-13}$ curie/g.

The analysis established that the cesium-137, antimony-125 and europium-155 contamination densities of the locality stand in the ratio $100 : 16.6 : 2.0$.

Thus, for levels of global contamination by cesium-137 of 80—150 mcurie/km^2, europium-155 contamination lies within the limits 1.6—3.0 mcurie/km^2. The power of the gamma-radiation dose at a height of 1 m is then of the order of 10^{-2} μroentgen/hour, i.e., very small compared with the power of the dose from the natural radioactivity of the soil and its contamination by cesium-137.

On the basis of data on the contamination of the locality by antimony-125 and europium-155, we can give a tentative estimate of the ratio of the yields of these isotopes (K_i) during fission.

According to /2/,

$$\frac{Q_1(t)}{Q_2(t)} = e^{-(\lambda_1 - \lambda_2) t} \; \frac{\lambda_1 \int\limits_{-\infty}^{t} e^{\lambda_1 t} q_1(t)\, dt}{\lambda_2 \int\limits_{-\infty}^{t} e^{\lambda_2 t} q_2(t)\, dt}, \tag{1}$$

where $Q_i(t)$ is the contamination density (curie/km^2) at time t; λ_i is the decay constant (sec^{-1}); $q_i(t)$ is the fallout (atom/km$^2 \cdot$ sec).

Functions $q_i(t)$ are not known exactly, and therefore we can conduct only very rough, tentative calculations of the ratio K_1/K_2. Subscripts 1 and 2 correspond to antimony-125 and europium-155, respectively.

We shall assume that the fallout of these isotopes obeys the same law and is proportional to their yield: $q_i(t) = K_i q(t)$.

Then (1) assumes the form

$$\frac{Q_1(t)}{Q_2(t)} = \frac{\lambda_1 K_1}{\lambda_2 K_2} f(t). \tag{2}$$

Due to the large period of half-decay of antimony-125, the ratio $q_1(t)/q_2(t)$ must actually grow with time. Therefore, on our assumption that $q_1(t)/q_2(t) = K_1/K_2$ the calculated value of $f(t)$ will be lower than the true value, independently of the form of function $q(t)$. The ratio K_1/K_2 determined by (2) will be correspondingly higher than the true value.

We assumed in calculating $f(t)$ that $q(t)$ changes with time in direct ratio to the concentration of europium-155 in air. The data on the concentration of europium for 1961—1967 were taken from /3/. The main contribution to the contamination of the locality was due to the 1962—1965 fallout. The calculated value of $f(t)$ was found to be 1.4, to which corresponds $K_1/K_2 = 7$.

The 1962—1967 fallout was almost completely due to thermonuclear weapons tests. The cumulative yield of antimony-125 for the fission reaction of uranium-238 into neutrons with energy of 14 MeV is known satisfactorily and is equal to 1%. Therefore, the yield of europium-155, according to the established ratio $K_1/K_2 = 7$, is $K_2 = 0.14\%$. This value coincides with the yield found from the ratio between the concentrations of europium-155 and cerium-144 in air for the period 1961—1967 /3/. Note that such an "exact" coincidence is due to chance. It is difficult to estimate the errors of our method. In any case they are not lower than 20%.

The practical absence in the radioactive global fallout of long-lived isotopes of europium-152 and europium-154 enables us to assume that even if they are formed during fission, their yield is very low, and at least smaller by an order of magnitude than for europium-155.

Long-lived radioisotopes of europium are formed in considerable quantities under activation by soil neutrons. Therefore we can assert that surface and underground explosions contribute little to contemporary global contamination of a locality.

BIBLIOGRAPHY

1. Z y s i n, Yu. A. et al. Vykhody produktov deleniya i ikh raspredelenie po massam (Yields of Fission Products and their Mass Distribution). — Moskva, Gosatomizdat. 1963.
2. K o g a n, R. M., I. M. N a z a r o v, and Sh. D. F r i d m a n. Osnovy gamma-spektrometrii prirodnykh sred (Foundations of Gamma-Spectroscopy of Natural Media). — Moskva, Atomizdat. 1969.
3. A a r k r o g, A. and I. L i p p e r t. Europium-155 in Debris from Nuclear Weapons. — Science, Vol. 157, No. 3787, 1967.
4. B o n n e r, N. A. and I. A. M i s k e l. Radioactivity. Distribution from Cratering in Basalt. — Science, Vol. 150, No. 3695. 1965.
5. K r i q u e r, H. L. The Measurement of Long-lived Radioisotopes in Soil by Gamma-Spectroscopy. — Health Physics, Vol. 11, No. 7. 1965.
6. Radioactive Fallout from Nuclear Weapon Tests. Proc. Second Conf., Germantown, Maryland. 1964. — AEC. 5 Symposium Series. 1965.
7. S a l t e r, L. P. and I. H. H a r l e y. "Trinitite" Cobalt-60, Cesium-137 and Europium-152. — Science, Vol. 148, No. 3672. 1965.
8. S v e n s s o n, G. K. and K. L i d e n. The Quantitative Accumulation of $Zr^{25} + Nb^{95}$ and $Ba^{140} + La^{140}$ in Carpets of Forest Moss. A Field Study. — Health Physics, Vol. 11, No. 9. 1965.

UDC 551.576.1

SOME CHARACTERISTICS OF UPPER CLOUDS AND SUGGESTIONS REGARDING THE UTILIZATION OF RADIOACTIVE TRACERS IN MERIDIONAL FLOWS

N. N. Romanov

The analysis of numerous reports of aircraft pilots and observations by the author himself during research flights in TU-104 and IL-18 aircraft lead to the establishment of a relationship between the development of upper clouds and the direction of wind with a large meridional component. Independently of the character of the baric field, the clouds develop under southern and southwestern stable flows and are destroyed (or are absent) by northern and northeastern flows.

This relationship is expressed more strongly in low latitudes and is weaker in high latitudes. It is assumed that such a relationship results from stable vertical currents of positive or negative sign, appearing in meridional flows on the rotating Earth. It is suggested that direct measurement of vertical motions be conducted with the aid of radioactive tracers during a rationally selected synoptic situation.

The utilization of both artificial and natural radioactive tracers for solving specific meteorological problems is on the increase. Some of the advantages of radioactive tracers, which enable us to follow the motion of air masses of relatively limited volume, are well known. The prospect of measuring ordered vertical air motion, so important in weather formation and so unreliably determined by other methods (including theoretical models of the atmosphere), is very tempting.

However, the utilization of radioactive tracers for a reliable assessment of the vertical motions in any synoptic situation is evidently associated with large, and at times insurmountable, difficulties. Experience in studying atmospheric processes on a synoptic scale shows that the fields of vertical currents in the atmosphere are frequently unstable. Therefore the experimental measurement of these currents at different levels should be conducted for situations in which there is reason to believe that at least the sign of the vertical velocities will be stable during a period of several hours at least.

Some considerations regarding the selection of suitable circulation conditions arise as a result of investigations into the dynamics of upper clouds.

Low clouds are weakly correlated with wind direction at the altitude of the clouds. At heights from 500 to 200 mb, there already exist preferential wind directions to which correspond either clouds (at the same heights) or clear sky. The correlation is expressed very clearly in large-scale flows possessing uniform direction and a considerable meridional wind component.

The analysis of several thousand aircraft reports and the subsequent results of the author's research flights in TU-104 and IL-18 aircraft (totaling over 1 mil. km flight) established that upper clouds develop strongly in southern and southwestern flows in the upper troposphere and lower stratosphere and are destroyed (or quite absent) under considerable northern and northeastern wind components. It is important to stress that the character of the high baric field and the form of the heat advection clearly play a secondary role. Thus, in spite of ordinary synoptic concepts, in large inversion troughs (with axis directed from south to north) clouds develop at the back of the trough and not at its front; in the front they are rapidly destroyed. The more intense and better organized the meridionality of the flows, the clearer this law. With the accumulation of satellite meteorological information we can even observe this fact from TV images of clouds, by comparing them carefully with baric topography charts. However, this is not all.

A more detailed investigation of both air and ground observations of upper clouds led to the detection of a clearly expressed latitudinal effect of the dynamics of clouds in meridional flows. This effect consists mainly of the following. *

In lower latitudes, the dependence of cloud development on wind directions (with large meridional component) is more sharply expressed, and decreases with increasing latitude.

In other words, if we select similar circulation conditions in different latitudinal ranges, the southern high flows in low latitudes are accompanied by more developed upper clouds than in high latitudes, and the destructive effect of northern flows is intensified with displacement to the south. We can assume on the basis of available data that this relationship is nonexistent in polar regions.

This fact leads to a number of consequences. It explains prefrontal clouds ahead of cold fronts, the different degree of development of cloud systems on warm fronts, cloud characteristics near "diving" cyclones, and so on.

It is natural to conclude that the large meridional shifts of air masses on the rotating Earth are accompanied by stable vertical currents. The currents caused by orographic or other factors are apparently weaker than the first ones (recall that we speak only of currents above 500 mb).

However, this assumption is still in need of direct corroboration. The necessity of the direct measurement of vertical motions during the synoptic situation mentioned above is obvious. It is important to conduct the experiment under conditions as ideal as possible. Competent selection of the situation must be guaranteed.

It is probably possible to use here both natural and artificial tracers. Since the experiment can be limited to a duration of 15—20 hours, the complications caused by artificial tracer diffusion will not be considerable. As to the cloud-tracer along the horizontal caused by vertical wind shifts, it is unimportant in this problem. It therefore appears more effective to use here a suitably selected, safe artificial tracer.

---

* The upper clouds were studied between 30 and 70° N and 0 and 90° E.

UDC 551

MEAN AND TURBULENT TRANSFER OF SUBSTANCES OVER THE USSR

I. G. Guterman

The relation is examined between the mean and turbulent fluxes of substances at the limit of the atmospheric boundary layer (1.5 km) in January and July over the USSR. It is shown that the intensity of macroturbulent fluctuations, characterized by the ratio of the vectorial standard deviation of wind σ_v to the modulus of the resultant wind $|\vec{V_r}|$, is equal to 100—500 % in winter and 200—2,000 % in summer. This results mainly from the decrease in mean transfer, since the macroturbulent component of the motion σ_v in summer is of the same order as in winter.

Turbulent heat fluxes in January hardly attain 1—3 % of the fluxes due to the mean motion, while in July this ratio increases to 4—7 %. Therefore, the practically horizontal heat fluxes at that level can be calculated from data on the mean temperature and resultant wind. The streamlines of turbulent heat fluxes coincide with the direction of the temperature gradient and, over the USSR in both January and July, are generally opposite to or intersect at right angles the streamlines plotted on the basis of the average wind speed vector. Hence the total heat fluxes are vectorially somewhat smaller than the mean heat fluxes.

Horizontal turbulent moisture fluxes make a more important contribution to the total moisture flux. At 1.5 km, the ratio of the turbulent moisture flux to the moisture carried by the mean motion fluctuates between 20 and 180 %, and in July between 40 and 140 %. Over the USSR, within a single season the regions of increased and reduced turbulence of the fluxes of the three considered substances coincide roughly, although the relative annual range of fluctuations for the different substances is different.

The direction of the turbulent moisture fluxes almost coincides with that of the horizontal gradients of mean absolute humidity. Over the USSR we isolated regions where the turbulent moisture fluxes are integrated with the mean moisture fluxes, and, on the other hand, regions where the total moisture fluxes are weakened sharply as a result of oppositely directed fluxes of the two kinds.

INTRODUCTION

Data are available which enable one to estimate the character of the atmospheric transfer of heat, moisture, momentum, energy, contamination products, and so on. We have in mind aeroclimatic wind characteristics at various levels or mean characteristics in layers of different thickness, published during 1961—1968 /2, 3, 12/. The atlas of mean wind characteristics over the northern hemisphere is used extensively for solving problems associated with the transfer of substances. It contains extensive information concerning mean winds, such as the mean (resultant) wind in a layer, its magnitude and direction, the vectorial standard deviation of the mean wind, and also 8-point wind roses of the mean wind and corresponding mean velocities.

The study of air currents over the USSR, and as a whole over the western hemisphere /6/, established the considerable scatter of winds with respect to their mean values calculated for a period of several (8 to 10) years. Wind scatter is estimated by the vectorial standard deviation. The utilization of this statistical characteristic enables one to calculate the turbulent atmospheric transfer of substances in addition to the mean transfer, evaluated on the basis of the resultant wind vector. The overall transfer comprises the mean and macroturbulent components of the motions. In regions where macroturbulent fluctuations of the currents are large compared with the mean flux, the total flux can exceed considerably the flux due to the mean current alone.

We shall establish in this paper the part played by the macroturbulent component of the fluxes of mass, heat and moisture in the overall (total) horizontal transfer, and shall compare it with the mean flux of these substances over the USSR. The solution of this problem is of great scientific and practical value.

Knowledge of the fluxes of substances is necessary for calculating their convergence after the substance balance has been established. The balances of heat, moisture, energy, angular momentum, are basic factors, which determine the climate and the general circulation of the atmosphere /7, 9/.

We examine the magnitude and direction ratios of the mean turbulent fluxes of heat and moisture at 1.5 km above sea level, i. e., roughly at the upper limit of the boundary layer. The investigation is based on the data of 96 USSR aerological stations, processed for the period 1957—1964 /13/.

The mean (resultant) transfer, calculated for a given period, reflects in some cases, sufficiently closely, the dominant transfer of substances. However, it does not suffice for estimating the changes (deviations) of individual fluxes with respect to the mean flux, occurring as a result of changes in circulation types (cyclones and anticyclones) /6, 10/. We must recognize that fluctuations calculated on the basis of radiosonde observations conducted over a six-hour period reflect atmospheric macroturbulence on a scale exceeding a hundred kilometers along the horizontal. Fluctuations of shorter period and smaller horizontal scale are not always recorded during 6-hour observation periods /11/.

When calculating total horizontal fluxes of substances as sums of the individual fluxes, we detect not only a variation in wind and in the substance with time, but also the existence of a correlation between the two characteristics. The time variation in the wind and substance cannot be expressed as a function. The degree to which they are related is characterized by the correlation coefficient, which fluctuates widely. Thus, when calculating turbulent fluxes of angular momentum we established (to within ±0.4) correlation coefficients between zonal and meridional components of the wind vector, depending on height, time of year, and circulation and relief conditions /7/. The coefficients of correlation between changes in heat or moisture and wind speed are low (of the order of hundredths), while between the same substances and wind directions they are higher, of the order of 0.2±0.3.

§1. MACROTURBULENCE IN THE ATMOSPHERE

The turbulence intensity in the velocity field can be characterized by the ratio of the vectorial standard deviation σ_v of wind to the modulus of the resultant vector $|\vec{V_r}|$, expressed as a percentage. The macroturbulence intensity in the atmosphere compared with the intensity of the ordered motion will be larger, the larger the calculated relative value.

In January at 1.5 km, the ratio $\sigma_v/|\vec{V_r}|$ over a large part of the USSR attains 100 and even 200% (Table 1).

TABLE 1. Vectorial standard deviation σ_v (m/sec), modulus of the resultant wind $|\vec{V_r}|$ (m/sec) and turbulence intensity $\sigma_v/|\vec{V_r}|$ (%) over the USSR (at 1.5 km)

Station	σ_v	$|\vec{V_r}|$	$\sigma_v/|\vec{V_r}|$	Station	σ_v	$|\vec{V_r}|$	$\sigma_v/|\vec{V_r}|$
January				Khar'kov	8.1	0.8	1070
Murmansk	12.0	4.2	300	Rostov-on-Don	8.3	0.5	1650
Petrozavodsk	11.3	4.2	262	Volgograd	7.8	1.5	520
Arkhangel'sk	10.4	3.1	333	Kursk	8.3	1.1	755
Vologda	11.2	4.3	260	Tambov	8.7	1.1	780
Odessa	9.3	3.3	280	Kazan'	7.6	1.3	585
Khar'kov	10.4	4.0	260	Sverdlovsk	8.3	2.4	350
Vladivostok	9.4	11.0	85	Aleksandrovskoe	8.3	1.9	440
Borzya	7.7	7.9	87	Tobol'sk	8.7	2.5	350
Chita	6.9	7.3	94	Omsk	7.6	1.6	475
Kirensk	7.5	8.2	91	Aktyubinsk	7.8	2.4	320
Vitim	7.3	9.0	81	Aral Sea	7.4	3.5	210
Troitskii Priisk	4.4	4.7	93	Chardzhou	5.5	6.9	78
Nizhne-Udinsk	8.3	8.6	96	Novosibirsk	8.0	0.3	2600
Krasnoyarsk	9.9	10.7	92	Krasnoyarsk	7.1	0.5	1420
Alma-Ata	3.7	0.5	740	Podkamennaya Tunguska	7.6	0.6	1260
Balkhash	8.8	2.5	350	Nizhne-Udinsk	6.1	1.0	610
Aral Sea	9.9	3.0	330	Irkutsk	6.7	2.1	320
Mys Vasil'eva	9.5	2.8	340	Chita	7.0	6.1	110
Petropavlovsk-Kamchatskii	11.2	2.4	470	Kyzyl	4.9	1.4	350
Bering I.	10.7	2.5	430	Kirensk	6.3	1.8	350
Klyuchi	10.3	2.3	450	Krasnyi Chikoi	5.9	1.2	490
Anadyr'	10.4	2.6	400	Vitim	6.4	1.4	460
Nagaevo	9.2	3.4	270	Troitskii Priisk	5.2	1.3	400
Gizhiga	10.3	3.2	320	Aldan	6.8	0.4	1700
				Yakutsk	7.2	0.8	900
July				Blagoveshchensk	9.2	0.6	1530
Kaunas	7.9	3.5	223	Ayan	8.0	1.1	730
Brest	7.6	3.3	230	Vladivostok	8.0	4.1	190
L'vov	7.2	3.1	230	Yuzhno-Sakhalinsk	8.7	3.0	290
Arkhangel'sk	8.2	0.9	910	Yuzhno-Kuril'sk	8.0	3.7	290
Kirov	7.8	0.8	975	Petropavlovsk-Kamchatskii	8.0	0.7	1140
Pechora	8.1	0.9	900	Mys Vasil'eva	9.8	1.2	820
Salekhard	8.5	1.4	607	Bering I.	8.7	1.2	720
Moscow	8.8	1.4	630				

For example, at the northwestern and southwestern parts of European USSR there are regions where the macroturbulent component of the motion exceeds the mean motion component by a factor of 2.5. Along the line of increased mean transfer from the Maritime Territory to the Baikal region and Eastern Siberia, the ratio $\sigma_v/|\vec{V_r}|$ is minimal (85—100%). Over the elevations of Soviet Central Asia the turbulence intensity is considerable (Alma-Ata); over the surrounding plains (Balkhash, Chardzhou) it decreases.

A clear predominance of macroturbulent fluctuations in air streams over the mean stream is seen above the Kamchatka peninsula, where the ratio $\sigma_v/|\vec{V_r}|$ attains 450%. The increased turbulence in January in this region is associated with a frequent reversal in the direction of transfer from the Pacific Ocean: from the Sea of Okhotsk into the system of moving cyclones.

Very weak resultant flows are observed in July at 1.5 km; their mean velocity compared with the value in January decreases by a factor of two to five, and over certain regions even by an order of magnitude. The wind scatters σ_v in January and July are roughly equal (Table 1). As a result the ratio $\sigma_v/|\vec{V_r}|$% in July is large and within the territory of the USSR fluctuates between 100 and 1,000%. Over some regions the ratio $\sigma_v/|\vec{V_r}|$ for a weak resultant wind speed attains 2,000%.

The distribution of turbulence intensity over the territory follows a pattern. At the west of European USSR it is low ($\sim$200%), to the east over the central part the fluctuations increase, reaching 1,000% over some stations. To the east of the Ural mountains over Asian USSR we distinguish two zones of reduced turbulence intensity: the first one comprising Sverdlovsk, Omsk and Chelyabinsk, and the second Irkutsk, Chita, Krasnyi Chikoi and Troitskii Priisk; and two regions of increased turbulence intensities: one over Western Siberia (Novosibirsk, Krasnoyarsk, Podkamennaya Tunpuska), the other over the south of Yakutia and the Amur region (Aldan, Blagoveshchensk). Over the southern part of the Maritime Territory (Vladivostok), Yuzhno-Sakhalinsk, Yuzhno-Kuril'sk and over the Sea of Okhotsk, the fluctuations exceed the mean flows by no more than 200—300%.

In July, as in January, there remains considerable macroturbulence over the Kamchatka peninsula. The frequent change in the paths of cyclones from the Pacific Ocean and from the Sea of Japan leads to a sharp drop in the resultant motion component, and the ratio $\sigma_v/|\vec{V_r}|$ attains a maximum reaching 1,142% over Petropavlovsk-Kamchatskii.

§2. RATIO BETWEEN THE MACROTURBULENT AND MEAN HEAT FLUXES

We shall estimate the intensity of turbulent heat fluxes from the ratio between the turbulent heat flux F_T' and the mean heat flux F_T at the limit of the boundary layer (Figure 1).

In January at 1.5 km, the fluctuating heat flux over the USSR is negligibly small (0.5—3% of the mean flux). The minimum of ratio F_T'/F_T is 0.5%, observed over Transbaikalia and Maritime Territory. Here one observes in winter a strong continental monsoon, characterized by the northwestern transfer of all the substances.

Over Yakutia, Chukchi National District, the Kamchatka peninsula and the Sea of Okhotsk the intensity of turbulent heat fluxes is large and the ratio F'_T/F_T attains $2-3\%$. Another center of turbulence increase in heat flux is observed along the western boundary of the USSR, where F'_T/F_T reaches 2%.

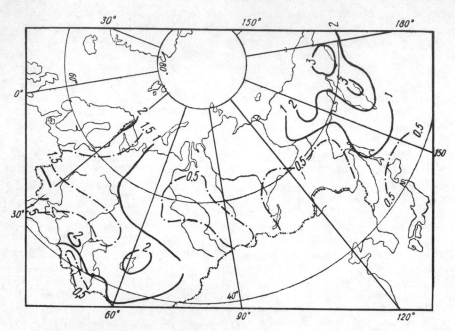

FIGURE 1.   Ratio between turbulent and mean heat fluxes (%) in January at 1.5 km.

In July (Figure 2), the ratio between the turbulent and mean heat fluxes increases as against January. Over the USSR we observe an alternation of zones of increased and decreased intensity of the turbulent heat fluxes. Over the central regions of European USSR, a region of high ratios F'_T/F_T is localized, whose magnitude to the north of the Sea of Azov reaches $6-7\%$. Over the Urals the ratio F'_T/F_T drops to 1%. Over Eastern Siberia, a second center of increased intensity of the turbulence of the heat fluxes is observed, at the center of which F'_T/F_T attains 5%. Over Transbaikalia, a center of low turbulent heat flux values is again in evidence. The center of increased turbulent heat flux is localized over the south of Yakutia and the Amur region. Here, at the very center (the Aldan station) the ratio between the turbulent and mean heat fluxes attains 7%.

At the south of Maritime Territory and the Khabarovsk littoral the ratio drops to 1%. A further drop in turbulent heat fluxes is observed over the Sea of Okhotsk, when in summer the marine monsoonal heat flux plays a predominant role. Finally, over the Kamchatka peninsula, in the same way as over the extreme north of Eastern Siberia and Chukchi, some increase in the ratio is observed (up to $3-4\%$).

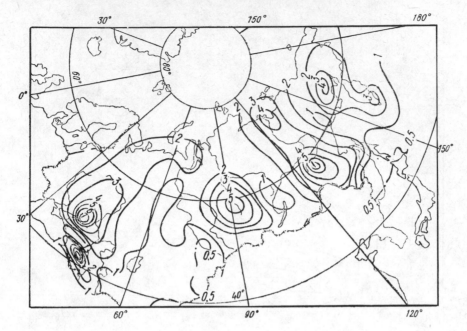

FIGURE 2. Ratio between turbulent and mean heat fluxes (%) in July at 1.5 km.

§3. PERTURBATION OF MOISTURE FLUXES

The turbulent component of the moisture flux contributes considerably to the total moisture flux over the USSR. The turbulence intensity, characterized by the ratio of the turbulent flux F'_a to the mean moisture flux F_a, reaches 100% and more (Figure 3). Within the USSR at the 1.5-km level in January, it varies between 20% in regions possessing minimum intensity of the turbulence of the heat fluxes (such as Transbaikalia, to the south of Yakutia, the Amur region and Maritime Territory, where a strong mean transfer is dominant in the continental monsoon system) and 180% over Kamchatka, where a frequent change is observed in the direction and magnitude of the moisture flux in passing cyclones /1, 7/.

Turbulent fluxes play a more considerable role in the total moisture flux over the central and northwestern parts of European USSR. Another center of large turbulent moisture fluxes is observed in January over Kazakhstan. Over Balkhash, the ratio between the turbulent moisture flux and the mean flux attains 120%. Over the remaining part of the USSR the ratio F'_a/F_a is 40—60%, i.e., the contribution of moisture transfer by turbulent eddies is half that of the mean moisture transfer /5, 7, 8/.

In July at 1.5 km (Figure 4), over the USSR, one cannot observe a sharp increase in the part played by turbulent fluxes in the total moisture transfer, such as we saw in the analysis of turbulent heat fluxes and macroturbulence in the velocity field. Thus, the annual cycle of the turbulence intensity of fluxes of different substances varies.

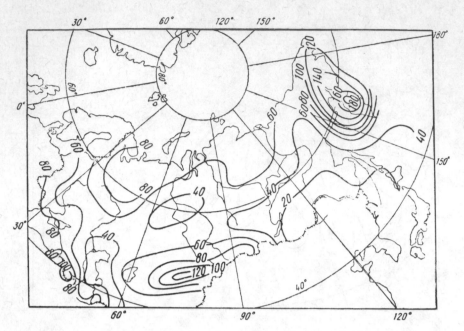

FIGURE 3. Ratio between turbulent and mean moisture fluxes (%) in January at 1.5 km.

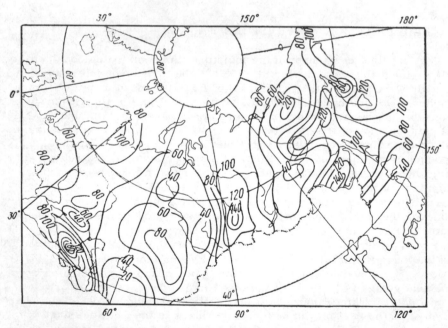

FIGURE 4. Ratio between turbulent and mean moisture fluxes (%) in July at 1.5 km.

Over the USSR, the intensity of the moisture turbulence in July varies strongly. We find centers of minimum intensity with ratio F'_a/F_a equal to 20—40% over Soviet Central Asia and up to 140% at the centers of maximum intensity over Eastern Siberia and the Amur region. To the south of Maritime Territory (Vladivostok) the ratio of turbulent fluxes to mean moisture fluxes drops to 40—50%.

The field of the turbulence intensity of moisture fluxes over the USSR in January, and especially in July, is split into a number of alternating centers of high and low intensity. There exist about four such waves in July over the USSR in a latitudinal direction. A similar pattern is observed in July as regards the distribution of the intensity of turbulent heat fluxes over the USSR.

§4. DIRECTION OF THE MEAN FLUXES OF SUBSTANCES

We examined above the ratio between macroturbulent and mean fluxes of mass, heat, and moisture in the atmosphere at the 1.5-km level. We shall estimate now the ratio between the directions of these fluxes.

The directions of the mean fluxes of the substances will naturally be the same and coincide with the direction of the resulting wind vector. The directions of the turbulent fluxes, which are determined by the direction of the horizontal gradient of the substance, will differ from substance to substance. The directions of the total fluxes of the substances will also differ, since they represent the vectorial sum of the mean and fluctuating fluxes.

We shall estimate the direction of the mean fluxes from the streamlines of the resulting velocity vector at the 1.5-km level in January (Figure 5) and July (Figure 6). The January streamlines characterize the predominance of west-east transfer over European USSR and most of Siberia, especially in its northern regions. Over Soviet Central Asia and in part over the south of European USSR, southwestern and west-southwest fluxes dominate. At the extreme northeast of the USSR there is a predominate eastern mean transfer in the system of the frontal and northern parts of the baric depression. Intensifying fluxes in a northwesterly direction are observed over the south of Yakutia, the south of Khabarovsk Territory, and Maritime Territory. This is the northwest winter transfer of substances into the system of mean fluxes from the continent to the ocean. At that part of the littoral farther to the east of the estuary of the Amur River until Vladivostok, the fluxes are directed almost normal to the littoral line. Over Kamchatka and the Sea of Okhotsk the mean fluxes of substances have an almost northerly direction.

The analysis of the resultant velocities (Table 1) indicated a sharp drop in July compared with January. The mean streamlines also differ. In July (Figure 6), westerly and southwesterly directions predominate over the northern half of European USSR. As is evident from the thickening of the streamlines, larger velocities are observed here. The streamlines bend to the south of European USSR and over the Turan depression. Instead of the northwesterly direction over the southwest of European USSR, they acquire north, northeast, and even eastern directions.

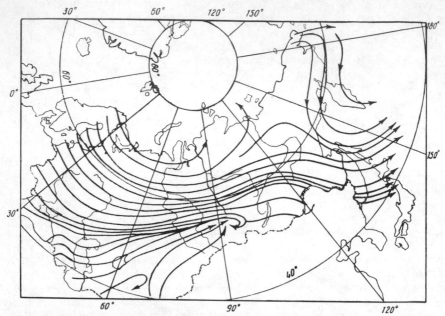

FIGURE 5. Mean transfer streamlines in January at 1.5 km.

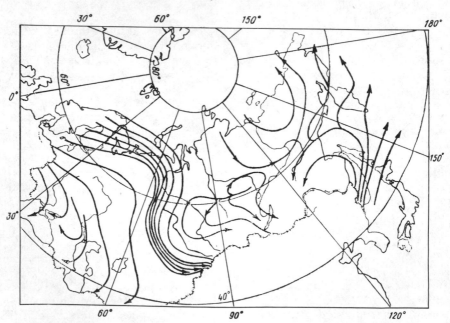

FIGURE 6. Mean transfer streamlines in July at 1.5 km.

Unstable mean fluxes with a mainly northern component are observed to the east of the Urals over Siberia. In the belt of moderate latitudes 50—55°N over Eastern Siberia, weak eastern fluxes dominate. Intensifying western and southwestern fluxes dominate to the north and south of the region of easterly winds, in particular over Maritime Territory.

§5. DIRECTION OF TURBULENT HEAT AND
MOISTURE FLUXES IN JANUARY

The direction of turbulent heat and moisture fluxes in January is illustrated on Figures 7 and 8, respectively. In January, the direction of the turbulent heat fluxes is very similar to that of the horizontal temperature gradients. At 1.5 km above sea level they are oriented in general from south to southwest in the western parts of the territory, and from the east (from the Ocean) in the eastern parts. For example, over the northwest of European USSR the direction of turbulent heat fluxes approximates that of the mean flux, and as a result the total flux here is intensified. Over the remaining part of the territory, up to the axis of the cold depression over Yakutia, the turbulent heat fluxes possess a large southern component and so do not contribute substantially to the total heat flux. The conclusion, that here the total heat flux can be calculated in practice from mean climatic data on wind and temperature, is also corroborated by the fact that the turbulent flux F_T' over most of the USSR is in winter 0.5—1% of the mean flux (in absolute value, $5—10 \cdot 10^3$ W·m/kg).

Of great interest is the analysis of the direction of turbulent heat fluxes to the east of the Yakutia cold depression. Along the axis of this depression (120—125°E) one observes a convergence of turbulent heat fluxes from the west and southwest and eastern fluxes directed from the Pacific Ocean. Such convergent fluxes create a region of turbulent heat outflow in the cold depression over Yakutia. Naturally, to the east of the cold axis the turbulent heat fluxes, which in winter possess a direction almost opposing that of the mean heat flux, must in spite of their small relative value (1—3%, Figure 1) nevertheless lower the total transport of heat from the continent to the ocean in the winter monsoon system.

The streamlines of turbulent moisture transfer (Figure 8) generally intersect the absolute humidity isolines (g/m^3) at right angles over the USSR. Thus in the turbulent field, moisture does not in practice diffuse against the gradient. An exception is represented by the winter conditions over Maritime Territory, characterized by coincidence between the northwestern direction of the mean transfer streamlines (Figure 5) and the direction of the turbulent transfer streamlines (Figure 8). The moisture content at the 1.5-km level increases along the streamlines from the continent toward the sea, which indicates countergradient turbulent diffusion. However, the data on flux ratios in Figure 3 show that the turbulent moisture flux is here small and represents less than 20% of the mean flux.

51

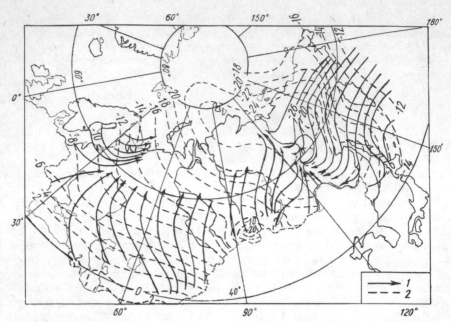

FIGURE 7. Field of mean temperature and streamlines of turbulent heat flux in January at 1.5 km:

1) streamlines; 2) isotherms.

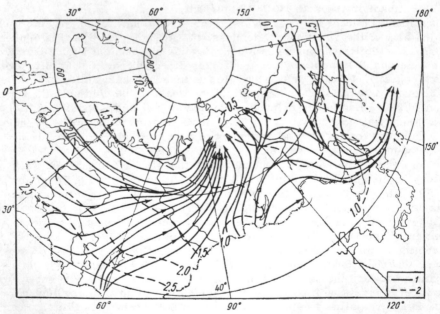

FIGURE 8. Field of mean absolute humidity and streamlines of turbulent moisture flux in January at 1.5 km:

1) streamlines; 2) isolines of absolute humidity (10^{-3} kg/m^3).

At the height (1.5 km) studied, the turbulent transport of moisture from the east, i. e., from the ocean inside Yakutia, is expressed much more clearly. Indeed, a moisture outflow is formed along the dry air tongue extending from Yakutia to the northern part of the Amur region. The convergence of turbulent fluxes is created at the expense of moisture brought from the relatively warm and moist regions of the Sea of Okhotsk and the Pacific Ocean, and also at the expense of moisture entering from the northwest. The turbulent moisture fluxes in January over the extreme northeast of Siberia, as along the north of the Sea of Okhotsk, coincide in direction with the streamlines of the mean motion (Figure 5). Since atmospheric humidity inside the continent decreases (see the isolines on Figure 8), coincidence of the fluxes indicates a considerable moisture influx in winter from the sea to the littoral. Over Chukchi and Kamchatka one can therefore observe overcast skies and considerable precipitation /1/.

Such an addition of mean and turbulent moisture fluxes entering the continent from the Atlantic is evident at the northwest of European USSR and to the east, up to the Northern Urals. Cloudiness and precipitation charts /1/ corroborate the presence here of a considerable transport of humid air to the continent.

§6. DIRECTION OF TURBULENT FLUXES OF HEAT
AND MOISTURE IN JULY

In July, the total horizontal heat fluxes remain smaller than in January, in spite of the sharp increase in the turbulent component. At the same time, the part played by turbulent heat fluxes increases in July by a factor of 2 to 5 compared with January. In order to estimate the heat balance within the USSR territory it is important to determine regions where the directions of turbulent heat flux streamlines coincide with the directions of the mean motion streamlines, resulting in the intensification of the total heat fluxes.

In July (Figure 9), as in January, turbulent heat fluxes are mainly directed along the temperature gradient. Over European USSR the turbulent fluxes are directed from the southeast, from the warm regions of Soviet Central Asia. Over the extreme south regions the mean monthly air temperature is highest (28°C). Over the south of European USSR the turbulent fluxes are directed against the mean heat fluxes (Figures 6 and 9). Over Central and Eastern Siberia turbulent heat fluxes have a southerly direction. Turbulent heat outflow exists in the summer cold depression, oriented toward the lower reaches of the Ob' and Enisei rivers. Over Maritime Territory the streamlines of the turbulent and mean heat fluxes coincide, hence increasing the total heat flux, directed from the overheated territory of Northern China to the north of the Sea of Japan.

Over the Sea of Okhotsk and the Far East littoral, the two heat fluxes are directed in opposing directions (the mean-motion fluxes, sustaining the monsoon circulation, have an easterly direction, while the turbulent fluxes have an almost westerly one, coinciding with the horizontal temperature gradient). At the heat crest, directed from Transbaikalia to the Kolyma estuary (East Siberia Sea) (Figure 9), the two heat fluxes probably combine.

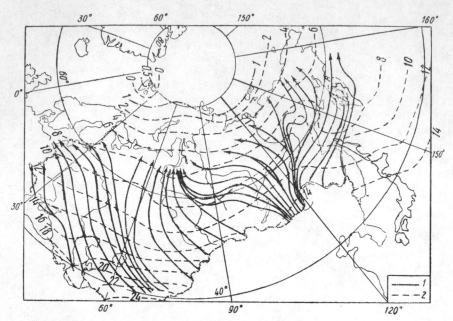

FIGURE 9. Field of mean temperature and streamlines of turbulent heat flux in July at 1.5 km.
Legend as in Figure 7.

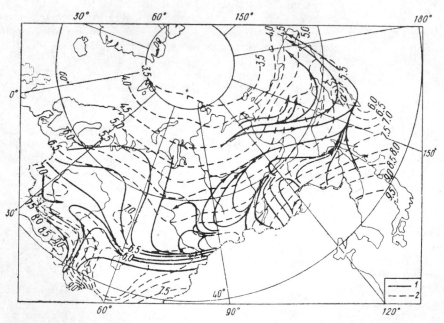

FIGURE 10. Field of mean absolute humidity and streamlines of turbulent moisture flux in July at 1.5 km.
Legend as in Figure 8.

The turbulent heat fluxes in July over most of the USSR have southwesterly and westerly directions. Over the northwest of the USSR and over Maritime Territory the absolute humidity gradients have an almost westerly direction and, as seen from Figure 10, the turbulent fluxes over these regions are deflected to the west (toward the leading flux) from the direction of the moisture gradient.

Two outflow regions of the turbulent moisture fluxes are observed in July over the Turan depression and over the region between the Don and Volga rivers. Dry air tongues are clearly observed in both regions. Moisture outflow is observed here as a result of its influx from the Caspian Sea in the first region and from the Sea of Azov, and somewhat from the Black Sea in the other region.

Over Maritime Territory and over Kamchatka the turbulent moisture fluxes are oriented from the southwest and west, i. e., from the continent to the sea. Their direction coincides in general with the absolute humidity gradient (Figure 10), which in summer is higher over the continent than over the sea. As a result, rapid moistening and much precipitation occurs in summer over the Sea of Okhotsk and over Kamchatka.

Other relations between the directions of turbulent and mean moisture fluxes are observed over the western part of the Sea of Okhotsk, the Lower Amur region, southern Yakutia, the Amur region and Cisbaikalia. The summer monsoon fluxes (Figure 6) here have an easterly direction. At the 1.5-km level they extend to 120°E, i. e., to Transbaikalia, where convergence occurs along the mean streamlines. Over these regions, on the other hand, turbulent fluxes have an almost westerly direction. The total moisture flux in the summer monsoon will be negligibly small owing to the vectorial addition of the two components. It can be assumed that cloudiness and precipitation over Transbaikalia, over the Amur region, and somewhat over southern Yakutia are probably due to the cyclonic activity at the Mongolian front, although the Pacific front cyclones, connected by the system of south-eastern monsoons, might play a part /1, 7, 8/.

BIBLIOGRAPHY

1. Alisov, B. P. Klimat SSSR (The Climate of the USSR).— Izdatel'stvo MGU. 1956.
2. Aeroklimaticheskii atlas kharakteristik vetra Severnogo polushariya (Aeroclimatic Atlas of Northern Hemisphere Wind Characteristics).— Moskva, Rotaprint, NIIAK. 1963.
3. Aeroklimaticheskii spravochnik kharakteristik vetra v uzlakh koordinatnoi setki Severnogo polushariya (Aeroclimatic Handbook of Wind Characteristics at Network Points of the Northern Hemisphere).— Moskva, Rotaprint, NIIAK. 1965.
4. Budyko, M. I. Teplovoi balans zemnoi poverkhnosti (Heat Balance of the Earth's Surface).— Leningrad, Gidrometeoizdat. 1956.
5. Vereshchagin, M. A. O gorizontal'nykh perenosakh skrytogo tepla v atmosfere (Horizontal Transfer of Latent Heat in the Atmosphere).— Trudy GGO, No. 245. 1969.
6. Guterman, I. G. Raspredelenie vetra nad Severnym polushariem (Wind Distribution over the Northern Hemisphere).— Leningrad, Gidrometeoizdat. 1965.
7. Drozdov, O. A. and A. S. Grigor'eva. Vlagooborot v atmosfere (Hydrologic Cycle in the Atmosphere).— Leningrad, Gidrometeoizdat. 1963.
8. Kornienko, V. I. Sootnoshenie srednego i turbulentnogo potokov vlagi v atmosfere nad Zabaikal'em (Ratio of Mean and Turbulent Moisture Flows in the Atmosphere over Transbaikalia).— Trudy GGO, No. 245. 1969.

9. Creasey, A.R. Water Vapor Balance for 1958 on a Hemispheric Scale.—In: Humidity and Moisture, Vol. 2, Section 6. Meteorology, Report of the International Symposium on Hygrometry. Washington, 1963. Reinhold. 1965.

10. Monin, A.S. Dinamicheskaya turbulentnost' v atmosfere (Dynamic Turbulence in the Atmosphere).—Izvestiya AN SSSR, Seriya Geograficheskaya i Geofizicheskaya, Vol. 14, No. 3. 1950.

11. Pinus, N.Z. Spektry gorizontal'nogo turbulentnogo perenosa kolichestva dvizheniya i tepla v troposfere i stratosfere (Spectra of Horizontal Turbulent Transfer of Momentum and Heat in the Troposphere and Stratosphere).—Meteorologiya i Gidrologiya, No. 11. 1969.

12. Spravochnik klimaticheskikh kharakteristik vetra svobodnoi atmosfery po otdel'nym stantsiyam Severnogo polushariya (Handbook of Climatic Wind Characteristics in the Free Atmosphere at Individual Stations of the Northern Hemisphere).—Moskva, Rotaprint, NIIAK. 1968.

13. Materialy po klimatu i tsirkulyatsii svobodnoi atmosfery nad SSSR (Data on the Climate and Circulation of the Free Atmosphere over the USSR).—Moskva, Gidrometeoizdat. 1970.

II. ACCUMULATION OF RADIOACTIVE PRODUCTS OF NUCLEAR BLASTS ON THE UNDERLYING SURFACE

UDC 551.510.72

RATE OF ATMOSPHERIC FALLOUT OF CESIUM-137 AND STRONTIUM-90 AEROSOLS

A. S. Zykova, E. L. Telushkina, V. P. Rublevskii,
G. P. Efremova, and G. A. Kuznetsova

Data are given on the fallout density of Cs^{137} and Sr^{90} aerosols in Moscow for the period 1962 to 1968 and on the concentration of these isotopes in the ground layer of atmospheric air.

It is shown that the ratio of Cs^{137} and Sr^{90} aerosols in radioactive precipitation in these years was always larger than the analogous ratio between these isotopes in air. This leads us to suppose that the fallout rate of aerosols carrying Cs^{137} is somewhat larger than the fallout rate of aerosols carrying Sr^{90}.

An assessment of the fallout rate of these aerosols established that, on the average, for the period 1962 to 1968 the fallout rate of Cs^{137} aerosols was 1.7 ± 0.4 cm/sec, and of Sr^{90} aerosols 1.5 ± 0.4 cm/sec, i. e., the fallout rate of Cs^{137} aerosols is larger by 14% than the fallout rate of Sr^{90} aerosols.

As of 1957, systematic observations have been conducted in Moscow of the fallout of radioactive aerosols and their concentration in the ground layer of atmospheric air /1/.

We present here the results of studies conducted from 1962 to 1967 to determine the fallout of Cs^{137} and Sr^{90} on the earth's surface, to determine their concentration in the ground layer of atmospheric air, and to study the ratio between Cs^{137} and Sr^{90} in radioactive fallout and in air.

Air samples for the determination of radioactive isotopes were selected by means of a specially designed UAS-1 suction installation with output 350—400 m^3/hour /2/. Beginning with 1966, more powerful installations were used, based on the 12TsS-34 fan, with output reaching 1,200 m^3/hour. The filtering material consisted of FPP-15—1.7 cloth. The daily sampling duration was 5—6 hours. Filters were changed every 5 to 10 days.

Radioactive fallout was collected continuously at several stations in cuvettes measuring $60 \times 50 \times 10$ cm, with bottom covered by filter paper. The cuvettes were exposed for 10 days.

In the course of three years the fallout was collected in parallel in a cuvette and in a high-wall tank. In all, 95 precipitation samples were collected. Statistical processing of the obtained data established that the difference between the mean values of the radioactive fallout density obtained by the two methods is not significant. Accordingly, we can regard the efficiency of precipitation collection by the cuvette as equal to the collection efficiency of the high-wall tanks, taken as 100%.

Processing of the samples and determination of their radioactive isotopes Cs^{137} and Sr^{90} were conducted according to standard radiometric and radiochemical procedures /3/.

The density of Cs^{137} and Sr^{90} fallout from atmospheric air from 1962 to 1968 is presented in Table 1.

The largest amount of Cs^{137} and Sr^{90} in the fallout was observed in 1962—1963. Starting with 1964, the fallout levels of these isotopes began gradually to decrease and dropped in 1968 by a factor of roughly 10. The ratio of Cs^{137} to Sr^{90} fluctuated in the considered period between 1.15 and 2.0

TABLE 1. Fallout of cesium-137 and strontium-90 ($mcurie/km^2 \cdot year$) in Moscow

Year	Cs^{137}	Sr^{90}	$\dfrac{Cs^{137}}{Sr^{90}}$
1962	11.8	6.75	1.75
1963	14.65	7.8	1.9
1964	7.7	5.1	1.5
1965	4.6	4.0	1.15
1966	3.3	2.1	1.6
1967	1.9	0.96	2.0
1968	1.3	0.7	1.8

TABLE 2. Concentration of cesium-137 and strontium-90 (10^{-17} curie/liter) in the atmospheric air of Moscow

Year	Cs^{137}	Sr^{90}	$\dfrac{Cs^{137}}{Sr^{90}}$
1962	2.4	1.4	1.7
1963	2.4	2.0	1.2
1964	1.6	1.3	1.2
1965	1.0	1.0	1.0
1967	0.25	0.18	1.4
1968	0.15	0.1	1.5

Table 2 gives mean annual concentrations of Cs^{137} and Sr^{90} in the ground layer of the atmospheric air of Moscow. It is seen that the largest concentrations of Cs^{137} and Sr^{90} aerosols in atmospheric air were observed in 1962 and 1963, i.e., during the period of nuclear tests and immediately afterward. In subsequent years the content of these isotopes in air decreased gradually and dropped in 1968 by a factor of 16—20. The ratio of Cs^{137} to Sr^{90} in air during the observation period fluctuated between 1 and 1.7.

The change in the concentration of Cs^{137} and Sr^{90} in atmospheric air during these years agrees satisfactorily with the dynamics governing the density of their fallout in Moscow during the same period.

Analysis of the data on the ratio of Cs^{137} to Sr^{90} in fallout and in air (Tables 1 and 2) implies that in the course of the entire observation period the ratio of Cs^{137} to Sr^{90} was higher in fallout than in air. The ratio of Cs^{137} to Sr^{90} in fallout during the spring-summer period (from April to September when the troposphere receives the main amount of radioactive substances from the atmosphere, and during the autumn-winter period (from October to March of the next year), when this influx is negligible, was also determine

Table 3 indicates that this ratio is generally greater in the spring-summer period and near the relative yield of isotopes during the fission of nuclear fuel. This fact can probably be explained by the different fallout rates of aerosols carrying Cs^{137} and Sr^{90}.

TABLE 3. Ratio of the amount of cesium-137 to strontium-90 in fallout

$\dfrac{Cs^{137}}{Sr^{90}}$	Date	$\dfrac{Cs^{137}}{Sr^{90}}$	Date
2.58	April—September 1960	1.71	October 1960—March 1961
1.55	April—September 1961	1.22	October 1961—March 1962
1.87	April—September 1962	1.51	October 1962—March 1963
1.94	April—September 1963	1.17	October 1963—March 1964
1.87	April—September 1964	1.15	October 1964—March 1965
1.22	April—September 1965	1.44	October 1965—March 1966
1.49	April—September 1966	1.76	October 1966—March 1967
1.91	April—September 1967	1.18	October 1967—March 1968
1.84	April—September 1968	—	—
Average 1.80		1.50	

TABLE 4. Mean-annual rate (cm/sec) of fallout of cesium-137 and strontium-90 aerosols, v_g

Year	Cs^{137}	Sr^{90}
1962	1.56	1.52
1963	1.93	1.22
1964	1.48	1.23
1965	1.46	1.27
1967	2.40	2.29
1968	1.38	1.23
Average	1.7 ± 0.4	1.5 ± 0.4

The rate of aerosol fallout from the troposphere is given by the formula $v_g = P/q$, where v_g is the rate of aerosol fallout from the troposphere, P the density of aerosol fallout, and q their concentration in the lower troposphere.

Table 4 gives the mean-annual rate of fallout of Sr^{90} and Cs^{137} aerosols. It is seen that the fallout rate from the troposphere of cesium-137 and strontium-90 aerosols is the same, to within the accuracy limits.

BIBLIOGRAPHY

1. Zykova,A.S., E.L.Telushkina, G.P.Efremova, and V.P.Rublevskii. Uroven' radioaktivnosti atmosfernogo vozdukha Moskvy v 1957—1961gg.(Radioactivity Level of the Atmosphere over Moscow in 1957—1961).— Gigiena i Sanitariya, No.9. 1963.

2. Rublevskii,V.P. Aspiratsionnaya ustanovka dlya opredeleniya kontsentratsii dolgozhivushchikh radioaktivnykh veshchestv v atmosfere (Suction Installation for the Determination of Concentrations of Long-Lived Radioactive Substances in the Atmosphere).— Gigiena i Sanitariya, No. 9. 1964.
3. Dozimetricheskie i radiometricheskie metodiki (Dosimetric and Radiometric Methods).— Atomizdat. 1966.

UDC 550.378

ACCUMULATION OF STRONTIUM-90 IN SOILS

E. B. Tyuryukanova

A very uneven distribution of Sr^{90} is observed in the soils of the Russian Plain. The content of this radio-active nuclide in sandy soils is lower than in loamy soils, and depends on the amount of soil humus and its qualitative composition. The accumulation of Sr^{90} in soils is determined both by its physicochemical composition, and by the landscape and geochemical conditions. Of great importance is the character of the runoff. In most soils Sr^{90} is concentrated in the upper layer (0—5 to 0—20 cm).

The peaceful uses of atomic energy and large-scale tests of nuclear weapons have given a global character to radioactive fallout. The soil is a natural barrier retaining the radioactive fission products falling from the atmosphere. The intensity of their accumulation in the surface layers of soil depends on its physical and chemical properties, the absorption thickness, the filtration capacity, the cation-anion composition, and so on. In the period from 1961 to 1965, a continuous increase in the content of Sr^{90} in soils was observed over the Russian Plain (Table 1). Subsequently, the content of Sr^{90} in the soils of the forest zone decreased somewhat, associated with the decreased influx of this radionuclide from the atmosphere and with its geochemical redistribution in the landscape.

TABLE 1. Content of Sr^{90} (10^{-9} curie/m^2) in the 0—60 cm soil layer of Russian Plain soils

Zone and dominant soil type	Period of observations, year						
	1961	1962	1963	1964	1965	1966	1967
Forest, sod-podzolic	$\frac{8\ 95}{15}$	$\frac{8\ 41}{21}$	$\frac{15\ 50}{25}$	$\frac{5\ 50}{44}$	$\frac{17-134}{62}$	$\frac{37-76}{53}$	$\frac{20-110}{48}$
Forest-steppe, gray forest	$\frac{16-40}{25}$	—	$\frac{11-60}{35}$	—	—	$\frac{45-160}{100}$	—
Steppe, chernozem	$\frac{20-40}{30}$	—	$\frac{30-50}{45}$	$\frac{90-175}{125}$	—	$\frac{150-290}{170}$	—
Dry-steppe, chestnut and saline ...	$\frac{8-26}{20}$	—	—	—	—	$\frac{8-109}{40}$	—

Note. The numerator gives the range, the denominator the mean values of a multitude of samples.

Since radionuclide accumulation in a soil depends on its physical and chemical properties /9—12/, the content of Sr^{90} in different types of soil increases differently with time (Table 1). The most intense increase was observed in chernozem soils of the steppe zone, characterized by the highest absorbing capacity, and the lowest in soils of the forest zone. Extensive areas of the forest zone at the center of the Russian Plain are occupied by sandur landscapes with sandy soils, characterized by high filtration capacity and low absorbing capacity. It was established that in sandur landscapes a considerable amount of radioactive strontium penetrates yearly into the groundwater. For example, in 1966 the content of Sr^{90} in subsoil waters of sandy podzolic soil was $0.9—8.8 \cdot 10^{-12}$ curie/liter. Taking into account that the mean-annual runoff range in these regions is $5—6$ liter/sec/km^2, the transport of Sr^{90} from sandy soils represents 6% of its overall reserve.

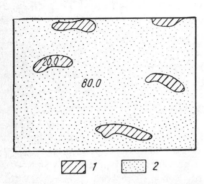

FIGURE 1. Distribution of Sr^{90} in sand podzolic soils (10^{-9} curie/m^2) in the $0—30$-cm layer:

1) Hylocomium pine forest; 2) Convallaria majalis pine forest.

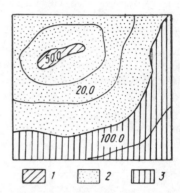

FIGURE 2. Distribution of Sr^{90} in myrtle whortleberry soils (10^{-9} curie/m^2) in the $0—30$-cm layer:

1) Cladonia, podzolic; 2) myrtle whortleberry with reedgrass, podzolic; 3) myrtle whortleberry, sod-podzolic, ferruginous soils.

Thus, in sandy soil regions we can expect a more rapid drop in the content of Sr^{90} in the root layer owing to its vertical migration, the rate of which exceeds that of the radioactive decay of this radionuclide. In addition to considerable zonal differences in the accumulation of Sr^{90} in soils, noticeable deviations in the contents of Sr^{90} from the mean values were observed within the limits of each soil-climatic zone. This is due to the geochemical migration of Sr^{90}. It follows from studies conducted elsewhere regarding the geochemical migration of Sr^{90} in soils /1, 2, 4—6/ that in sandy soils of the forest zone Sr^{90} migrates easily downward along the soil profile. Since in this zone one observes closure of the currents descending from the shallow subsoil waters, Sr^{90} is carried out. A certain part of the migrating Sr^{90} is retained in the sod and peaty-gley loamy floodplain soils, located in the region of petering out of the subsoil waters.

The deposition of Sr^{90} occurs as a result of changes in the redox and alkaline-acid conditions in the region of the landscape-geochemical barriers characterized by an increased content of Fe, Ca, Sr and S. In the forest zone a nonuniform distribution of Sr^{90} was observed even over territory occupied by one biogeocenosis, due to the inhomogeneity of the phytocenoses, and the different conditions of moisture and nutrition of the soils (Figures 1 and 2). It was detected that the ferruginous sod-podzolic soils, formed under conditions of increased moistening and favorable nutrition, are characterized by a content of Sr^{90} which is five times higher than the surrounding territories (Figure 2). The soils of Pleurozium schrebe-ri clumps in Convallaria majalis pine forest with a more intense podzol process were characterized by a content of Sr^{90} which was four times lower (Figure 1).

The variation of the Sr^{90} content in soils is due to the inhomogeneity of the soil cover, the considerable fluctuations in the thickness of the forest floor, the degree of its mineralization and its content of humus. It was established that in soils characterized by a high content of soft humus Sr^{90} is retained more strongly and carried out to a lesser extent than in soils with a low content of humus or with a high content of coarse, peaty organic substance. The content of Sr^{90} in forest podzol soils is seen to depend on the forest floor mineralization, its content of humus and qualitative composition (Figure 3).

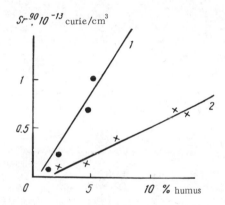

FIGURE 3. Content of Sr^{90} in the forest floor as a function of its content of humus:

1) humus litter; 2) peat litter.

In the forest-steppe and steppe zones one also observes considerable fluctuations in the content of Sr^{90} in soils (Table 2). For example, in the forest-steppe zone over a 1-ha plot of soil the sections occupied by gray forest soils under oak forest (p. 4/66) were characterized by a four times lower content of Sr^{90} than the ordinary chernozems occupying the watershed topsoils (p. 3/66). In the steppe zone the ordinary solonetzic arable chernozems and chestnut soils, covering large territories at the watersheds (p. 10/66, 5/66), contain several times more radioactive strontium than the hydromorphous soils (meadow and seashore solonchaks) located in depressions (ravines flooded in spring and seashores, p. 11/66, 6/66).

TABLE 2. Content of Sr^{90} in soils (10^{-9} curie/m^2)

Soil	Horizon	Depth, cm	Content of Sr^{90}
Ordinary loamy chernozem, arable, p. 3/66	A_{ar}	0—12	79.0
	A_{ar}	12—32	82.0
	A	32—43	2.7
	B	43—62	4.5
	B	62—78	4.9
	BC	78—85	1.0
	BC	85—96	Traces
	Total	0—30	161.0
Gray forest, loamy. Oak forest, p. 4/66	A_1	0—10	35.0
	A_1	10—17	1.7
	A_2B	17—37	6.8
	A_2B	37—53	2.0
	B	53—67	4.3
	B	67—78	1.9
	Total	0—30	43.5
Ordinary solonetzic chernozem, arable, p. 10/66	A_{ar}	0—5	Traces
	A	5—22	282.0
	B_1	22—43	11.1
	B_2	43—59	3.3
	$B\kappa$	59—68	Traces
	Total	0—30	290.0
Light chestnut solonetzic, loamy, p. 5/66	Vegetation		17.9
	A_1'	0—5	70.0
	B'	5—23	21.2
	B_2	23—52	4.3
	C	52—80	10.3
	C	80—110	29.5
	Total	0—30	109.1
Meadow solonchak, p. 11/66	Vegetation		0.2
	$A\kappa_1$	0—8	16.2
	$A\kappa$	8—26	27.6
	B	26—46	Traces
	B	46—68	Traces
	Total	0—30	44.0
Wet seashore solonchak, p. 6/66	Layer I	0—10	3.4
	Layer I	10—25	2.8
	Layer II	25—36	Traces
	Total	0—30	6.2

In chernozem soils Sr^{90} is accumulated in the upper part of the soil profile. Its negligible migration downward along the soil profile is associated not only with the high sorption properties of the surface soil horizons, but also with the absence in them of a flushing regime. The latter, in all probability, contributes to the carrying out of Sr^{90} from the soils of ravine and seashore depressions. The results of long-term investigations indicate that Sr^{90} is concentrated in most types of soils in the top 10-cm soil layer /3, 7, 8/. Thus, in sandy podzolic soils the maximum content of Sr^{90} is observed in the lower part of the floor and the upper layer of the humus horizon (Figure 4). The content of Sr^{90} in the upper horizons of podzolic soils is determined to a considerable extent by the type of forest floor (Table 3).

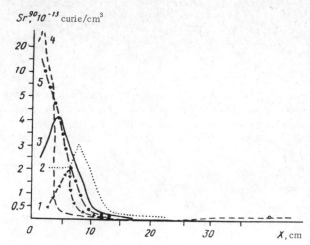

FIGURE 4. Vertical distribution of Sr^{90} in pine forest soils:

1) 1961; 2) 1962; 3) 1963; 4) 1964; 5) 1967.

TABLE 3. Content of Sr^{90} (10^{-12} curie/cm³) in the forest floor of podzolic soils

Type of floor	$\dfrac{A_0'}{0-2\,cm}$	$\dfrac{A_0''}{2-5\,cm}$
Oak	$\dfrac{4.2-7.5}{5.0}$	$\dfrac{1.6-1.7}{1.6}$
Small-leaved species	$\dfrac{2.8-3.0}{2.9}$	$\dfrac{1.7-1.8}{1.6}$
Pine	$\dfrac{1.5-2.0}{1.7}$	$\dfrac{2.3-12.8}{6.0}$

Note. The numerator gives the range, the denominator the mean results of several determinations.

The content of Sr^{90} in the surface vegetation is determined by its type. For example, in the forest zone mosses are characterized by a somewhat higher content of Sr^{90} than grassy plants and undershrubs (Table 4).

It follows that the accumulation in soil of radioactive strontium falling from the atmosphere depends both on the soil physicochemical properties and on the characteristics of the landscape and geochemical conditions.

TABLE 4. Content of Sr^{90} in the surface phytomass in 1967 (10^{-9} curie/m^2)

Plant cover					
Pleurozium schreberi	Cladonia sylvanica	Sphagnum	Myrtle whortleberry	Convallaria majalis	Reedgrass
$\dfrac{5-8}{6}$	$\dfrac{1-4}{3}$	$\dfrac{14-20}{17}$	$\dfrac{0.1-0.3}{0.2}$	$\dfrac{0.4-0.5}{0.45}$	$\dfrac{0.1-0.3}{0.2}$

Note. See Table 3.

In addition to accumulation in soils there occurs a biogeochemical migration of Sr^{90}; it is also carried out from some soils and secondary accumulation occurs in others. The motley character of the landscape and geochemical conditions determines the different content of Sr^{90} in the various soils.

BIBLIOGRAPHY

1. Novikova,S.K. and E.B.Tyuryukanova. Raspredelenie strontsiya-90 v pochvakh lugovo-stepnoi zony (Distribution of Strontium-90 in Soils of Meadow-Steppe Zone).—Pochvovedenie, No. 12. 1968.
2. Pavlotskaya,F.I. and E.B.Tyuryukanova. O vliyanii prirodnykh uslovii na soderzhanie i raspredelenie radioaktivnogo strontsiya v pochvennom pokrove (The Effect of Natural Conditions on the Content and Distribution of Radioactive Strontium in the Soil Cover).—Atomnaya Energiya, Vol. 23, No. 3. 1967.
3. Rosyanov,S.P.,V.K.Vinogradova,P.I.Gustova,and L.I.Gedeonov. Raspredelenie strontsiya-90 i tseziya po profilyu pochv v prirodnykh usloviyakh v 1964 g. (Distribution of Strontium-90 and Cesium Along the Soil Profile in Natural Conditions in 1964).—Atomizdat. 1967.
4. Tyuryukanova,E.B. et al. O migratsii i raspredelenii Sr^{90} i Ce^{144} v pochvakh Moskovskoi oblasti (Migration and Distribution of Sr^{90} and Ce^{144} in Soils of Moscow Region).—Pochvovedenie, No. 10. 1964.
5. Tyuryukanova,E.B., F.I.Pavlotskaya, A.N.Tyuryukanov, and V.I.Baranov. Raspredelenie Sr^{90} v poverkhnostnykh gorizontakh pochv v zavisimosti ot ikh tipa i landshafta (Distribution of Sr^{90} in the Surface of Horizons of Soils as a Function of their Type and Landscape).—Pochvovedeni No. 8. 1964.
6. Tyuryukanova,E.B., F.I.Pavlotskaya, and V.I.Baranov. Osobennosti raspredeleniya Sr^{90} v razlichnykh tipakh pochv Evropeiskoi chasti SSSR v 1961 g. (Characteristics of the Distribution of Sr^{90} in Different Types of Soils of European USSR in 1961).— In: "Radioaktivnost' pochv i metody ee opredeleniya" ("Soil Radioactivity and Methods for its Determination"). Moskva, "Nauka." 1966.
7. Alexander,L.T., E.P.Hardy, T.W.Meyer, J.S.Allen,and V.T.Valassis. Vertical Distribution of Strontium-90 in Sandy Soils in May 1965.—HASL-171, p. 1075. 1966.
8. Kulp,I.S. Radionuclides in Man from Nuclear Tests.—In: Radioactive Fallout in Soils, Plants, Food, Man, p. 247, edited by E.B.Fowler. Amsterdam—London—New York, Elsevier. 1965.
9. Miller,R. and R.F.Reitemier. Sr^{90} and Cs^{137} Leaching from Soils.—Soil Sci., Vol. 27, No. 2. 1963.
10. Mortensen,L., E.C.Marcusin, and N.Holowayechuk. Strontium Exchange Characteristics of Soils.—Ohio J. Sci., Vol. 63, No. 5. 1963.
11. Reissig,H. Untersuchungen über die Sr^{90} Auswaschung in Boden.—Chem. Erde, Vol. 25, No. 3. 1966.
12. Schilling,G. and D.Richter. Über das Verhalten von Sr^{90} and Y^{90} in mitteldeutschen Boden.—Albrecht-Ihaer-Arch., Vol. 8, Nos. 1—3. 1964.

UDC 550.378

CESIUM-137, STRONTIUM-90 AND LEAD-210 IN SOIL OF THE FAR NORTH REGIONS

M. N. Troitskaya, M. S. Ibatullin, B. Ya. Litver,
A. N. Nizhnikov, P. V. Ramzaev, and L. A. Teplykh

The part played by soil in the pollution of subsequent links of the chain of natural and artificial radio-nuclides in regions of the Far North is considered.

It is shown that while a geographic variation exists of the levels of artificial contamination of the soils, the ratio of cesium-137 to strontium-90 in all regions remains between 1.3 and 1.6.

Experimental data are given on the mechanism governing the contamination of lichen (the main fodder of reindeer) by natural and artificial nuclides.

An analysis is given of museum samples (1900–1945), indicating the absence of any connection between the high levels of lead-210 in the North and nuclear tests.

The levels of plutonium-239 content in the vegetation of some regions of the Far North are determined.

The part played by soil as one of the intermediate links in the migration of radionuclides has been studied in detail by Soviet scientists (V. M. Klechkovskii, I. V. Gulyakin, F. I. Pavlotskaya, E. B. Tyuryukanova, Yu. M. Svirezhev and others) [1, 2]. Soil is the main custodian of nuclides falling onto the soil surface and its contamination levels are an indicator of the contamination of subsequent links in the migration under conditions of root uptake. However, the hygienic importance of soil in the conditions of the Far North is not treated in the literature.

In the Far North the part played by soil in radioecological systems differs substantially from that in middle latitudes, for which migration schemes have been developed. The existence of permafrost in soil and the duration of the snow cover create unusual conditions both for the emanation of radon and for the fixation of fallout. The agricultural utilization of soil, not to speak of its physicochemical properties, is specific. Grain cultivation and agriculture in general are practically impossible.

The entry of long-lived nuclides via cereals (bread)—the main form of uptake of these nuclides by the organism of the inhabitants of the central regions and towns of the North—bears no relation to the contamination of the local soil, since the bread consumed is not produced locally. The soil contamination of these regions can be of importance for the population mainly through the chain, soil—plant—products of animal origin—man, and especially through the chain, lichen—reindeer—man. It is this latter chain which was considered in our examination of the part played by soil contaminated by the principal long-lived radionuclides of artificial and natural origin.

Soil samples were taken (at a depth of 5 cm) together with the vegetation on them. Three or four samples were taken per point in different regions of the Far North over several years, starting with 1962. The data for 1965, when the intense global fallout had already ceased, are presented in Table 1.

The given levels of cesium-137 and strontium-90 reflect accordingly the total sum of fallout against whose background the radiation environment was formed in the investigated regions.

Along the whole littoral of the Arctic Ocean (67—70° latitude) in 1962—1965, the radioactive contamination levels of the soil (by cesium-137 and strontium-90) were smaller by a factor of 1.5 — 2 than the average values over the USSR and over the northern hemisphere. Reliable differences (a factor of 2) in the soil contamination of different northern regions were also noted.

TABLE 1. Soil radioactivity in the 0—5-cm layer (together with the vegetation) in mcurie/mm^2 (March 1965)

Region	Cesium-137 (according to radiochemical analysis)	Strontium-90	$\dfrac{\text{Cesium-137}}{\text{Strontium-90}}$
Murmansk Region	46 ± 4	35 ± 4	1.4 ± 0.1
Nenets National District	51 ± 9	41 ± 10	1.3 ± 0.1
Jamal-Nenets National District	48 ± 8	34 ± 6	1.4 ± 0.1
Taimyr National District	28 ± 6	18 ± 4	1.6 ± 0.1
Yakut ASSR	34 ± 6	23 ± 3	1.5 ± 0.1
Chukchi National District	34 ± 2	21 ± 2	1.6 ± 0.1
Average for the USSR	—	67	—

The highest contamination was and is observed in the Murmansk Region and the Nenets National District, and the lowest in the eastern regions (Taimyr, Yakut ASSR, Chukchi National District). These differences are consistent with the similar variation in the amount of atmospheric precipitation. For example, in the Murmansk Region, during the years with intense radionuclide fallout (1962—1964), there fell about 500 mm annual precipitation, while in the eastern regions (such as the north of Yakut ASSR) the figure was only 200 mm.

The ratio of cesium-137 to strontium-90 in soil (plus vegetation) is almost the same in all regions (1.3—1.6) and corresponds to fallout data.

As regards the main northern cattle-breeding industry — reindeer breeding — in many regions of the Far North the basic fodder during 8—9 months of the year is lichen, which has no root system.

The question of the part played by soil in lichen contamination, which has a direct bearing on the forecast of the radiation environment in the northern chain, is not treated in the literature. It is assumed that direct fallout is the main, if not the only source of their radioactive contamination [3].

However, in spite of the high sorption properties of lichen, the nuclides are far from being 100% extracted by them from fallout. Our separate analysis of soil and the lichen on it established that roughly half the total radioactivity is recorded in the soil (Table 2).

TABLE 2. Cesium-137 in soil and in the lichen on it (the mean ± the standard deviation is given in mcurie/km^2)

Region	Sampling date	Lichen weight, kg/m^2	According to chemical analysis		According to gamma-spectrometry	
			lichen	soil	lichen	soil
Murmansk Region	Dec. 1965	0.70	25 ± 6 (6)	24 ± 3	52 ± 10 (9)	117 ± 14
Komi ASSR	Feb. 1967	0.60	—	—	25 ± 12 (1)	60 ± 6
Yakut ASSR	Jan. 1967	0.56	15 ± 1 (6)	11 ± 1	12 ± 3 (8)	33 ± 4
Chukchi National District .	Dec. 1966	1.12	8 ± 2 (1)	29 ± 6	12 ± 2 (1)	8 ± 2

We designed special experiments to study the possibility of uptake and migration of cesium-137 and strontium-90 from the soil into the lichen. Soil portions (10 × 10 × 5 cm) with the lichen on them were taken from the tundra. By means of a syringe, 50 μcurie cesium-137 and strontium-90 in an aqueous solution were injected simultaneously in all the portions of the upper soil layer to a depth of 0.2 — 0.5 cm. All the contaminated soil portions were placed in stainless steel vessels and exposed on the roof of a building. Through 2, 7, 30, 45, 83 and 105 days lichen was cut at a height of 1 cm from the soil layer from the different portions, in order to determine their nuclide content (as % of the amount introduced). The results are presented in Table 3.

TABLE 3. Migration of cesium-137 and strontium-90 from soil to lichen (as % of the amount introduced into the soil)

Duration of experiment, days	Cesium-137		Strontium-90	
	obtained in the experiment	reduced to the lichen density, 1 dry kg/m^2	obtained in the experiment	reduced to the lichen density, 1 dry kg/m^2
2	0.013	0.039	0.0004	0.0014
7	0.024	0.040	0.0017	0.0039
30	0.170	1.250	0.0011	0.0820
45	1.230	1.750	0.1140	0.1270
83	1.430	2.060	0.2330	0.3420
105	1.990	3.840	0.1500	0.3100

In spite of all expectations, the lichens, although they have no root system, are capable of uptaking very efficiently radionuclides from the uppermost contaminated soil layer.

After three months we find in the lichens 2 to 4% of the cesium-137 introduced into the soil, and only 0.1—0.3% of the strontium-90. During such a period of time, grass takes from the soil through its roots about 0.01% cesium and 0.1% strontium /4/. In other words, during the same period the rootless lichen extracts from soil 200 to 400 times more cesium-137 than grass.

The experiments imply that in the absence of fallout the soil contamination mechanism maintains a predominance of cesium-137 in the chain radioactivity over strontium-90, as with surface contamination.

In addition to artificial radionuclides, natural radionuclides are of undoubted interest in the northern chain, since absorbed doses of them in subsequent migration links in reindeer and man are very considerable.

The levels of natural radioactivity of the soil and vegetation of Far North regions are given in Tables 4 and 5.

TABLE 4. Content of polonium-210 and lead-210 (mcurie/km^2) in soil of Far North regions

Region	Polonium-210	Lead-210	Po/Pb
Murmansk Region	146	—	—
Komi ASSR	60	60	1.0
Taimyr National District	135	80	1.7
Yakut ASSR	37	37	1.0
Chukchi National District	29	24	1.2

TABLE 5. Natural radioactivity of lichen (10^{-9} curie/kg dry weight)

Region	Polonium-210	Lead-210	Radium-226	Thorium-228
Murmansk Region	9.4 ± 2.2	9.4 ± 0.8	0.27 ± 0.10	0.06 ± 0.02
Komi ASSR	4.9 ± 0.5	4.9 ± 0.7	0.34 ± 0.09	0.10 ± 0.07
Taimyr National District	9.1 ± 0.2	7.1 ± 0.8	0.08 (2)	0.06 (2)
Yakut ASSR	7.6 ± 0.5	6.7 ± 0.8	0.30 ± 0.10	0.23 ± 0.05
Chukchi National District	3.9 ± 0.1	3.6; 3.1	0.37 ± 0.11	0.08 ± 0.01

Comparison of levels of the polonium-210—lead-210 content in the lichens and soils of the corresponding regions of the North show that the concentration of polonium-210 in lichens exceeds two- to fivefold the levels of this isotope content in soil. Besides, there exists a geographical variation in the levels of natural radioactivity of soil and lichen, reaching a factor of two to five. The highest levels are observed in the Murmansk Region and the lowest in the Chukchi National District and Yakut ASSR.

The mechanism of polonium-210—lead-210 cumulation on lichen is unanimously explained by the sorption of these nuclides from atmospheric air. It might be thought that there exists in addition a root uptake of radioisotopes from the soil. However, this assumption is still in need of experimental corroboration.

The ecological parameters in lichens in relation to lead-210 and polonium-210 (sorption, soil uptake, scavenging rate, etc.) have not been studied much. No agreement has yet been reached as to the origin of these nuclides.

The natural origin of these nuclides, at least as regards their main bulk, is not in doubt. It is known from literature sources that 1 liter rain contains 2.5 pcurie lead-210. For an annual total precipitation of 500 mm the fallout is 1.25 mcurie/km^2 per year.

The equilibrium content of lead-210 on the soil surface, without allowing for washout, must be about 30 mcurie/km^2, if only fallout is considered.

The actual content in many regions is about two or three times higher, pointing to its formation directly in the soil. If the process of lead-210 washout is substantial, the part played by the formation of the isotope in soil can be even more important.

In order to refine the hypothesis about the link between the high levels of lead-210—polonium-210 in the North with nuclear tests, we investigated museum samples of lichens taken prior to the tests.

The concentration of lead-210 in equilibrium with polonium-210 in lichen is characterized by the following values:

	Prior to 1900	1900—1945	1958—1966
Lichen, 10^{-9} curie/kg dry weight	16.9	23.6 ± 9.3	7.2 ± 1.4

Hence the probability of a link between the high levels of these nuclides in the northern chain and nuclear tests is low, and they probably pertain to the whole period of existence of the ecological system of the North.

In our study the concentration of plutonium-239 in the lichens of some regions of the Far North was also determined for the first time; the figures are $(1.1—1.7) \cdot 10^{-10}$ curie/kg.

BIBLIOGRAPHY

1. Gulyakin,I.V. and A.A.Yudintseva. Postuplenie radioaktivnykh izotopov v rasteniya (Penetration of Radioactive Isotopes in Plants).—DAN SSSR, Vol. 3, No. 3, pp. 709—712. 1965.
2. Klechkovskii,V.M., L.N.Sokolova, and G.N.Tselishcheva. Sorbtsiya mikrokolichestv strontsiya i tseziya v pochvakh (Sorption of Microamounts of Strontium and Cesium in Soils).— Reports of Soviet Scientists, Proc. Geneva Conf., Vol. 5. 1958.
3. Liden,K. and M.Gustaffson. Relationship and Seasonal Variation of Cs^{137} in Lichen, Reindeer and Man in Northern Sweden, 1966.—Symposium on Radioecology, Sweden. 1966.
4. Kriger,II., B.Kahn, and S.Cummings. Deposition and Uptake of Sr^{90} and Cs^{137} in Established Pasture.—Symposium on Radioecology, Sweden. 1966.

UDC 550.378

COMPARATIVE DISTRIBUTION OF STRONTIUM-90 AND CESIUM-137 IN DIFFERENT TYPES OF SOILS

E. I. Belova and Z. G. Antropova

Results are presented of investigations into the distribution of strontium-90 and cesium-137 along the profile of five types of virgin soil 10 years after their contamination. The investigations were conducted under natural conditions on artificially contaminated plots of sod podzolic, gray forest, leached chernozem, meadow solod and solonchak soils. It is shown that by the tenth year some characteristic features are observed in the distribution of the investigated radioisotopes along the profile of different types of soils. The influence of the forest cover on the migration rate and distribution of radioisotopes along the soil profile is noted. The soils are arranged in the following series according to the content of cesium-137 in the upper layer (0—4 cm): meadow solod < sod podzolic < gray forest < solonchak < leached chernozem. The series for strontium-90 content is as follows: meadow solod < sod podzolic < solonchak < gray forest < leached chernozem.

Accumulations of the products of global fallout in soil depend not only on the levels of their entry from the atmosphere, but also on the natural situation in which they fall /1—4/.

The soil-formation process is a powerful geochemical factor, which alters to a considerable extent the form of the radioactive element compounds, so determining the rate of radionuclide migration both along the soil profile and in the "soil-plant" system.

We present in this paper the results of investigations into the distribution of strontium-90 and cesium-137 along the profile of five types of soils as a function of physicochemical properties.

The radionuclide distribution in soils was studied on virgin experimental plots comprising sod-podzolic, gray forest, leached chernozem, meadow solod and solonchak soils. A mixture of radioisotopes of strontium-90 and cesium-137 was sprayed on the soil surface in the form of a solution of nitrates. Soil sections were cut on each portion, and layer-by-layer soil sampling was carried out 3 or 4 times along the profile of each section. The thickness of the sampled layers was 2 cm down to a depth of 20 cm, and 5 cm in the 20—30-cm layer. In each soil sample the strontium-90 was determined by the radiochemical method and the cesium-137 content by the gamma-spectrometric method.

The main physicochemical properties of the studied soils are given in Table 1. We see that the soils used in the experiments were fully representative of each type of soil as regards their basic physicochemical indices. The mean annual precipitation in the region of the experimental areas is 370—390 mm.

The distribution of strontium-90 and cesium-137 in soils 10 years after radionuclide spraying on the soil surface is given in Table 2.

TABLE 1. Physicochemical properties of soils (A horizon)

Soil	Humus, %	pH	Absorption capacity, mg·eq/100g	Degree of saturation of soils by bases, %	Content of the clay fraction, %
Sod podzolic	3.0	4.7	20.0	75.2	13.5
Gray forest	4.7	5.2	25.8	89.0	12.5
Leached chernozem	9.4	6.0	45.2	90.5	9.3
Meadow solod	6.6	5.4	15.0	89.0	15.8
Solonchak	0.8	8.3	36.6	—	18.9

TABLE 2. Distribution of strontium-90 and cesium-137 along the profile of different types of soil (as % of the total content along the profile)

Depth, cm	Sod podzolic		Gray forest		Chernozem		Meadow solod		Solonchak	
	strontium-90	cesium-137	strontium-90	cesium-137	strontium-90	cesium-137	strontium-90	cesium-137	strontium-90	cesium-137
0—2	20.0	30.4	48.0	63.3	29.4	42.9	8.0	11.0	46.2	67.7
2—4	27.2	19.5	28.0	12.1	50.3	49.1	25.3	27.8	28.8	25.0
4—6	13.0	5.7	9.0	4.1	7.6	4.1	22.0	40.8	6.7	2.1
6—8	3.0	4.1	2.7	2.4	8.0	1.5	14.4	5.2	5.2	0.8
8—10	3.3	3.2	1.3	1.9	2.5	0.7	9.5	1.9	4.2	0.6
10—12	2.5	4.1	1.4	2.0	0.7	0.4	4.3	1.7	2.6	0.4
12—14	4.2	11.4	1.0	1.0	0.9	0.3	3.5	1.9	2.2	0.4
14—16	3.6	2.4	0.5	0.7	0.1	0.1	2.6	0.5	0.9	0.3
16—18	7.8	3.2	1.3	1.4	0.1	0.2	2.7	1.1	0.9	0.5
18—20	3.6	3.2	1.1	0.9	0.1	0.1	1.5	0.5	0.3	0.3
20—25	11.8	12.8	3.3	3.5	0.2	0.3	6.2	7.6	1.0	1.1
25—30	—	—	2.4	7.3	0.1	0.3	—	—	1.0	0.8

The observation results of the distribution of strontium-90 and cesium-137 along the profile of the investigated soils established that the bulk of the isotopes (40—90%) is located in a 5-cm thick layer by the tenth year of their residence in the soil. However, some isotope distribution features become clear during that period along the profile of the different types of soils.

Table 2 shows that the migration rate of radionuclides along the profile of sod podzolic soil and meadow solod soil is much higher than in gray forest and chernozem soil. This can evidently be explained by the development of solodized soils under conditions of temporary excessive moistening.

Unlike sod podzolic soil, the radionuclide distribution along the profile of solodized soil is smoother. Apparently, the higher moisture content and the existence of a downward moisture flow create favorable conditions for the displacement of radioisotopes both in the diffusion process and in the process of mechanical migration. The high humus content combined with the relatively heavy texture and the absence of downward moisture flow cause a much lower rate of radioisotope migration in chernozem than in sod podzolic and solod soils.

For forest-covered soils (sod podzolic, gray forest and meadow solod), the rate of migration and the distribution of strontium-90 and cesium-137 along the soil profile are affected by the nature and structure of the forest floor. On the experimental solod area the cover consists of aspen litter, which differs from the litter of coniferous woods on sod podzolic soil by a higher rate of decomposition. As a result the radioisotope content in the solod forest floor cover 10 years after contamination was considerably lower than in the cover of sod podzolic soil.

One characteristic feature is observed in the distribution of strontium-90 along the soil profile: in the course of time there occurs a migration of the maximum radioisotope content from the upper surface layer of the soil to lower layers. Natural deactivation of the surface layer occurs under the influence of climatic and soil-formation factors. This phenomenon can be associated with the restoration of organogenic layers (litter, peat) and the washout of radioisotopes from the upper layers of the soil by atmospheric precipitation.

In order to compare the migration rates of two radioisotopes (strontium-90 and cesium-137) along the soil profile, we give in Table 3 data on the content of these isotopes in the 0—4-cm and 4—30-cm layers. It is seen that the distribution of cesium-137 along the soil profile in the 10-th year after contamination is similar to the distribution of strontium-90. The content of cesium-137, as of strontium-90, in the 4-cm layer of the sod podzolic soil and the solod is about 50%. In the other soils that we studied the main bulk of the radioisotopes (75—93%) is contained in this layer.

TABLE 3. Distribution of strontium-90 and cesium-137 in soils (as % of the total content in the 0—30-cm layer)

Soil	Strontium-90		Cesium-137	
	0—4 cm	4—30 cm	0—4 cm	4—30 cm
Sod podzolic	47.2	52.8	49.9	50.1
Gray forest	76.0	24.0	75.4	24.6
Chernozem	79.7	20.3	92.7	7.3
Solod	33.3	66.7	38.8	61.2
Solonchak	75.0	25.0	92.7	7.3

Thus, although the mechanisms of interaction of the studied isotopes with soil differ in many respects, the soil series as regards cesium-137 content in the upper soil layer (meadow solod < sod podzolic < gray forest < solonchak < < chernozem) differs little from the corresponding series for strontium-90 (meadow solod < sod podzolic < solonchak < gray forest < chernozem).

BIBLIOGRAPHY

1. Makhonina, G.I. et al. Raspredelenie Fe^{59}, Co^{60}, Zn^{65}, Sr^{90}, Ru^{106}, Cs^{137}, Ce^{144} po komponentam biogeotsenoza (Distribution of Fe^{59}, Co^{60}, Zn^{65}, Sr^{90}, Ru^{106}, Cs^{137}, Ce^{144} by Biogeocenosis Components). — Trudy Instituta Biologii UFAN SSSR, No. 45. 1965.

2. Rosyanov,S.P., V.K.Vinogradova,L.I.Gustova, and L.I.Gedeonov. Raspredelenie strontsiya-90 i tseziya-137 po profilyu pochv v prirodnykh usloviyakh v 1964 g. (Distribution of Strontium-90 and Cesium-137 Along the Soil Profile Under Natural Conditions in 1964).—Gosudarstvennyi Komitet po ispol'zovaniyu atomnoi energii. Moskva, Atomizdat. 1967.

3. Tyuryukanova,E.B., F.I.Pavlotskaya, and V.I.Baranov. Raspredelenie radioaktivnogo strontsiya v pochvakh razlichnykh prirodnykh zon (Distribution of Radioactive Strontium in Soils of Different Natural Zones).—Gosudarstvennyi Komitet po ispol'zovaniyu atomnoi energii. Moskva, Atomizdat. 1967.

4. Squire,H.M. and L.Z.Middleton. Behavior of Cs^{137} in Soils and Pastures: A Long-Term Experiment.— Radiation Botany, Vol. 6, No. 5. 1966.

UDC 550.378

DISTRIBUTION AND MIGRATION OF STRONTIUM-90 IN SOILS

L. I. Gedeonov, S. P. Rosyanov, and V. K. Vinogradova

Results are given of a study of Sr^{90} distribution along soil profiles. This enables us to estimate the radioactive contamination of the soil cover and the rate of Sr^{90} migration deep into soil. These data can be used in an attempt to study the mechanism of Sr^{90} migration in soil. Soil samples taken at depths down to 30 cm were subjected to radiochemical analysis for Sr^{90}. It was found that Sr^{90} in 1964—1965 was mainly retained in a 15-cm soil layer. Measurable amounts of Sr^{90} were found in the 25—30-cm layer. The distribution of Sr^{90} along the profile of loamy soils can be described in a first approximation by a power law. Calculations with its aid show that Sr^{90} penetrates deeper than 40—60 cm.

The motion of radioactive fission products inside the soil cover involves a combination of different physicochemical processes in the soil, the most important of which are Sr^{90} migration by diffusion and isotope migration together with the soil solution. The dependence of the rate of Sr^{90} diffusion on the soil moisture content and temperature was determined. It was found that the diffusion coefficients in chernozem and sod podzolic soils for yearly averages of the moisture content are $0.49 \cdot 10^{-7}$ and $0.84 \cdot 10^{-7}$ cm^2/sec, respectively.

The vertical distribution of Sr^{90} in soils resulting from diffusion alone was calculated with the aid of the coefficients found. Comparison of the calculated distribution of Sr^{90} with the distribution obtained by radiochemical determination of Sr^{90} showed that in loamy chernozem Sr^{90} migrates mainly by diffusion. In sandy sod podzolic soil this process is of the same order as the others.

This paper treats the distribution of Sr^{90} along the profile of soils contaminated by global radioactive fallout. The results are useful for evaluating the cumulative deposition of Sr^{90} falling from the atmosphere, and also the rate and mechanism of Sr^{90} migration deep into soil.

The soil samples were taken from flat meadow areas at a depth of up to 30 cm by means of a sample collector of rectangular shape measuring 20×20 cm. The samples were dried, marked, and subjected to analysis. Sr^{90} was determined radiochemically by the sulfate method /1,5/. The yttrium activity was measured on a low-background installation (1—1.5 counts/min) /2/. The chemical yield was determined by the flame photometry method. The accuracy of the method of Sr^{90} determination used in the work was evaluated on the basis of results of an analysis of standard samples obtained from the International Atomic Energy Agency and was not less than 10%.

The soil sample properties are given in Table 1. Standard soil-science methods /3/ were used to determine the specific gravity and volume weight, the content of humus in the soil, the pH of the aqueous extract, and the absorption capacity of the soil. Table 2 gives results of Sr^{90} determination at various depths in different soils. The results show that the upper 3-cm soil layer contains 26—72 % of the observed amount of Sr^{90}, and the 10-cm layer 42—90%. Deeper Sr^{90} is distributed more or less uniformly, and is sometimes observed even at a depth of 25—30 cm. This indicates that it penetrates even deeper than 30 cm. This amount can be estimated if the relationship between Sr^{90} concentration and its penetration depth is expressed by an empirical formula. For soils of loamy composition the best approximation is given by the power law

$$y = ax^{-b},$$

where y is the Sr^{90} content in the soil layer, x the layer depth, and a and b are constants. This relationship has been plotted in Figure 1. On the basis of these data one may assume that in loamy soils Sr^{90} penetrated to a depth of 30—40 cm, with 5 to 10% of the amount observed in the 30-cm layer found below 30 cm. In chestnut soils Sr^{90} penetrated deeper than 1 m, and correspondingly 40—50% of Sr^{90} penetrated below the 30-cm layer.

TABLE 1. Some soil characteristics (0—5-cm soil layer)

Section No.	Soil type	Specific gravity, g/cm³	Bulk weight, g/cm³	Porosity, %	Absorption capacity, mg · eq/100 g	Humus content, %	pH of the aqueous suspension	Exchange calcium, mg · eq/100 g
1	Sod podzolic, sandy	2.4	1.4	43	4	2.6	5.8	9.8
2	Sod podzolic, sandy loamy	2.3	1.1	51	19	3.4	5.2	7.4
3	Sod podzolic, heavy loamy	2.4	1.2	50	10	3.4	5.5	8.7
4	Chernozem leached, heavy loamy	2.5	1.1	56	38	6.9	5.9	25.0 .
5	Meadow-chernozem, loamy	2.2	1.1	50	22	4.2	6.2	34.0
6	Chestnut, loamy	2.6	1.0	62	33	4.0	5.9	27.0
7	Meadow-alluvial, loamy . .	2.4	1.3	46	21	2.1	6.1	

The vertical distribution of Sr^{90} along the soil profile is presented on Figure 2, from which we see that the level of radioactive contamination of loamy soils is higher than that of sandy soils. Besides, the distribution of Sr^{90} in the soils was found to be inhomogeneous. Two types of distribution were observed. One of them is characterized by a rapid drop in Sr^{90} concentration with depth, characteristic of clayey soils. The other type of distribution, corresponding to sandy loamy soils, is characterized by the formation of an additional peak corresponding to a depth of 10—15 cm. Due to the variety of soils and moistening conditions, there must exist intermediate Sr^{90} distributions along the soil profile. Differences in the Sr^{90} distributions can be explained as follows.

Strontium-90, which is easily dissolved in water, can migrate together with the filterable surface water into the depth of the soil. At the same time, being in an ion-exchange state, Sr^{90} participates in the diffusion

TABLE 2. Distribution of Sr^{90} in soils in 1964

Layer depth, cm	Sod podzolic, loamy		Sod podzolic, sandy loamy		Sod podzolic, loamy		Chernozem-leached, loamy		Meadow-chernozem, loamy		Chestnut, loamy		Meadow-alluvial, loamy	
	10^{-12}, curie/cm^3	%	10^{-12}, curie/cm^3	%	10^{-12}, curie/cm^3	%	10^{-12}, curie/cm^3	%	10^{-12}, curie/cm^3	%	10^{-12}, curie/cm^3	%	10^{-12}, curie/cm^3	%
0–1	1.73	12.0	2.53	12.4	9.30	64.6	5.75	32.0	5.35	27.5	2.60	19.3	2.28	32.6
2–3	1.25	17.3	1.33	13.0	0.60	8.3	2.75	30.5	3.04	31.5	1.12	16.6	0.77	22.0
4–5	0.62	8.6	0.23	2.5	0.53	7.4	0.98	10.8	1.35	14.1	0.91	13.5	0.24	6.9
6–7	0.38	5.3	0.85	8.3	0.34	4.7	0.55	6.1	0.42	4.3	0.36	5.4	0.14	4.2
8–10	0.58	12.0	0.74	10.9	0.22	4.5	0.35	5.9	0.50	7.7	0.52	11.6	0.12	5.2
11–15	1.01	35.0	0.79	19.3	0.13	4.1	0.22	6.3	0.18	4.7	0.34	12.5	0.12	8.6
16–20	0.10	3.3	0.58	14.2	0.05	1.7	0.10	2.8	0.16	4.0	0.23	8.7	0.10	6.9
21–25	0.16	5.0	0.75	18.4	0.10	3.3	0.12	3.5	0.13	3.3	0.18	6.7	0.12	8.7
26–30	0.05	1.7	0.05	1.2	0.05	1.7	0.08	2.1	0.10	2.7	0.13	4.8	0.07	5.1

process, moving in the soil by diffusion. The efficiency of the process of Sr^{90} filtration or of diffusion is determined by the moistening regime and the soil properties. In clayey soils, with poor water permeability, and therefore with low filtration capacity, the determining process of Sr^{90} migration is diffusion, while in sandy soils the process of filtrative leaching is of great importance.

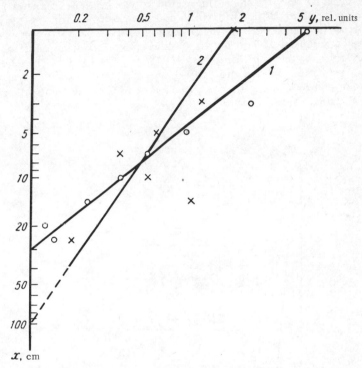

FIGURE 1. Content of Sr^{90} as a function of penetration depth in the soil:

1) leached chernozem, heavy loamy; 2) sod podzolic, sandy loam.

In order to estimate the contribution of diffusion in the distribution of Sr^{90} along the soil profile, the diffusion coefficient of Sr^{90} was determined in laboratory conditions. The procedure used in the experiment can be found elsewhere /4/.

The values of the diffusion coefficients of Sr^{90} for the investigated soils are tabulated in Table 3 and lie between $0.1 \cdot 10^{-7}$ and $2.4 \cdot 10^{-7}$ cm^2/sec. Relatively larger values of D are characteristic of sod podzolic soil, and lower ones of leached chernozem. The dependence of the diffusion coefficient of Sr^{90} on the soil moisture and temperature was determined (Tables 3 and 4). The diffusion coefficient increases with increasing moisture and temperature. These data enable us to calculate the mean diffusion coefficient, which reflects changes in soil moisture and temperature under natural conditions. The calculations were conducted by the formula

$$D_{av} = \frac{D_1 t_1 + D_2 t_2}{t_1 + t_2},$$

where D_1 and D_2 are the diffusion coefficients determined with the aid of averaged values of soil moisture and temperature in the warm period t_1 (April — October) and in the cold period t_2 (November — March), respectively. The average values of the moisture and temperature for the soils investigated by us, necessary for calculating the diffusion coefficients, were established from published data. The average diffusion coefficient for sod podzolic soils was found to be $0.84 \cdot 10^{-7} \, cm^2/sec$, and for leached chernozem $0.49 \cdot 10^{-7} \, cm^2/sec$. Once the diffusion coefficient of Sr^{90} in these soils is known, one can calculate the distribution of Sr^{90} along the soil profile as a result of diffusion.

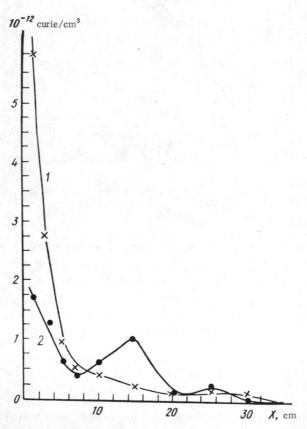

FIGURE 2. Distribution of Sr^{90} along the soil profile:

1) leached chernozem, heavy loamy; 2) sod podzolic, sandy loamy.

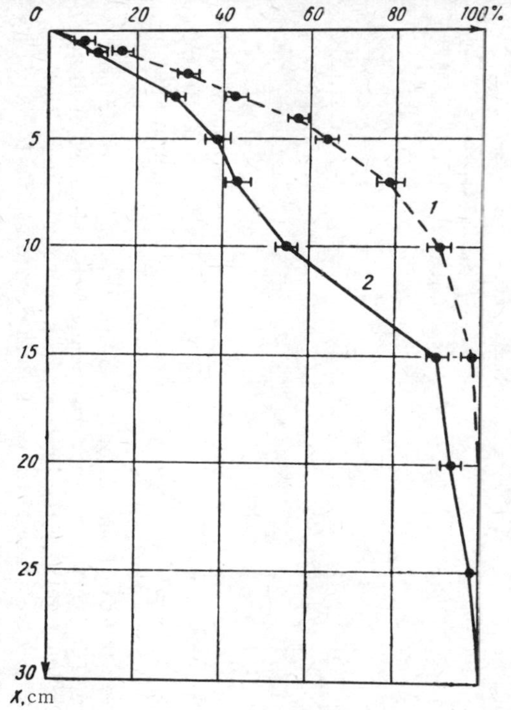

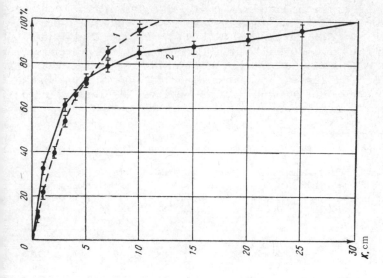

FIGURE 3. Reserve of Sr^{90} in sod podzolic, sandy soil (No.1) down to a depth of 30 cm:

1) according to calculated data ($D = 0.84 \cdot 10^{-7} \mathrm{cm}^2/\mathrm{sec}$);
2) according to data of the radiochemical determination of Sr^{90}.

FIGURE 4. Reserve of Sr^{90} in leached chernozem (No. 4) down to a depth of 30 cm:

1) according to calculated data ($D = 0.49 \cdot 10^{-7} \mathrm{cm}^2/\mathrm{sec}$);
2) according to data of the radiochemical determination of Sr^{90}.

Comparison of the calculated distribution of Sr^{90} with that observed in nature enables one to determine which is the dominant process. Figures 3 and 4 present the actual and calculated diffusion distributions of Sr^{90} in soils. The shape of the curves indicate that in sandy-loam soil Sr^{90} migrates more rapidly than the rate explained by diffusion alone. Together with the diffusion migration of Sr^{90} there probably also exists transfer from the soil solution. Calculation indicates that in this soil, 78 % of the total amount of Sr^{90} in the 0—30-cm layer is to be found in the 0—7-cm layer, while actually only 43 % is observed. The probable error in the determination of Sr^{90}, expressed as a fraction of its total amount, is estimated as 6—8 %; it can therefore be assumed that the observed discrepancy in the shape of the curves is significant.

TABLE 3. Diffusion coefficient D ($10^{-7} cm^2$/sec) as a function of soil moisture f (as % of dry soil weight)

Sod podzolic, sandy loam soil		Leached chernozem, heavy loamy soil		Sod podzolic, sandy loam soil		Leached chernozem, heavy loamy soil	
f	D	f	D	f	D	f	D
10.8	0.12	12.4	0.12	16.7	0.76	22.0	0.83
12.2	0.20	18.0	0.25	16.8	1.09	23.9	0.85
14.1	0.30	18.8	0.28	18.6	1.47	24.1	1.10
14.6	0.40	19.1	0.25	19.4	1.77	25.0	1.40
15.0	0.50	20.0	0.33	20.5	1.76	26.8	1.80
15.0	0.55	21.6	0.45	22.8	2.40	27.0	2.06
15.2	0.41			23.0	2.30		

TABLE 4. Diffusion coefficient of Sr^{90} in moist soil at various temperatures

Sod podzolic soil			Leached chernozem, heavy loamy soil		
t, °C	f, volume fraction	D, $10^{-7} cm^2$/sec	t, °C	f, volume fraction	D, $10^{-7} cm^2$/sec
18 ± 2	0.31	2.3 ± 0.16	18 ± 2	0.36	1.80 ± 0.16
18 ± 2	0.31	2.4 ± 0.15	18 ± 2	0.36	2.06 ± 0.15
−2 ± 0.5	0.33	0.74 ± 0.03	−2 ± 0.5	0.33	0.65 ± 0.05
−2 ± 0.5	0.33	0.78 ± 0.03	−2 ± 0.5	0.34	0.52 ± 0.05

For chernozem soil, the curves of Sr^{90} distribution almost coincide and only a negligible difference between them is observed at a depth of 10 cm. This points to the dominance of the diffusion process over other migration processes.

Figure 5 illustrates the distribution of Sr^{90} along the profile of some types of soil observed in 1964 under natural conditions. It is seen that the distribution of Sr^{90} depends on the type of soil. However, it was not possible to detect a clear relation between the vertical distribution of Sr^{90} and the zonality of the soils. The migration of Sr^{90} depends on many factors: texture and structure of the soil, content and composition of humus, content of calcium and pH of the soil solution, moisture, soil temperature, and so on. These factors affect differently the migration of strontium-90: some contribute to its migration within the soil, while others retard the migration.

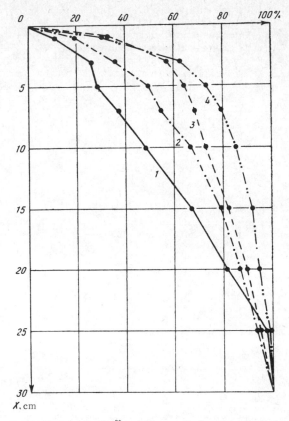

FIGURE 5. Reserve of Sr^{90} in different soils down to a depth of 30 cm:

1) sod podzolic, sandy loamy (No. 2); 2) chestnut, loamy (No. 6); 3) meadow, alluvial (No. 7); 4) meadow-chernozem, loamy (No. 5).

Diffusion as a continuous process occupies an important place in Sr^{90} migration. In clayey and loamy soils it can play the most important role, while in sandy and sandy loamy soils its importance is apparently commensurate with other migration processes.

BIBLIOGRAPHY

1. Arinushkina, E.V. Khimicheskii analiz pochv i gruntov (Chemical Analysis of Soils and Grounds). — Moskva, Izd. AN SSSR. 1952.

2. Zinov'eva, V.K., M.I. Zhilkina, V.P. Shvedov, and G.V. Yakovleva. Metodika vydeleniya strontsiya iz pochvy i opredelenie Sr^{90} (Procedure for Extracting Strontium from the Soil and Sr^{90} Determination). —Radiokhimiya, Vol. 1, p. 613. 1959.

3. Lavrukhina, A.K., T.V. Malysheva, and F.I. Pavlotskaya. Radiokhimicheskii analiz (Radiochemical Analysis). —Moskva, Izd. AN SSSR. 1963.

4. Prokhorov, V.M. O diffuzii strontsiya-90 v pochve i peske (Diffusion of Strontium-90 in Soil and Sand). —Radiokhimiya, Vol. 4, No. 2. 1962.

5. Shvedov, V.P. and S.P. Shirokov (editors). Radioaktivnye zagryazneniya vneshnei sredy (Radioactive Contamination of the Environment). —Moskva, Gosatomizdat. 1962.

UDC 551.482.214

HORIZONTAL WATER MIGRATION OF STRONTIUM-90

I. G. Vodovozova

During spring snowmelting, radioactive strontium deposited on the earth's surface participates with melted snow in migration processes.

This paper presents data on the physicochemical state of strontium-90 migrating with water; 73% of strontium-90 falling with snow is in cationic form. Atmospheric precipitation is deposited in the soil, participates in the migration processes, and subsequently leaches mainly soluble strontium-90 from the soil and its proportion in cationic form in the melted snow and river water increases to 100%.

Existing in an easily mobile cationic form, strontium-90 is discharged in the river together with floodwaters.

Radioisotopes deposited on the earth's surface due to global fallout are involved, together with the stable elements, in the cycle of substances in nature. It is known that, biologically, the most dangerous is strontium-90, which plays an active role in the natural biological cycle.

Many papers have been published, both in the Soviet Union and elsewhere, on the horizontal water migration of strontium-90 under different conditions. Depending on the experimental conditions, values of the horizontal water migration of strontium-90 were found to fluctuate between 1 and 80% /4, 5/. The horizontal redistribution of strontium-90, both falling with atmospheric precipitation and already deposited on the soil, accompanies surface water runoff, which is mainly observed during spring snowmelting. In this period large amounts of melted snow form in the drainage basin of a river, and although they do not interact with the soil for long, the low mineralization of this water contributes to the leaching of soluble soil compounds, and therefore of strontium-90, since 80—90% of the latter is in soluble form /1—3/.

This report presents data on the horizontal migration of strontium-90 falling with snow, and on the physicochemical forms in which it migrates.

The horizontal migration of strontium-90 with surface runoff water was studied in 1965—1966 at three drainage basins, which were selected with due allowance for their afforestation and the agrotechnical state of the soil. Thus, the first drainage basin was arable land, the second partly arable land and partly birch wood, while the third was located in a pine wood. The relief of the drainage basins was slightly hilly. The woods in the drainage basins were mainly birch, pine, and mixed (birch-pine) plantations. The local soils are sod-podzolic at the watersheds and the upper parts of the slopes, while gray wood and dark-colored meadow soils occupy the middle and lower parts of slopes. During spring floods the melted snow flows into the river, whose main supply originates from that source. High water occurs in April and lasts for about 30 days.

Samples of snow, spring snowmelt and soil were taken by the usual procedures. Samples of virgin soil were taken at a depth of 5 cm, and of

arable land at a depth of 10 cm. In these samples strontium-90 was determined by the radiochemical method, calcium by the flame-photometric
method, and strontium by the spectral method.

In order to determine the physicochemical state of strontium-90 in
water, the latter was passed through a column with cationite KU-2 in H^+-form
immediately after its collection. Resin was also analyzed for strontium-90,
calcium and stable strontium content.

In 1968 the strontium-90 content in snow was $20 \cdot 10^{-12}$ curie/liter and
in 1966, $2.6 \cdot 10^{-12}$ curie/liter. The decrease in global radioactive fallout
evidently led to an eightfold decrease in the content of strontium-90 in snow.

In the first period of snowmelting, when the drainage basin is still completely covered by snow, the activity of floodwater originating from snow is
considerable. At drainage basin I, the contribution of strontium-90 originating from snow was 41% in 1965 and 23% in 1966.

The strontium-90 decrease in global radioactive fallout probably
caused a drop in its content in the floodwater during the first period of
snowmelting. Figure 1 illustrates strontium-90 content as a function of the
snowmelting periods. The content of strontium-90 increases in period II
of the snowmelting, when the element is washed intensively from the soil.
In period I there is no contact between the water and soil. Almost all the
strontium-90 from atmospheric precipitation passes into runoff water (the
proportion of strontium-90 in the activity is 22%); 80% of strontium-90
originating from snow is found in floodwater.

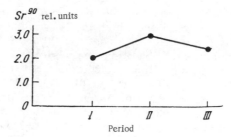

FIGURE 1. Strontium-90 content in floodwater as
a function of snowmelting periods.

However in period II, when the floodwaters flow over soil half-freed
from snow, the interaction of water with the soil is considerable, and as a
result the strontium-90 content in melted snow increases.

Finally, in period III, when very little snow remains on the drainage
basins but runoff still continues, the content of strontium-90 in the water
drops. This is possibly due to the fact that the soil in that period is de-
frosted and absorbs moisture, and runoff is realized at the expense of the
remaining snow on the moistened soil.

The content of stable elements (potassium, sodium, calcium) in floodwater during the different snowmelting periods is likewise different.

The physicochemical state of strontium-90 migrating with water was
also studied. Samples of snow, floodwater, water from brooks flowing
into the river, and water from the river itself were passed through columns

with cationite KU-2 in H^+-form. The determinations of the content of stable strontium, strontium-90 and calcium in the original water and on the resin are tabulated in Table 1. It is seen that 73 % of the strontium-90 falling with snow is in cationic form. Subsequently, after being deposited on the soil and included in the migration processes, atmospheric precipitation leaches mainly soluble strontium-90 from the water, and so its proportion in cationic form contained in the melted snow and the river water increases from 70 to 100%. Therefore strontium-90, migrating with the water, is almost completely in cationic form.

TABLE 1. Stable strontium, strontium-90 and calcium in cationic form (%) in water

Sample	Sr^{90}	Sr	Ca
Snow	73	80	39
Meltwater	83	80	45
Brook:			
1	100	37	42
2	79	—	55
3	93	74	62
4	97	88	66
River in spring	82	58	85
River in autumn	81	100	68

The content of stable strontium, and especially of calcium in cationic form, is somewhat different from that of strontium-90. This is probably explained by the fact that equilibrium has not yet been reached between strontium-90 and stable strontium and calcium, even in such a mobile system as water.

BIBLIOGRAPHY

1. Baranov, V.I. and V.I. Vilenskii. Opredelenie dolgozhivushchikh beta-izluchatelei v atmosfernykh vypadeniyakh (Determination of Long-Lived β-Emitters in Atmospheric Fallout). — Radiokhimiya, Vol. 4, No. 4, p. 486. 1962.
2. Dibolcs, I.K. et al. Global'nye vypadeniya strontsiya-90 na territorii Urala v period 1961—1966 gg. (Total Fallout of Strontium-90 Over the Territory of the Urals in the Period 1961—1966). — Moskva, Atomizdat. 1967.
3. Pavlotskaya, F.I. and L.N. Zatsepina. K voprosu ob izuchenii form postupleniya nekotorykh produktov deleniya na zemnuyu poverkhnost' (Study of the Forms of Arrival of Some Fission Products at the Earth's Surface). — Moskva, Atomizdat. 1965.
4. Martell, E.A. Atmospheric Aspects of Strontium-90 Fallout. — Science, Vol. 129, No. 3357. 1959.
5. Welford, G.A. and W.R. Collins. Fallout in New York during 1958. — Science, Vol. 131, No. 3415. 1960.

III. RADIOACTIVE AEROSOLS AND THEIR PROPERTIES

UDC 621.039.58

FORMATION OF RADIOACTIVE PARTICLES DURING NUCLEAR BURSTS IN THE TROPOSPHERE

Yu. A. Izrael' and A. A. Ter-Saakov

A theoretical model of aerosol radioactivation in the fireball of a nuclear burst is examined. Formulas are derived for the distribution of the radioactivity of isotopes on the aerosol particles as a function of particle radius. Three mechanisms of particle radioactivation are treated. In the first case, condensation of radioactive isotope vapors occurs at temperatures higher than the vaporization temperature of the soil particles ($\sim 2,300°C$), i.e., under conditions far removed from thermodynamic equilibrium. Such is the case for isotopes of zirconium lanthanum, yttrium and other refractory elements. In the second case the condensation of radioisotopes occurs on the surface of fused soil particles, i.e., under conditions of thermodynamic equilibrium (in the temperature range 2,300—1,400°C). In the third case aerosol activation is determined by radioisotope sorption on the surface of solid particles. Such is the case for isotopes which have gaseous precursors with half-decay periods from tens of seconds to several minutes (Sr^{89}, Sr^{90}, Cs^{137}, Ba^{140}). The influence of the precipitation of large particles from a cloud at the moment of radioactivation is taken into account.

This paper proposes several possible mechanisms of the formation (activation) of radioactive particles in the fireball and cloud during nuclear bursts in the troposphere. The characteristics of radioactive particle formation affect substantially the degree of radioisotope fragmentation and determine the dependence of particle activity on its size. Correct allowance for these effects is necessary when forecasting the radioactive contamination of natural media by different radioisotopes.

During fireball cooling, isotopes of zirconium, yttrium, strontium and other refractory elements condense on the fused soil particles trapped in it at temperatures higher than their vaporization temperature ($\sim 2,300°C$), i.e., under conditions far removed from thermodynamic equilibrium. In this case the activation of fused particles must proceed rapidly, and the condensation coefficient is near to unity. Under such conditions the amount of condensed radioisotope atoms on the particles is proportional to their surface, and therefore the volume concentration σ_0 will depend on the size of the particles.

In the temperature range $\sim 2,300 — 1,400°C$ (between the vaporization and solidification temperatures of the soil matter) the condensation of radioisotopes on the surface of fused soil particles will proceeed under conditions close to thermodynamic equilibrium. The condensation coefficient may differ substantially from unity. At the onset of equilibrium the ratio between the number of atoms of the i-th isotope in the gaseous and liquid phases will be determined by the saturation vapor pressure in the given volume at the given temperature in accordance with Raoult's law.* For small particles

---

* Actually, exact thermodynamic equilibrium is not established due to the thermal inertia of the particles, but the deviation from equilibrium will not be substantial.

(such as those produced in air bursts) or for long activation times (in bursts of high energy) constant volume condensation is established in particles of different size. For larger particles and shorter activation times the concentration of the i-th radioisotope in the external volume layer of a particle will be equalized through diffusion in the particle body (quasi-equilibrium case).

After solidification of the soil particles their activation will be determined by radioisotope sorption on the surface of the particles. Taking into account that radioisotopes such as strontium-89, -90, yttrium-91, cesium-137, -138, barium-140 and others have gaseous precursors with half-decay periods from tens of seconds to several minutes, the sorption process of these isotopes can last several tens of minutes. In this case the fallout of large particles from the activation zone under gravity can substantially affect the fractionation of the given group of isotopes.

We shall examine the scheme of particle activation for the cases mentioned above. In accordance with other results presented elsewhere /1—5/, we shall introduce various assumptions for surface bursts.

1. The temperature change in the fireball is exponential /1/ in the second stage of flow (after the second maximum), while the time of particle solidification is determined by /2/

$$t_l = 0.67\sqrt{W} \text{ sec,} \qquad (1)$$

where W is the burst strength in kilotons.

2. The radioactive products of the burst and the soil fragments are distributed uniformly throughout the fireball or a part of it, and can be estimated from data of Onufriev /3/, who examined the development of the cloud of a burst. If in accordance with the latter paper we assume that the cloud, at the beginning of its formation, passes through the stage of a vortex ring, the magnitude of the circulation of the external flow Γ_0 yields the linear particle velocity v in different zones of the formed torus:

$$v = \frac{\Gamma_0}{2\pi a} \simeq 5.3W^{0.2} \text{ m/sec,} \qquad (2)$$

where a is the torus radius, in m. The proportion δ of the fireball volume occupied by radioactive products of the burst and trapped fragmented soil is then found to be ~ 10—20%.

3. The amount of fused soil (in the form of fused particles) is about 200 t/kt according to Freiling /4/. The chemical composition of the soil is determined by its main component (SiO_2), the vaporization temperature of the soil matter ($\sim 2,300°C$), and the temperature of fusion ($\sim 1,400°C$).

4. The size distribution of the number (mass) of fused soil particles is approximated by a lognormal law /4/.

5. The saturation vapor pressure changes with temperature in accordance with data given in /5/; the rate of isotope molecule diffusion in fused particles is in accordance with data of /1/.

a. The Nonequilibrium Case

In this case the vaporization temperature of isotope matter is higher than that of the soil particle matter. The stream of atoms (molecules) of the i-th isotope, impinging per unit time on a unit surface of soil particle carriers, is given by

$$I_i = \frac{n_i \bar{v}_i}{4} \cdots, \tag{3}$$

where $n_i(t)$ is the concentration of atoms of the i-th isotope in the fireball at time t and $\bar{v}_i$ is the mean atom velocity of the i-th isotope, equal to $\sqrt{\frac{8kT}{\pi m_i}}$ (m_i is the mass of the atom, k the Boltzmann constant, and T the absolute temperature).

If there is no re-evaporation of atoms and we can use first-order kinetics, the condensation rate of the atoms of the i-th isotope (the intensity of their decrease in the fireball) is expressed in the form

$$\frac{dn_i}{dt} = -\alpha I_i \frac{S}{V} = -\alpha \frac{n_i(t)}{V} \frac{\bar{v}_i S}{4}, \tag{4}$$

where α is the condensation coefficient (in our case, starting at some time which can be considered as the effective beginning of the condensation, α increases sharply and approaches unity); S is the total surface of all the fused soil particles suspended in the fireball; V is the mean value of the fireball volume or of that part of it in which are distributed radioactive products and particles of trapped soil, while the atoms of the i-th isotope are being condensed on the fused particles. If $\alpha \approx 1$ (condensation conditions far removed from equilibrium), then

$$n_i(t) = n_{0i} e^{-\frac{\bar{v}_i S}{4V} t} = n_0 e^{-\frac{t}{t_V}}, \tag{5}$$

where n_{0i} is the initial number of atoms of the i-th isotope in the fireball; $t_V = \frac{4V}{\bar{v}_i S}$ is the mean residence time of the atoms of the i-th isotope in the gaseous phase.

The distribution density function of the number (mass) of particles as a function of their dimensions is approximated by a lognormal law. Therefor

$$S = \frac{3G_0}{\rho \xi_N e^{13.2\sigma^2}} = \frac{3G_0 e^{2.7\sigma^2}}{\rho \xi_m} \tag{6}$$

and

$$\frac{4\bar{V}\rho \xi_N e^{13.2\sigma^2}}{3\bar{v}_i G_0} = \frac{4\bar{V}\rho \xi_m}{3\bar{v}_i G_0 e^{2.7\sigma^2}}, \tag{7}$$

where G_0 is the total weight of fused particles, equal to $\sim 200\,t/kt$; ϱ is the particle density, equal to $\sim 2.5\,g/cm^3$; ξ_m and σ are the distribution parameter of the mass of fused particles with respect to their dimensions: $\xi_m = 100\mu$ and $\sigma = 0.76$ /4/.

In accordance with /6/ the volume of the fireball (at the time of separation of the shock wave front) is about 10^6 m^3/kt. Hence

$$t_V \simeq 4 \cdot 10^{-4} \text{ sec.}$$

The period during which 99% of the initial number of atoms of the i-th isotope in the fireball pass into the fused particles lasts about $2 \cdot 10^{-3}$ sec.

In this case the dependence of the activity of the i-th isotope in the particles on their size is given by

$$a_i(r) = 4\pi r^2 \frac{n_0 \lambda_i}{S} = \frac{4\pi r^2 n_0 \lambda_i \rho \xi_m}{3G_0 e^{2 \cdot 7\sigma^2}}, \tag{8}$$

where λ_i is the decay constant.

b.   The Quasi-equilibrium Case

In examining this case we shall assume that, in the temperature range of 2,300—1,400°C during each successive (small) time interval, thermodynamic equilibrium is established. This equilibrium is then disturbed, due to the more rapid cooling of the vapor phase compared with the liquid phase. This approximation gives a better accuracy for high-power blasts, in which cooling of the fireball at temperatures 2,300—1,400°C is much slower than in blasts of lower intensity. At the beginning of the process the inflow of atoms of the i-th isotope in the particle is proportional to their surface, and therefore the volume concentration of the i-th radioisotope in the surface layer (σ_V) for smaller particles will be higher than for larger particles. This leads to an increase in the vapor pressure of the soluble component remaining in the vapor phase over the finer particles, and to more rapid condensation on the larger particles. The Thompson effect (increase in saturation vapor pressure above the finest particles), caused by the surface curvature for particles larger than 0.1 μ, can be neglected in the case of a blast /7/.

In this case, the distribution of the total particle volume $V(r)$ and the volume containing the i-th isotope $V_i(r, t_l)$ (at the time of solidification of the particles t_l) according to particle size will be different. Clearly

$$V_i(r, t_l) = V(r)\xi_i(r, t_l),$$

where

$$\xi_i(r, t_l) = \frac{\frac{4}{3}\pi\{r^3 - [r - r_0(t_0, t_l)]^3\}}{\frac{4}{3}\pi r^3} = \frac{3r_0}{r} - \frac{3r_0^2}{r^2} + \frac{r_0^3}{r^3},$$

and

$$r_0(t_0, t_l) = \sqrt{2 \int_{t_0}^{t_l} D_i(t)\, dt}$$

when

$$r_0 \geqslant r, \quad \xi_i(r, t_l) = 1$$

(D_i is the diffusion coefficient of the i-th isotope and t_0 the time of onset of activation).

This case is most characteristic for isotopes of the intermediate group, which fall entirely or partly inside particles with temperatures close to the particle solidification temperature, i. e., under conditions close to thermodynamic equilibrium.

c.   Adsorption on the Surface of Solidifying Particles

After solidification of the particles, their activation will be determined by the adsorption both of atoms of radioisotopes having gaseous precursors, and of atoms of radioisotopes whose vaporization temperature is lower than the fusion temperature of the mass of soil particles.

The process rate has great importance when considering adsorption. The value of t_V, estimated with allowance for formula (7) at a time near to cloud stabilization (7—10 min after the blast) and at an ambient temperature of ~20°, is maximum for the period of cloud formation and equals ~5 sec (the cloud volume at the time of its stabilization was calculated by the formula for an ellipsoid with diameters /6, 8/ $D_x = D_y = 3\sqrt[3]{W}, D_z = \sqrt[3]{W}$, where W is the strength of the blast in kt). Therefore, in the absence of desorption, i. e., under conditions for which the vaporization temperature of the i-th radioisotope is higher than the temperature of the particle surface, the adsorption time of the main amount of atoms (99%) will be roughly equal to 30 sec.

During the ascent of the blast cloud, the large soil particles will leave the activation zone under the action of gravity. As a result the total surface of the soil particles in the radioactive cloud will decrease with time:

$$S_\Sigma(t) = S_{\Sigma_0} - 4\pi N_0 \int_{r(t)}^{\infty} r^2 f(r)\, dr...,$$

where $S_\Sigma(t)$ is the total surface of the soil particles at time t; S_{Σ_0} is the total surface of the soil particles at the beginning of the formation of the blast cloud, equal to $4\pi N_0 \int_0^{\infty} f(r)\, r^2 dr$ and determined with the aid of formula (6). $S(r)$ is the density function of the particle size distribution, approximated by a lognormal law; N_0 is the total number of soil particles trapped in the fireball:

$$N_0 = \frac{G}{\frac{4}{3}\pi\rho \int\limits_0^\infty r^3 f(r)\, dr} \; ;$$

$r(t)$ is the radius of particles situated at time t beyond the limits of the radioactive cloud. This latter radius can be determined tentatively from the rate of gravitational precipitation of particles:

$$u(r) = \frac{R_{\text{cl}}(t)}{t} .$$

For radioisotopes which do not have gaseous precursors, the dependence of activity on particle size is thus given by

$$a_i(r) = 4\pi r^2 \frac{n_i \lambda_i}{S_{\Sigma_0} - 4\pi \int\limits_{r(t)}^\infty N_0 r^2 f(r)\, dr} = \frac{1.45 \cdot 10^{23} V_i r^2 \lambda_i}{\frac{r(t)}{N_0 \int\limits_0^{} r^2 f(r)\, dr}}, \tag{9}$$

where $n_i(t) = n_{0i} e^{-\lambda t}$ is the number of atoms of the i-th radioisotope at time t; λ_i is the decay constant of the i-th radioisotope; V_i is the yield of the i-th radioisotope upon fission. For radioisotopes having gaseous precursors, particle activity as a function of size is expressed as follows:

$$a_i(r) = \frac{n_{2i}(t)\lambda_{2i}}{N_0 \int\limits_0^{r(t)} r^2 f(r)\, dr} r^2, \tag{10}$$

where $n_{2i}(l) = \frac{\lambda_{1i} n_{1l}}{\lambda_{2l} - \lambda_{1l}} [e^{-\lambda_{1i}t} - e^{-\lambda_{2i}t}]$ is the number of atoms of the daughter isotope in the i-th mass chain at time t; λ_{1i} and λ_{2i} are the decay constants of the mother (gaseous) and daughter radioisotopes.

For fine particles ($r < r_0$) which do not succeed in getting beyond the blast cloud during the entire activation time, expression (10) assumes the form

$$a_i(r) = \frac{n_{2i}(t)\lambda_{2i}}{N_0 \int\limits_0^{r_0} r^2 f(r)\, dr} r^2. \tag{11}$$

BIBLIOGRAPHY

1. Freiling, E.C. Formation of Fission Fragments in Nuclear Blasts.— In: Radioaktivnye Vypadeniya ot Yadernykh Vzryvov (Radioactive Fallout from Nuclear Explosions), edited by Yu.A.Izrael'. Moskva, Izdatel'stvo "Mir." 1968. [Russian translation.]
2. Anderson, A.D. A Theory for Close-in Fallout from Land-Surface Nuclear Bursts.—J.Met., Vol.18, No.4. 1961.

3. Onufriev, A.T. Teoriya dvizheniya vikhrevogo kol'tsa pod deistviem sily tyazhesti. Pod"em oblaka atomnogo vzryva (Theory of Vortex Ring Motion under the Effect of Gravity. Ascent of the Cloud of a Nuclear Explosion).— PMTF, No. 2. 1967.

4. Freiling, E.C. Fractionation in Surface Bursts. "Radioactive Fallout from Nuclear Weapon Tests I." TID-7632. 1962.

5. Glushko, V.P. et al. (editors). Termodinamicheskie svoistva individual'nykh veshchestv (Thermodynamic Properties of Individual Substances). Handbook.— Moskva, Izd. AN SSSR. 1962.

6. Operation of Nuclear Weapons. [Russian translation, 1963.]

7. Junge, C. Air Chemistry and Radioactivity.— New York, Academic Press. 1963.

8. Fedorov, E.K. (editor). Meteorology and Atomic Energy. [Russian translation, 1959.]

UDC 621.039.58

CALCULATION OF FRACTIONATION EFFECTS IN ATMOSPHERIC NUCLEAR BURSTS

Yu. A. Izrael'

A theoretical calculation is given of the coefficients of fractionation of radioactive isotopes in aerosols, formed during nuclear bursts. The calculations are conducted on the assumption of thermodynamic equilibrium between the liquid and gaseous fractions with the utilization of Raoult's law. The results are given of the calculation of the fraction of radioactive isotopes of the most important mass chains condensing on the aerosols as a function of the time after the burst. Also calculated are the coefficients of fractionation $f_{i, 95}$ for the isotopes Te^{132}, Sr^{90}, Sr^{89} and Cs^{137} in the form of functions of particle radius (the time of particle solidification is 7 sec). The calculations are performed for the nearest trace of the surface blast. The derived theoretical correlation curve of fractionation of the series of isotopes agrees satisfactorily with measurements of isotope fractionation at the nearest trace of the "Small Boy" low-strength American nuclear explosion.

A model for calculating the fractionation of radioactive products in nuclear bursts was suggested earlier /1, 2/. The model took into account the complex nuclear and physicochemical processes taking place simultaneously in the fireball. It was assumed that the soil trapped in the fireball has the form of separate, first fused and then solidified particles, on the surface of which exist condensed isotopes in the form of different elements with different physicochemical properties. Their condensation takes place at different times, so leading to a different ratio of isotopes in particles of different size, i.e., to the fractionation of the isotopes.

These models /1, 2/ contained some simplifications which affected the calculation results: a model of particle activation was used, according to which the isotopes were able to diffuse to the full depth of the particles /1/ (equilibrium case, which is apparently true only for high-intensity air or surface bursts); during the condensation of isotopes in the liquid phase only the vaporization temperature was taken into account, i.e., it was assumed that condensation occurs discontinuously and not in accordance with the saturation vapor pressure /2/; particle precipitation from the cloud during condensation on the particle surface was disregarded, etc.

This paper presents an improved model for computing fractionation effects, using the model of particle activation by radioactive isotopes in the fireball described in /3/.

If we assume the existence of thermodynamic equilibrium in the fireball, the ratio between the amounts of substances of the i-th component in the vapor n_i^0 and liquid n_i phases (in accordance with Raoult's law) assumes the form

$$\frac{n_i^0}{n_i} = \frac{P_i^0 V_n}{(n_i + n_j) RT},$$ (1)

where P_i^0 is the vapor pressure above the one-component liquid i; n_i, n_j are the numbers of moles of the i-th and j-th components in the solution (melt); n_i^0 is the number of moles in the vapor phase of volume V_n; T is the temperature; R is the gas constant.

We can calculate from here the amount of a given element, in whose form is found some given explosion product converted to the liquid phase at temperature T in the fireball.

The model for calculating the isotope composition at each moment /2/, data on the thermodynamic properties of the individual substances /4/ and calculation of the temperature relationships in the fireball /3/ together enabled us to calculate $F_i(t)$, the fraction of isotopes belonging to the i-th mass chain condensed up to time t.

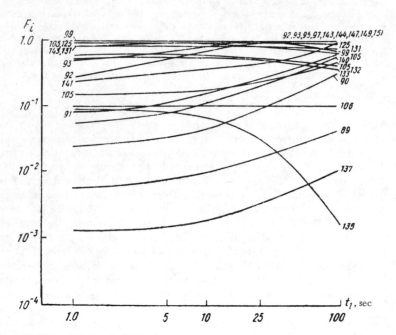

FIGURE 1.   Fraction $F_i(t)$ of refractory products in the mass chains as a function of the time up to fission.

Figure 1 presents the relationship $F_i(t)$ for the most important mass chains, and seems more accurate than that given in /2/. For known time of soil particle solidification for explosions of different intensity, we can find with the aid of Figure 1 the fraction of each isotope trapped inside the

particles (up to solidification) and distributed over the volume of these
particles:

$$F_i(t) = \frac{Q_i^V(t)}{Q_i(t)},\tag{2}$$

where $Q_i(t)$, $Q_i^{V,S}(t)$ are respectively the total activity of the i-th isotope and
the number of particles distributed in the volume (over the surface).
According to /1/, the fractionation coefficient is given by

$$f_{i,j}(r,\ t) = \frac{Y_j \lambda_j e^{-\lambda_i t}}{Y_i \lambda_i e^{-\lambda_i t}}\ \frac{N_i^V(r,\ t) + N_i^S(r,\ t)}{N_j^V(r,\ t) + N_j^S(r,\ t)},\tag{3}$$

where $N_i^V(r,\ t)$, $N_i^S(r,\ t)$ and $N_i(r,\ t)$ are respectively the particle-size density
distribution functions of the volume, surface and total activities of the i-th
isotope at time t, with $\int_0^\infty N_i(r,\ t)\,dr = Q_i(t)$; $Y_{i,j}$ is the yield of isotopes during
fission; $\lambda_{i,j}$ is the decay constant.

During activation, in the case of uniform particle contamination (equilibrium case, volume contamination $\bar{\sigma}_{V_i} = \text{const}$),

$$N_i^V(r) = V(r)\bar{\sigma}_{V_i},\tag{4}$$

where $\bar{\sigma}_{V_i} = \dfrac{Q_i^V(t)}{\int_0^\infty V(r)\,dr}$ and $V(r)$ is the particle size distribution of the total
volume.

For rapid activation, when the flux of nuclides across the surface of the
particles is constant,

$$N_i^V(r) = \beta S(r),\tag{5}$$

where $\beta = \dfrac{Q_i^V(t)}{\int_0^\infty S(r)\,dr}$, and $S(r)$ is the particle size distribution of the total
surface. For the most general case (during the equalization of volume
concentration in the layer into which isotopes penetrate as a result of
diffusion, $\sigma_V' = \text{const}$),

$$N_i^V(r) = V(r)\xi_i(r)\sigma_{V_i}',\tag{6}$$

where $\sigma_{V_i}' = \dfrac{Q_i^V(t)}{\int_0^\infty V(r)\xi_i(r)\,dr}$; $\xi_i(r)$ is the ratio of the volume in the particles of
given size occupied by the diffusing i-th isotope (at the moment of solidifica-
tion of particles) to the total volume of particles of this size /3/. Similarly

$$N_i^S(r) = \varkappa S(r),\tag{7}$$

where

$$\varkappa = \frac{Q_i^S(t)}{\int_0^\infty S(r)\,dr}.$$

Here

$$Q_i^S(t) = Q_i(t)\left\{\sum_z [1 - F_{zi}(t_l)]\,P_i(t_l,Z) - P_i^\wedge(t_l,Z) + \right.$$

$$\left. + \int_{t_l}^t U_i(t')f(r,t')\,dt'\right\} = Q_i(t)\,Y_i^S(r,t,t_l), \tag{8}$$

where F_{zi} is the value of F_i for an individual isotope of atomic number Z; $P_i(t_l,Z)$ is the isotope fraction belonging to the i-th mass chain with atomic number Z at time t_l; $P_i^\wedge(t_l,Z)$ is the same for the "volatile" isotopes, existin in the form of elements not condensing even on cold particles; $U_i(t)$ is the rate of formation of nonvolatile isotopes from volatile isotopes, such that

$$\int_{t_l}^\infty U_i(t)\,dt = \sum_z [F_{zi}(\infty) - F_{zi}(t_l)], \tag{9}$$

$f(r,t)$ being the fraction of particles of size r remaining in the cloud at tim t. If volatile isotopes form from less volatile or nonvolatile isotopes (for instance, in chains with $Z = 131-135$), then in formula (8) $U_i(t)$ assumes negative values, and we must then assume here that $f(r,t) = 1$.

Substitution of the values obtained for $N_{i,j}^V$ and $N_{i,j}^S$ in formula (3) yields the final expression for $f_i(r)$. Assuming that the fractionation of the i-th isotope is determined with respect to the refractory one (for instance, to Zr^{95}), we obtain in the most general case

$$f_{i.95}(r,t,t_l) = \frac{Y_{95}\lambda_{95}e^{-\lambda_{95}t}}{Y_i\lambda_i e^{-\lambda_i t}} \cdot \frac{V_i'(r,t_l)Q_i^V(t,t_l) + S'(r)\,Q_i^S(t,t_l)}{V_{95}'(r,t_l)\,Q_{95}(t)} =$$

$$= \frac{V_i'(r,t_l)\,F_i(t_l) + S'(r)\,Y_i^S(r,t,t_l)}{V_{95}'(r)}, \tag{10}$$

where

$$V_i'(r) = \frac{V(r)\varepsilon_i(r)}{\int_0^\infty V(r)\,\varepsilon_i(r)\,dr}.$$

Figure 2 illustrates relationships between fractionation coefficient $f_{i.95}$ and particle size (radius) for the nearest trace of a surface burst for the isotopes Te^{132}, Sr^{90}, Sr^{89}, Cs^{137} and for $t_l = 7$ sec (low-strength burst), calculated by formula (10). The forms of $V(r)$ and $S(r)$ were derived with the aid of data in /5/, and the diffusion coefficients of the different isotope in fused soil are obtained using data of /6/.

Figures 1 and 2 show that the fractionation coefficients vary considerably with changes in particle size and are substantially different for the different isotopes.

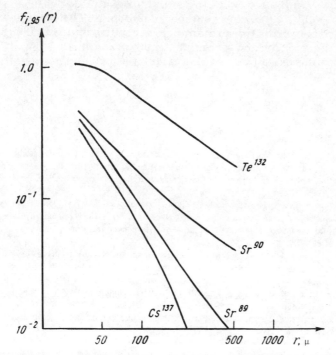

FIGURE 2. Fractionation coefficients as a function of particle radius for a low-strength surface nuclear burst.

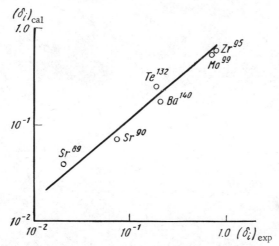

FIGURE 3. Correlation curve between calculated and experimental values of the fraction of various falling isotopes on the nearest trace of a low-strength surface nuclear burst.

Integration of the numerator of the right side of formula (10) within the limits of the particles sizes characteristic for any zone (such as the nearest trace) yields the fraction δ_i of a given isotope falling in this zone.

Figure 3 shows the correlation curve between the calculated $(\delta_i)_{cal}$ and experimental $(\delta_i)_{exp}$ values for a number of isotopes. The experimental values $(\delta_i)_{exp}$ for particles sizes (mean diameter) exceeding 90μ are taken from /6/ for the nearest trace of the low-strength American explosion "Small-Boy." It is seen that the experimental and calculated values are in satisfactory agreement.

BIBLIOGRAPHY

1. Izrael', Yu.A. Ob opredelenii koeffitsientov fraktsionirovaniya i biologicheskoi dostupnosti produktov yadernykh vzryvov v radioaktivnykh vypadeniyakh (Determining the Fractionation Efficiency and Biological Accessibility of Nuclear Burst Products in Radioactive Fallout).— DAN SSSR, Vol. 161, No. 2. 1965.

2. Grechushkina, M.P. and Yu.A.Izrael'. Fraktsionirovanie radioaktivnykh produktov yadernogo vzryva (Fractionation of Radioactive Products of a Nuclear Burst).— In: Radioaktivnye izotopy v atmosfere i ikh ispol'zovanie v meteorologii (Radioactive Isotopes in the Atmosphere and their Utilization in Meteorology). Moskva, Atomizdat. 1965.

3. Izrael', Yu.A. and A.A.Ter-Saakov. Obrazovanie radioaktivnykh chastits pri yadernykh vzryvakh v troposfere (Formation of Radioactive Particles during Nuclear Bursts in the Troposphere).— In this collection.

4. Glushko, V.P. et al.(editor). Termodinamicheskie svoistva individual'nykh veshchestv (Thermodynamic Properties of Individual Substances). Handbook.— Moskva, Izd. AN SSSR. 1962.

5. Freiling, E.C. Fractionation in Surface Bursts. "Radioactive Fallout from Nuclear Weapon Tests I." TID-7632, p. 25. 1962.

6. Freiling, E.C. et al. Formation of Fission Fragments in Nuclear Blasts.— In: Radioaktivnye Vypadeniya Yadernykh Vzryvov (Radioactive Fallout from Nuclear Explosions), edited by Yu.A.Izrael'. Moskva, Izdatel'stvo "Mir." 1968. [Russian translation.]

UDC 551.510.72

THE ATMOSPHERIC FORMATION OF SECONDARY AEROSOLS DURING VENTILATED UNDERGROUND NUCLEAR TESTS

V. N. Petrov and A. A. Ter-Saakov

In underground nuclear tests, some radioactive products may be discharged into the atmosphere through excess pressure or ventilation due to the destruction of rocks in the test area and the formation of cracks near to ground level.

The direct outflow into the atmosphere of nongaseous radioactive products is hardly probable, due to their sorption in the subsoil rock layer. It is therefore natural to assume that, in the main, chemically inert gases (such as the isotopes of krypton and xenon) are discharged into the atmosphere. The appearance of nonvolatile radioisotopes in the atmosphere can be associated with the decay of radioactive gases, which are the precursors of such isotopes in the corresponding chains of radioactive transformations. Nongaseous radioisotopes formed in the atmosphere are deposited on atmospheric dust particles and form so-called "secondary" aerosols.

A model of the atmospheric formation of the decay products of gaseous radioisotopes during underground nuclear tests is examined.

In underground nuclear tests, the destruction of rocks in the test zone, especially fractionation of rocks and the formation of a system of cracks, can create channels connecting the test cavity with the atmosphere. As a result of ventilation, excess pressure or diffusion, some radioactive products of the test may be discharged into the atmosphere /1, 2/.

It is natural to assume that these comprise mainly chemically weakly-active inert gases, such as the isotopes of krypton and xenon. The direct discharge into the atmosphere of nonvolatile radioisotopes is hardly probable, due to their sorption in thick layers of rock separating the test zone from the ground surface /3/. Accordingly, the appearance of nonvolatile long-lived radioisotopes in the atmosphere at large distances may be due to the decay of radioactive gaseous isotopes, which are the precursors of nongaseous isotopes in the corresponding chains of radioactive transformations. Such gaseous isotopes (mother and daughter) are $Kr^{89} - Rb^{89} - Sr^{89}$ and $Xe^{137} - Cs^{137}$. The nongaseous long-lived isotopes formed in the atmosphere are deposited on atmospheric dust particles and form so-called "secondary" aerosols.

This paper deals with a theoretical model of the atmospheric formation of decay products of gaseous radioisotopes discharged to the surface during underground nuclear tests.

We shall examine the transfer of radioactive gases due to ventilation of the test cavity. We shall assume that the discharge of radioactive gases into the atmosphere is exponential and takes place at a constant rate.

Denote by t' and t the respective times at which any portion of gases emerge from the test cavity and arrive at the ground surface, and by $t_0 = t - t'$ the time taken by this portion to reach the surface. Then the number of nuclei of the gaseous isotope (if it is the precursor of a radioactive chain) in the test cavity at time t' is $N_{1,0} e^{-(K+\lambda_1)t'}$, and the rate of outflow from the cavity is given by

$$\frac{dN_1}{dt} = -KN_{1,0} e^{-(K+\lambda_1)t'}, \tag{1}$$

where $N_{1,0}$ is the number of nuclei of the given isotope formed during the explosion: $N_{1,0} = 1.45 \cdot 10^{21} q_{fis} \nu$ (q_{fis} is the fission power of the explosion in 10^3 t, and ν is the yield of nuclei of the given isotope in %); λ is the radioactive decay constant of the given isotope; K is a constant characterizing the rate of transport of gases from the cavity (in the case of air ventilation of the cavity, K is equal to the ratio of the air discharge in the system to the cavity volume).

If we assume that, as a result of radioactive decay, each portion of nuclei of a given isotope leaving the cavity decreases by a factor of $e^{-\lambda_1 t_0}$ until its emergence to the surface, then the rate of discharge of gas in the atmosphere is given by the equation

$$\frac{dN_1}{dt} = -KN_{1,0} e^{-(K+\lambda_1)t'-\lambda_1 t_0}. \tag{2}$$

If the radioactive gas is a daughter product (second in the chain), the rate of discharge will be equal (in accordance with the theory of radioactive transformations) to

$$\frac{dN_2}{dt} = -K \left\{ N_{1,0} \frac{\lambda}{\lambda_2 + K - \lambda_1} [e^{-\lambda_1 t'} - e^{-(\lambda_2+K)t'}] + \right.$$
$$\left. + N_{2,0} e^{-(K+\lambda_2)t'} \right\} e^{-\lambda_2 t_0}. \tag{3}$$

Integration of equations (2) and (3) within the limits t, $t+\Delta t$ yields the number of nuclei of a gaseous isotope discharged into the atmosphere during that time interval. For the radioisotope which is the precursor of the chain, we obtain

$$N_1(t,t+\Delta t) = \frac{KN_{1,0}}{K+\lambda_1} e^{-\lambda_1 t_0 - t'(K+\lambda_1)} [1 - e^{-\Delta t(K+\lambda_1)}]. \tag{4}$$

Similar expressions hold for N_2, etc.

The activity yield of the i-th radioisotope (curie) per unit time is calculated by the formula

$$Q_i(t,t+\Delta t) = \frac{N_i(t,t+\Delta t)\lambda_i}{1.33 \cdot 10^{14}}. \tag{5}$$

Consider the portion of radioactive gases discharged into the atmosphere per unit time, which, upon decay, form nongaseous products.

The number of nuclei of the given nongaseous isotope N_2' in this portion at time τ is determined by the equation

$$N_2' = \frac{\lambda_1 N_1}{\lambda_2 - \lambda_1} [e^{-\lambda_1 \tau} - e^{-\lambda_2 \tau}]. \tag{6}$$

If the nongaseous isotope is third in the transformation chain (for instance, $Kr^{89} \rightarrow Rb^{89} \rightarrow Sr^{89}$), then

$$N_3' = N_1 \lambda_1 \lambda_2 \left[\frac{e^{-\lambda_1 \tau}}{(\lambda_2 - \lambda_1)(\lambda_3 - \lambda_1)} + \frac{e^{-\lambda_2 \tau}}{(\lambda_1 - \lambda_2)(\lambda_3 - \lambda_2)} + \frac{e^{-\lambda_3 \tau}}{(\lambda_1 - \lambda_3)(\lambda_2 - \lambda_3)} \right]. \tag{7}$$

For any unit portion of gases discharged into the atmosphere, the expression before the brackets in formulas (6) and (7) is constant.

Since the portion of gases emerging to the surface will be transferred to the atmosphere at the wind speed u, we can set

$$N_2' = \text{const}[e^{-\lambda_1 r/u} - e^{-\lambda_2 r/u}], \tag{8}$$

where r is the distance from the source of the emerging gases.

By specifying numerical values of K, and using formula (5) to compute the activity yield of the i-th radioisotope per unit time, we can estimate the concentration of radioactive gases in the atmosphere at different distances from the explosion using known solutions to the equation of turbulent diffusion for a continuously operating stationary source.

BIBLIOGRAPHY

1. Nikiforov, B.I. et al. Podzemnye yadernye vzryvy (Underground Nuclear Tests).— Moskva, Atomizdat. 1965.
2. Martell, E.A. Iodine-131 Fallout from Underground Tests.— Science, Vol. 143, No. 3602. 1964.
3. Radioactive Fallout from Nuclear Weapons Tests.— U.S. Atomic Energy Commission. 1965.

UDC 551.510.72

SIZE DISTRIBUTION OF HIGH-ACTIVITY
PARTICLES IN THE TROPOSPHERE IN
SEPTEMBER—DECEMBER 1967

Ya. I. Gaziev, S. G. Malakhov, and L. E. Nazarov

High-activity particles of artificial radioactive aerosols were observed in the troposphere in September—December 1967. The "age" of the aerosols at the beginning of the observation period was ~2.5 months. Radioactive particles of diameter $d \geqslant 0.9\,\mu$ were investigated.

According to the results obtained in the ground layer of the atmosphere and the upper troposphere, the integral and differential size distribution of these particles was exponential for $d \geqslant 0.9\,\mu$. On the average for the troposphere the exponent was equal to $(1.4 \pm 0.2)\,d$ micron^{-1}. For radioactive particles of diameter between 2 and 6 μ, the fractionation coefficients of the isotopes Ce^{144}, Ce^{141} and Ru^{103} were determined with respect to Zr^{95}. The values of these coefficients were roughly the same as those given earlier in the literature for micron particles of atmospheric nuclear blasts. The time of residence in the stratosphere of particles of diameter between 2.5 and 6 μ was roughly 4.5 months. The scavenging rate of radioactive particles of micron size ($d = 1$—$6\,\mu$) in the lower troposphere was close to 2 km/day.

Various observations show that, in periods of atmospheric nuclear weapons tests and in the first months after their completion, a considerable part of the radioactive products of the bursts is associated with aerosol particles possessing individual activities of the order of 10^{-12}—10^{-11} curie and above /6, 14/. Theoretical and experimental data have been published indicating that the behavior of these highly active particles in the atmosphere and their radioisotope composition may depend considerably on particle size /2—8, 12—18/. Therefore, the size distribution of the highly-active particles must be known in order to understand the space-time patterns of the contamination of the atmosphere and of the earth's surface by the products of nuclear blasts in the first six months after an explosion.

In September—December 1967 we observed in the troposphere highly active particles whose "age" at the beginning of September was ~2.5 months. On the eve of our observation period the stratosphere contained a large amount of "fresh" radioactive aerosols, and we could expect a considerable influx of highly active particles from the stratosphere into the troposphere. Figure 1 presents the results of American scientists /10/; they show that in August 1967 the maximum concentrations of radioactive aerosols in the lower stratosphere occurred at 45—60°N. Our own investigations were conducted in the same range of latitudes over European USSR. Aerosol samples in the ground layer of the atmosphere were taken by means of filtering installations and horizontal boards /9/. In the free atmosphere up to 12 km, samples were taken by special aircraft on FPP or FPA filtering materials. The β-count rates of the particles were measured by an MST-17 end counter or were determined from the size of the corresponding dark spots on autoradiographs. The thickness of the counter window was about 5 mg/cm². Radiography of the aerosol samples was carried out with RM-1 and RT-2 X-ray films. The particle distribution with respect to the β-count rates was determined from autoradiographs of the samples. Radioisotopic composition of the particles was studied by means of a scintillating gamma-spectrometer with NaJ (Ti) crystal of dimension 40×40 mm. The size-activity relation used had the form

$$d = \sqrt{\frac{6n}{\pi n_{\mathrm{un}}}},$$

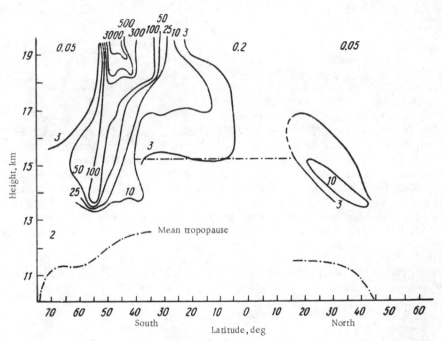

FIGURE 1. Concentration of Zr^{95} in the atmosphere in August 1967 /10/ in pcuric per m³ air, reduced to normal conditions ($T = 15°C$ and $P = 760$ mm Hg).

where d is the particle diameter, n its β-count rate, and n_{un} the unit volume β-count rate. According to published data, the unit volume β-count rates of micron particles of the considered "age" are, on the average, practically independent of their size /17, 18/. The size of 10 particles and their β-count rates were determined. The diameters of these particles lay between 2 and 6μ. The count rates n and n_{un} were naturally taken for the same particle age. The decrease in the β-count rates of the considered particles with time, for ages from 4 to 12 months, is described satisfactorily by the power law

$$n = n_1 (t/t_1)^{-1.3},$$

where n_1 is the β-count rate at time t_1.

As usual, in highly active particles we observed a substantial fractionation of isotopes. The fractionation coefficients of Ce^{144}, Ce^{141} and Ru^{103} with respect to Zr^{95} for particles of diameter between 2 and 6μ are given in Table 1. These coefficients were calculated for fission of U^{238} by thermonuclear neutrons.

TABLE 1. Fractionation coefficients of Ce^{144}, Ce^{141}, Ru^{103} with respect to $Zr^{95} + Nb^{95}$ in radioactive particles

Serial No.	Number of particles in the sample	Particle diameters, μ	Fractionation coefficient		
			$f\left(\dfrac{Ce^{144}}{Zr^{95}+Nb^{95}}\right)$	$f\left(\dfrac{Ce^{141}}{Zr^{95}+Nb^{95}}\right)$	$f\left(\dfrac{Ru^{103}}{Zr^{95}+Nb^{95}}\right)$
1	46	2–3.6	0.6–0.7	0.1–0.3	0.1–0.3
2	7	3–5.5	0.5–0.7	Undetermined	Undetermined
3	1	5	0–0.1	0.4–0.6	0–0.1
4	1	5.8	0–0.3	0–0.1	0–0.1

According to the measurements of four aircraft samples, the content of Zr^{95} in particles with diameters $d \geqslant (1.3-1.5)\mu$ in September—October 1967 fluctuated between 20 and 60% of the Zr^{95} content in aerosols as a whole.

Rectified integral distribution curves of highly active particles, plotted on the basis of samples taken in the ground layer of the atmosphere and at heights of 9—12 km, are presented in Figures 2 and 3. About 390 particles were used for plotting the first curve, and about 1,100 for the second one. The vertical segments indicate the standard deviations of the number of counted particles, and the horizontal segments the standard deviations of measurements of the unit β-count rate and the diameters of the dark spots on the autoradiographs.

According to the results, the considered distributions are exponential and can be expressed in the form

$$F(d) = e^{-\alpha(d-d^*)},$$

where $F(d)$ is the number of particles of diameter larger than d divided by the number of particles of diameter larger than $d^* = 0.9\mu$; $\alpha = 1.2\mu^{-1}$ for the ground air layer and $\alpha = 1.6\mu^{-1}$ for the upper troposphere. These results show that in September—December 1967, in the ground layer of the atmosphere, larger and more active particles were observed than in the upper troposphere. For the troposphere as a whole the value of α must lie within the limits of the values found above and can be taken as $(1.4 \pm 0.2)\mu^{-1}$. The differential particle size distribution function $f(d)$ is the derivative of the function $F(d)$, i.e.,

$$f(d) = \alpha e^{-\alpha(d-d^*)}.$$

Both $F(d)$ and $f(d)$ were derived for particle diameters larger than d^*. The range of smaller sizes was not examined in the present study.

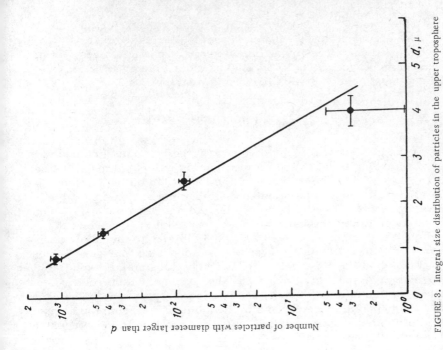

FIGURE 3. Integral size distribution of particles in the upper troposphere in September–December 1967.

Number of particles with diameter larger than d

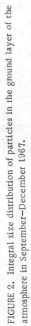
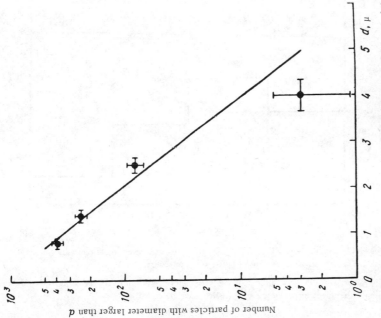

FIGURE 2. Integral size distribution of particles in the ground layer of the atmosphere in September–December 1967.

Number of particles with diameter larger than d

The simple form of the functions approximating the experimental particle-size distributions is probably associated with the fact that these distributions were obtained for a limited range of particle sizes. In the more general case, according to /6/, the particle size distribution in the troposphere must approximate a lognormal distribution:

$$f(d) = \frac{1}{\sqrt{2\pi}\sigma d} \exp\left[-\frac{1}{2\sigma^2}\left(\ln \frac{d}{d_d}\right)^2\right],$$

where d_d is the geometrical mean diameter of the particles (the logarithm of the diameter d_d is equal to the mean value of the logarithms of the particle diameters); σ^2 is the variance of the logarithm of the particle diameters. Naturally, more complicated distributions are also possible /5/.

The variance for highly active particles did not remain constant during the period under consideration, as can be seen from the change in the ratio of the number of particles between 2.5 and 6μ in size to the number of particles from 1 to 1.5μ in size (Figure 4). According to Figure 4, these ratios at the end of the observation period were substantially smaller than at its beginning. Especially strong was the decrease in the relative content of particles of diameter $d = 2.5-6\mu$ in the upper troposphere. The concentration of these particles decreased to the same extent from the beginning to the end of the observation period, while the variation in the concentration of particles of diameter $1-1.5\mu$ was small.

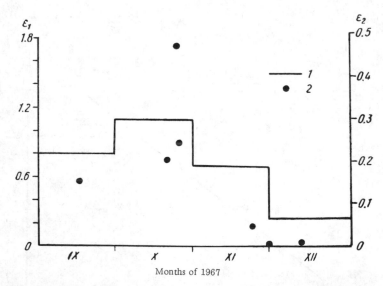

Months of 1967

FIGURE 4. Ratio (ɛ) of the number of particles with diameter d between 2.5 and 6μ to the number of particles with d between 1 and 1.5μ:

1) data for the ground layer of the atmosphere (scale of ratios on the left); 2) data for the upper troposphere (scale of ratios on the right).

The results show that at the end of November and beginning of December 1967, in the main, particles with dimensions of several microns were scavenged from the stratosphere. As a result, the entry of such particles from the stratosphere into the upper troposphere dropped sharply. Accordingly, the time of residence in the stratosphere of particles of diameter $d = 2.5-6\mu$ was about 4.5 months. This is roughly two to three times smaller than the time of residence in the northern-hemisphere stratosphere of radioactive particles of diameter of the order of tenths of a micron and less, the half-period of whose removal from the stratosphere is roughly 10 months /1, 11/.

The scavenging rate for the lower troposphere as regards highly active particles was found as usual from the ratio of the fallout intensity to the concentration of particles. For the considered fraction from September to December 1967 it was approximately 2 km/day.

In conclusion, the authors thank Bogacheva and Melin for their help in the analysis of the samples of highly active particles.

BIBLIOGRAPHY

1. Brendakov, V.F. et al. Urovni radioaktivnogo zagryazneniya prizemnogo sloya atmosfery i poverkhnosti zemli produktami yadernykh vzryvov v 1963–1965 gg. v Podmoskov'e (Levels of Radioactive Contamination of the Ground Layer of the Atmosphere and the Earth's Surface by Nuclear Burst Debris during 1963–1965 in the Moscow Area).— Moskva, Atomizdat. 1967.

2. Gaziev, Ya.I., S.G.Malakhov, and L.E.Nazarov. Fraktsionirovanie radioaktivnykh izotopov v goryachikh chastitsakh (Fractionation of Radioactive Isotopes in Hot Particles).— Atomnaya Energiya, Vol. 18, No.5. 1965.

3. Grechushkina, M.P. and Yu.A.Izrael'. Fraktsionirovanie radioaktivnykh produktov yadernogo vzryva (Fractionation of the Radioactive Products of Nuclear Weapons Tests).— In: Radioaktivnye izotopy v atmosfere i ikh ispol'zovanie v meteorologii (Radioactive Isotopes in the Atmosphere and their Utilization in Meteorology). Moskva, Atomizdat. 1965.

4. Izrael', Yu.A. and E.D.Stukin. Gamma-izluchenie radioaktivnykh vypadenii (Gamma-Emission of Radioactive Fallout).— Moskva, Atomizdat. 1967.

5. Lavrenchik, V.N. Global'noe vypadenie produktov yadernykh vzryvov (Global Fallout of the Products of Nuclear Bursts).— Moskva, Atomizdat. 1965.

6. Makhon'ko, K.P. and S.G.Malakhov. Rezul'taty sistematicheskikh nablyudenii za goryachimi chastitsami v prizemnom sloe atmosfery v Podmoskov'e s 1961 po 1963 g. (Results of Systematic Observations of Hot Particles in the Ground Layer of the Atmosphere in the Moscow Area from 1961 to 1963).— In: Radioaktivnye izotopy v atmosfere i ikh ispol'zovanie v meteorologii (Radioactive Isotopes in the Atmosphere and their Utilization in Meteorology). Moskva, Atomizdat. 1965.

7. Izrael', Yu.A. (editor). Radioaktivnye Vypadeniya ot Yadernykh Vzryvov (Radioactive Fallout from Nuclear Weapons Tests). Moskva, "Mir." 1968. [Russian translations from English.]

8. Bykhovskii, A.V., S.G.Malakhov, and G.A.Sereda (editors). Radioaktivnye Chastitsy v Atmosfere (Radioactive Particles in the Atmosphere).— Moskva, Atomizdat. 1963. [Russian translations from German.]

9. Sereda, G.A., N.K.Gasilina, I.M.Kutyrina, and Z.S. Shulenko. Sbornik metodik po opredeleniyu radioaktivnosti okruzhayushchei sredy (Collection of Procedures for the Determination of the Radioactivity of the Environment). Part. 1.— Moskva, Gidrometeoizdat. 1966.

10. Fallout Program.— Quarterly Summary Report. HASL-193. 1968.

11. Feely, H.W., H.Seitz, R.J.Lagomarsino, and P.E. Biscaye. Transport and Fallout of Stratospheric Radioactive Debris.— Tellus, Vol. 18, Nos. 2–3. 1966.

12. E d v a r s o n, K., K. Löw, and J. S i s e f s k y. Fractionation Phenomena in Nuclear Weapons Debris.—Nature, Vol. 184, No. 4701. 1959.

13. F r e i l i n g, E.C. Radionuclide Fractionation in Bomb Debris.— Science, Vol. 133, No. 3469. 1961.

14. F r e i l i n g, E.C. and M.A. K a y. Radionuclide Fractionation in Air Burst Debris.— Nature, Vol. 209, No. 5020. 1966.

15. H a l t e r, J., O. H u b e r, and M. G a s s e r. Messungen an heissen Teilchen in den Jahren 1962 und 1963.— Atomkernenergie, Vol. 10, Nos. 7—8. 1965.

16. M a m u r o, T. Physico-chemical Properties of Fallout Particles in Relation to Burst Conditions.— Atompraxis, Vol. 14, No. 1. 1968.

17. S i s e f s k y, J. Debris from Tests of Nuclear Weapons.— Science, Vol. 133, No. 3455. 1961.

18. S i s e f s k y, J. New Investigations of Size-Activity Relations for Nuclear Weapon Debris Particles Sampled in Sweden. Autumn 1961 — Summer 1962.—FOA4, Report Nos. 407—456. 1964.

UDC 550.35

STATE OF STRONTIUM-90, CESIUM-137 AND CERIUM-144 IN RADIOACTIVE FALLOUT

F. I. Pavlotskaya, R. Surotkevichiene, and G. P. Levina

Investigations into the state and chemical form of existence of Sr^{90}, Cs^{137} and Ce^{144} in global fallout during 1958—1968 are described.

Substantial differences are shown between the soluble and insoluble fractions in the distributions of the different radionuclides. Independently of the geographical location of the observation stations, the decreasing soluble fraction in the indicated period is preserved in the sequence $Sr^{90} > Cs^{137} > Ce^{144}$, the values being on the average 78, 62 and 16%, respectively.

The radionuclides in the insoluble fraction possess different mobilities. When treating the insoluble remainder by 1 N CH_3COONH_4 and 1N HCl, more than 90% of the Sr^{90} and up to 65—70% of the Cs^{137} and Ce^{144} pass into the solution. The latter indicates that most of the radionuclides in the insoluble fraction are in exchange and mobile states, and not in the form of slightly soluble compounds (such as CeO_2).

In a soluble state, the radionuclides are present in cationic, anionic and neutral forms. The ratios between the latter are different in the various radionuclides. The distribution between these three forms is 90, 6 and 4% for Sr^{90}, 72, 16 and 12% for Cs^{137}, 55, 18 and 27% for Ce^{144}. A certain trend is observed toward an increase in the relative fraction of Sr^{90} and Cs^{137} in anionic form and a decrease in the fraction in neutral form during the winter compared with the summer period.

The different mobility of the radionuclides in insoluble fractions and their existence in cationic, anionic and neutral forms in a soluble state indicate the formation of different compounds and the variety of forms of their arrival at the earth's surface.

The state of the different radionuclides in radioactive fallout is of great interest, both for elucidating the biogeochemical characteristics of their behavior on the earth's surface and for studying the geophysical aspects. Depending on the forms of their entry from the atmosphere, they are differently bound to the soil and subsequently participate in the processes of migration in the soil itself and in the soil—plant system. Besides, the forms of existence in the fallout substantially affect the absorption of radio- nuclides by the tissue surface of plants during their direct fall on above- ground organs. The observed fractionation of the radionuclides is possibly determined not only by the conditions of their formation, but also by the state in the atmosphere and the fallout.

The aim of the present work is to study the forms of existence of Sr^{90}, Cs^{137} and Ce^{144} in radioactive fallout collected during 1963—1968 in the region of Moscow, Vil'nyus and Elektrenai of Lithuanian SSR. The work also examines the results of other observations.

The data presented in Table 1 point to substantial differences in the distributions of the various radionuclides. Independently of the geographical location of the observation station, the following sequence of decrease in soluble fraction is preserved throughout the period 1958—1968: $Sr^{90} > > Cs^{137} > Ce^{144}$ (corresponding on the average to 78, 62, and 16%, respectively). We observe similar values of the relative content of Ce^{144} in the insoluble fraction of fallout collected at different stations; this also is an indirect proof of its presence in the form of compounds difficult to dissolve in water.

111

TABLE 1. Distribution of strontium-90, cesium-137 and cerium-144 between the soluble and insoluble fractions of radioactive fallout, %

Place of observation	Period of observation	Type of atmospheric fallout	Sr⁹⁰		Cs¹³⁷		Ce¹⁴⁴	
			soluble	insoluble	soluble	insoluble	soluble	insoluble
1	2	3	4	5	6	7	8	9
New York /12/	1958	Precipitation	95.6	0.03	70.0	22.6	42.0	57.3
Moscow /1/	1959—1961	"	—	5.6	—	42.5	—	73.2
Moscow	1963—1968	Total fallout	—	12.0	—	88.5	9.3 (4—13)	95.5
		Snow	52.5 (35—70)	47.5 (30—65)	33.0	67.0	21.8	90.7 (87—96)
		Total fallout	86.4 (67—98)	13.6 (2—33)	—	—	11.9	78.2
		Average	76.0	24.0	—	—	12	88.1
Elektrenai	1967—1968	Total fallout	84.9 (82—90)	15.1 (10—18)	62.8	37.2	16.8 (15—20)	83.2 (80—86)
Leningrad /2/	1961—1966	Precipitation	91 (84—96)	9 (4—16)	72 (52—78)	28 (23—48)	—	88
Ural territory /3/	1963—1964	Snow	71.0	29.0	(0—90)	(10—100)	5.5 (0—49)	94.5 (51—100)
		Total fallout	56.5 (2—97)	43.5	(36—50)	—	4.6 (0—15)	95.4
		Average	63.7 (20—92)	36.3 (13—29)	(50—64)	—	5.1 (0.2—16)	94.9
Stuttgart /9/	1961	Total fallout	76	24 (7—46)	—	—	—	—
	1962	The same	80 (71—87)	20	—	—	—	—
	1963	"	91 (54—93)	9 (5—19)	—	—	—	—
Czechoslovakia /8/	1964	"	73.7 (81—95)	26.3 (8—48)	44.9	55.1	—	19 (8—27)
Average	1958—1968	"	78 (52—92)	—	62 (32—64)	(36—68)	16	—

Note. Minimum and maximum values are given in parentheses.

112

The higher content of Cs^{137} in the insoluble fraction of the fallout in Moscow compared with elsewhere is probably due to the greater atmospheric pollution. According to data of /1/, in the Moscow region in summer, about $10 \, g/m^2$ dust containing ~20—30% organic matter falls on the average in the course of a month; in rainwater, the dust content is several tens mg/liter. It is noted elsewhere /4, 8, 11, 14/ that the fraction of the content of total β-activity, Sr^{90} and Cs^{137} in insoluble state increases with increase in the ground air layer and in the fallout of the amount of organic and inorganic contaminants (industrial aerosols, dust, soot, flower pollen, etc.). It seems, however, that the distribution between phases is affected strongly not simply by the amount of contaminants, but by their chemical composition. The latter is different not only from station to station, but also at the same station in the course of a year, and also depends on the type of precipitation. For instance, it was shown in /13/ that in mixed precipitation (rain with snow) the content of SiO_2, Ca^{2+}, Mg^{2+}, HCO_3^-, SO_4^{2-}, Cl^-, N_3^- and other ions increases considerably compared with rain. Therefore, depending on the content of different ions, the formation of different chemical compounds is possible, radionuclides present in micro-concentrations being included in the latter either isomorphously or otherwise.

TABLE 2. Percent extraction of strontium-90, cesium-137 and cerium-144 from the insoluble remainder

Radio-nuclide	Reagent	Moscow /5/		Vil'nyus	Elektrenai	Ural territory /3/	
		fresh snow	fallout	snow	fallout	snow	fallout
Sr^{90}	1N CH$_3$COONH$_4$	81 (67—94)	73 (57—89)	93 (90—96)	93 (91—95)	—	—
	1N HCl	—	—	5 (3—8)	6 (5—7)	23** (3—40)	24** (3—60)
	6N HCl	19* (6—33)	27* (11—43)	0	0	—	—
	HF	0	0	2 (1.7—2.4)	1 (0—2)	6 (4—20)	21 (4—71)
Cs^{137}	1N CH$_3$COONH$_4$	—	—	21 (16—26)	20 (20—20)	—	—
	1N HCl	—	—	44 (40—47)	45 (42—48)	—	—
	6N HCl	—	—	7 (5—9)	4 (0—7)	—	—
	HF	—	—	28† (28—29)	31† (30—33)	—	—
Ce^{144}	1N CH$_3$COONH$_4$	10 (9—12)	16 (2—30)	6 (3—8)	9 (7—11)	—	—
	1N HCl	—	79 (63—95)	70 (59—80)	57 (56—57)	60** (60—74)	55** (28—94)
	6N HCl	52* (40—62)	3 (0.6—5)	4 (0.5—8)	8 (4—13)	—	—
	HF	38 (24—52)	2 (2—2)	20† (13—29)	26† (20—32)	34† (25—100)	41† (4—72)

* Treatment by 1N HCl not carried out.
** Insoluble remainder treated in the course of 48 hr by 0.1N HNO_3.
† Treatment by NH_4F.
  (Minimum and maximum values are given in parentheses.)

As a result of the formation of different chemical compounds, radionuclides in the insoluble remainder possess different solubility or mobility (Table 2). The remainder was treated in succession by different reagents according to the procedure described earlier /5/. Fairly close values, characterizing the passage of the different radionuclides into the solution, are observed at the different observation stations. In all cases, Sr^{90} is in a more mobile state than Cs^{137} and Ce^{144}. However, most of the latter two radionuclides are also in exchange and mobile forms, extracted during treatment by solutions of $1N\ CH_3COONH_4$ and $1N\ HCl$ (according to the terminology adopted when investigating the mobility of macro- and micro-elements in soils). Similar values were obtained elsewhere /3/. Thus, when treating the insoluble remainder by $0.1N\ HNO_3$, up to 60% of Ce^{144} pass from the content in the whole sample. On the average, several per cent of Sr^{90} and up to 30—35% of Cs^{137} and Ce^{144} remain in a state which is difficult to dissolve (treatment by $6N\ HCl$ and HF).

The formation of chemical compounds of different composition is corroborated by the average data for four samples, illustrated in the form of the curve of Ce^{144} extraction from the insoluble remainder (Figure 1). Fractions were collected, each comprising 200 mliter. Note that, for all samples, similar values of the relative content of this excess were obtained in the different fractions; in only one sample was the maximum extraction observed not only in the first fraction of $1N\ HCl$, but in two.

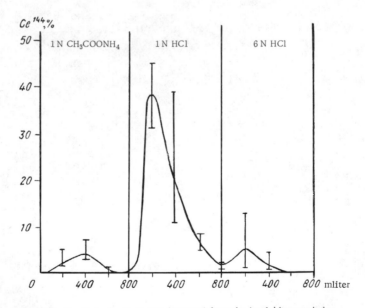

FIGURE 1. Fraction of cerium-144 extracted from the insoluble remainder.

The presented material indicates that most Ce^{144} in radioactive fallout is not in the form of dioxide which is difficult to dissolve, as is usually assumed in most investigations devoted to the study of global fallout.

Of great importance in the subsequent "fate" of the falling radionuclides are the forms of their existence in the soluble fraction of the fallout /5/. It was shown that strontium-90 and cerium-144 are present not only in cationic form, but in anionic and neutral forms too. Later investigations corroborated the existence of Sr^{90}, Cs^{137} and Ce^{144} in all three forms. The ratios between the latter differ substantially in the different radionuclides. Thus, on the average in the region of Moscow, Vil'nyus and Elektrenai, the content of Sr^{90} in cationic, anionic and neutral forms is 90, 6, and 4 %, respectively, which agrees satisfactorily with the data of /7/ (90, 9, and 1 %, respectively). The distribution of Cs^{137} among the observed three forms was 72, 16 and 12 %, and of Ce^{144}, 55, 18 and 27 %, respectively. It follows from Table 3 that a certain trend is observed toward an increase in the relative fraction of Sr^{90} and Cs^{137} existence in anionic form and a decrease in their existence in neutral form in the winter compared with the summer period. This trend is not very evident as regards Ce^{144}. The observed seasonality is probably explained by changes in the chemical composition of the air and atmospheric precipitation.

TABLE 3. Percent distribution of strontium-90, cesium-137 and cerium-144 in the soluble fraction of fallout during 1963—1968

Radio-nuclide	Place of ob-servation	June—November			December—May		
		cationic	anionic	neutral	cationic	anionic	neutral
Sr^{90}	Moscow	79*	13*	8*	88** (85—93)	12** (7—15)	0** (0—0)
		94 (80—100)	0.6 (0—2)	5 (0.5—18)	86 (81—94)	2 (0—4)	12 (3—18)
	Elektrenai	92 (91—93)	4 (1—6)	4 (1—8)	80	20	0
	England /7/	88 (79—95)	10 (3—19)	2 (0—4)	92 (82—97)	8 (3—18)	0 (0—0)
	Average	88	7	5	87	11	2
Cs^{137}	Moscow	62*	12*	26*	64**	15**	21**
	Vil'nyus	—	—	—	55	35	10
	Elektrenai	89 (88—90)	11 (9—12)	0.3 (0—0.7)	98	2	0
	Average	76	11	13	72	17	10
Ce^{144}	Moscow	78*	13*	9*	49** (43—56)	24** (15—30)	27** (13—39)
	Vil'nyus	—	—	—	56	19	25
	Elektrenai	46 (45—49)	22 (19—24)	32 (31—32)	84	6	10
	Average	62	18	20	63	16	21

* Rain.
** Fresh snow.

The above differences in the forms of existence of Sr^{90}, Cs^{137} and Ce^{144} in the soluble fraction of fallout are due to their chemical properties and to their different capacity to form radiocolloids and complex compounds. The latter can be of organic or inorganic nature and exist not only in the form of charged ions, but also in the form of slightly dissociated compounds. It has been shown /6, 10/ that different organic substances are present in atmospheric precipitation: acetic, valerian, butyric and other acids, amino acids (glycine, alanine, valine, glutamine, etc.), low-molecular amines (methylamine, dimethylamine, ethylamine, triethylamine, etc.), with many of which the alkaline-earth and rare-earth elements form complex compounds. Since ions of ammonium and alkaline elements are present in the atmosphere and precipitation, it is more probable that not pure organic acids but their salts participate in the formation of complex compounds. Cesium can also enter the composition of such compounds and replace the ions of ammonium or other alkaline elements. The formation of complex nitrates, carbonates and other compounds from inorganic compounds is possible.

Assumptions about the composition of radionuclides in radioactive fallout were made on the basis of the above material pertaining to the state and forms of existence of the different radioactive products of global fallout, the results of spectral analysis of the soluble and insoluble fractions, the published data on the formation of radionuclides in nuclear explosions, and the properties of the chemical compounds of the stable isotopes of these radionuclides. Most of the radionuclides are apparently not in the form of oxides or simple salts, but in the form of complex compounds. Thus, in soluble and easily mobile (exchange) states they are present both in the form of simple salts (nitrates, chlorides, cesium sulfate, strontium bicarbonate, double cerium sulfates, etc.) and in the form of complex compounds with different organic and inorganic ligands. On the assumption that Fe, Al, Si, Ca, Mg, Ti, Ni, Cu and other chemical elements were found in the radioactive fallout, we can assume the formation of different insoluble compounds in whose composition are found radionuclides and the elements listed above. There exist indications in the literature pointing to the nonuniform chemical composition of aerosol particles, caused by the gradual drop in the temperature of the gaseous phase, and to the possibility that most particles are mixtures or alloys of oxides. Moreover, while passing through the atmosphere the radioactive aerosols are subjected to the influence of the humidity CO_2 and other chemical components, which affect their chemical composition.

We stress in conclusion that radioactive fission products in global fallout are characterized by a variety of forms. This must be kept in mind when studying transfer processes and atmospheric washout of radionuclides and subsequent migration on the ground.

BIBLIOGRAPHY

1. B a r a n o v, V.I. and V.D. V i l e n s k i i. Opredelenie dolgozhivushchikh β- izluchatelei v atmosfernykh vypadeniyakh (Determination of Long- Lived β-Emitters in Atmospheric Fallout).—Radiokhimiya, Vol. 4, No. 4. 1962.

2. G e d e o n o v, L.I., M.I. Z h i l k i n a, Z.G. G r i t c h e n ko, and V.M. F l e g o n t o v. Forms of Radionuclides Residing in Atmospheric Precipitation.— In: Atmospheric Scavenging of Radioisotopes. Israel Program for Scientific Translations, Jerusalem. 1970.

3. Dibobes, I.K. et al. Global'nye vypadeniya strontsiya-90 na territorii Urala v period 1961–1966 gg. (Global Fallout of Strontium-90 over the Territory of the Urals in 1961–1966).—Moskva, Atomizdat. 1967.

4. Kozlova, M.V., I.P. Korenkov, Yu.V. Novikov, and D.D. Granovskaya. Izuchenie kontsentratsii dolgozhivushchikh radioaktivnykh aerozolei atmosfernogo vozdukha v zavisimosti ot ego zapylennosti (Study of the Concentration of Long-Lived Radioactive Aerosols of Atmospheric Air as a Function of its Pollution).—Gigiena i Sanitariya, No. 3. 1968.

5. Pavlotskaya, F.I. and L.N. Zatsepina. Ob izuchenii form postupleniya nekotorykh produktov deleniya na zemnuyu poverkhnost' (Study of the Forms of Arrival of Some Fission Products at the Earth's Surface).—Atomnaya Energiya, Vol. 20, No. 4. 1966.

6. Semenov, A.D., L.I. Nemtsova, T.S. Kishkinova, and A.P. Pashanova. O soderzhanii otdel'nykh grupp organicheskikh veshchestv v atmosfernykh osadkakh (On the Content of Different Groups of Organic Substances in Atmospheric Precipitation).—Gidrokhimicheskie Materialy, Vol. 42. 1966.

7. Brenan, C. and J.H. Lovatt. Ion Exchange Method of Estimation of Strontium-90 and Other Radionuclides in Rainwater.—Nature, Vol. 211, No. 5044. 1966.

8. Csupka, St. Der Aktivitätspegel in der löslichen und unlöslichen Fraktion des Fallouts im Jahre 1964.—Kernenergie, Vol. 8, No. 9. 1965.

9. Reintschler, W., W. Haussermann, and P.H. Wieser. Untersuchungen der künstlichen Radioaktivität von Boden, Luft, Niederschlag und Staub in Stuttgart–Hohenheim.—Atomkernenergie, Vol. 9, Nos. 7–8. 1964.

10. Sidle, A.B. Amino Acid Content of Atmospheric Precipitation.—Tellus, Vol. 19, No. 1. 1967.

11. Sood, B.S., A.K. Talwar, and R.Mohan. Measurement of Atmospheric Radioactivity at Chandigarh.—Res. Bull. Panjab Univ. Sci., Vol. 13, Nos. 3–4. 1962.

12. Welford, J.A. and W.R. Collins. An Evaluation of Existing Fallout Collection Methods.—Science, Vol. 131, No. 3416. 1960.

13. Whitehead, H.C. and J.H. Feth. Chemical Composition of Rain, Dry Fallout and Solid Precipitation at Menlo Park, California, 1957–1959.—J. Geophys. Res., Vol. 69, No. 16. 1964.

14. Zier, M. Der Wochengang des Staubgehaltes und der künstlichen Radioaktivität der bodennahen Luftschicht.—Radioaktivita Atmosfery. Sborník Prací Hydrometeorologického Ústavu ČSSR, Praha, No. 6. 1966.

IV. PROCESSES OF ATMOSPHERIC SCAVENGING

UDC 551.510.7

SOME THEORETICAL NOTIONS OF RADIOACTIVITY ACQUISITION BY RAINDROPS

A. S. Avramenko and K. P. Makhon'ko

An approximate model is given of the acquisition of radioactivity by raindrops during their formation and precipitation from a cloud. The processes taking place in a cloud with ordered ascending currents, leading to the size distribution of the specific radioactivity of raindrops observed on the earth, are examined. Comparison of theoretical calculations of the concentration of the products of nuclear bursts in raindrops of different sizes with experimental data enabled us to determine the value of the coefficient of radioactive aerosol-particle washout by cloud-borne droplets ($\sigma_0 \sim 10^{-3}$ sec^{-1}) and to establish the existence of an inverse relationship between the concentration of nuclear burst products in cloud-borne droplets and their radius. This relationship is near-inverse for raindrops. It is shown that the obtained size distribution of the specific radioactivity of raindrops can lead to an increase in the specific radioactivity of rainwater at the end of brief showers due to the decrease in raindrop size.

1. INTRODUCTION

Washout is the most important mechanism for the atmospheric scavenging of radioactive contaminants. So far, in the study of tropospheric scavenging attention has been paid mainly to the integral laws of radioactive dust washout by precipitation. However, our knowledge of washout processes remains very general. The mechanism of individual acts of dust particle capture by droplets has been studied more or less, but the general pattern of the radioactivation of raindrops falling on the earth, the relation linking the radioactivity of individual droplets to the specific radioactivity of precipitation and to changes in the process of raining have been studied very inadequately.

The present investigation aims at developing the first model of raindrop radioactivation by the products of nuclear weapons tests. We disregard the different mechanisms leading to the capture of dust particles by droplets. The model pertains to the next, less developed stage — the description of processes leading to the size distribution of the specific radioactivity of raindrops. We examine the influence of this distribution on the variation in the radioactivity of precipitation during its fall.

2. DETERMINATION OF THE COEFFICIENT OF RADIOACTIVE DUST WASHOUT BY CLOUD-BORNE DROPLETS

The capacity of raindrops to separate radioactive dust from air is usually characterized by the washout coefficient σ_0. In most investigations the value of σ_0 was determined from the integral characteristics of atmospheric processes /5/. We shall show that this quantity can be found by using the size distribution of the specific radioactivity of raindrops.

Consider the processes taking place in a cloud. They can be represented as follows in simplified form. Raindrops enter the cloud and grow by capturing cloud-borne droplets. We assume for simplicity that raindrops fall from the cloud when they reach a given size, and that their initial specific radioactivity is equal to that of the cloud water at the same level z. The final specific radioactivity of the raindrop will be determined by the radioactivity of the cloud-borne droplets captured during its fall from level z until it emerges from the cloud ($z = 0$). Raindrops of different size follow different paths in the cloud (Figure 1). Thus, if there exists some variation in the specific radioactivity of the cloud-borne droplets with altitude, resulting from the vertical radioactivity concentration profile in the cloud air, the specific radioactivity of the various drops will be different. In most cases the appearance of a vertical profile of radioactivity concentration in the cloud air can be regarded as the result of an influx of radioactive substance across the lower base of the cloud. The capture of radioactive dust particles by cloud-borne droplets and the gradual decrease in the concentration of radioactive dust in the air is observed with height.

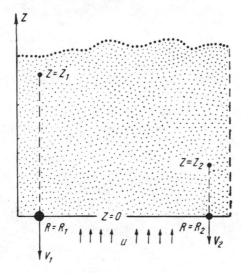

FIGURE 1. Diagram of raindrop growth in a cloud
during the acquisition of radioactivity.

Following Styro et al. /9, 10/, we shall use the following simplifying assumption in our calculations: 1) the cloud consists of monodisperse droplets; 2) the radioactive aerosols are monodisperse; 3) the gravitational speed of the fall of cloud-borne droplets is compensated by the speed u of the ascending air current; 4) all the processes are steady; 5) the cloud and the concentration field of the radioactive dust are isotropic along the horizontal.

Let the process of dust particle capture by droplets be described by the Smoluchowsky equation

$$\frac{dq}{dt} = -KNq, \tag{1}$$

where q is the concentration of radioactivity in the air; N is the droplet concentration; K is the factor of coagulation of dust particles with the droplets (taken here as constant); and $t = z/u$ is the time of air-mass ascent from level $z = 0$ to level z. Integration of (1) with respect to height z for $u = $ = const yields

$$q = q_0 \exp\left(-\frac{\sigma_0}{u} z\right), \tag{2}$$

where $\sigma_0 = KN$ is the washout coefficient.

Formula (2) may be regarded only as some approximation of the actual, fairly complex pattern. The derived radioactivity profile corresponds to clouds with ordered ascending currents, and therefore negligible turbulence. Therefore the model of raindrop radioactivation considered below will apply only to heavy strati with low lateral trapping of the surrounding air.

Since the specific radioactivity of cloud water C_z is proportional to the concentration of radioactivity in the air q, the profile of specific radioactivity of the cloud water can be expressed in the form

$$C_z = C_{0z} \exp\left(\frac{\sigma_0}{u} z\right), \tag{3}$$

where C_{0z} is the concentration at level $z = 0$.

During the process of falling, the radioactivity of the droplets changes owing to their coalescence, and also grows as a result of the diffusion currents of radioactive dust particles directed to the surface of the falling droplets. The raindrop size grows from $\sim 10\mu$ to $\sim 100\mu$ as a result of falling in the cloud. Comparative evaluations of the coagulation and diffusion radioactivity fluxes on droplets of this size, conducted by us on the basis of /3/, established that the radioactivity flux on the raindrop resulting from its capture of raindrops of 7μ radius /12/ is larger by 2—3 orders of magnitude than the flux due to the convective-diffusive capture of radioactive dust particles of radius 0.3μ, corresponding to the mean size of radioactive dust particles of global origin /18/. Thus, in the process of its fall and growth in the cloud the raindrop alters its radioactivity, mainly as a result of coalescence with cloud-borne droplets and not as a result of the capture of radioactive dust particles from the air; the latter effect can therefore be neglected. If the specific radioactivity of the raindrop is then given by $C = A/m$, where A is the total radioactivity of droplets of mass m, its increase is

$$dC = \frac{\partial}{\partial A}\left(\frac{A}{m}\right) dA + \frac{\partial}{\partial m}\left(\frac{A}{m}\right) dm =$$
$$= \frac{m dA - A dm}{m^2}. \tag{4}$$

Substituting $dA = C_z dm$, $dm = 4\pi\rho r^2 dr$ in (4) and using (3), we obtain the following equation relating the specific radioactivity of the droplet to its radius:

$$\frac{dC}{dr} + \frac{3}{r}C = \frac{3}{r}C_z, \tag{5}$$

where C_z is the specific radioactivity of cloud water level z.

We shall introduce the relation between the raindrop radius r and the level z of its location in the cloud, derived from the equation of droplet coagulation growth /6/:

$$z = -\frac{4\rho}{\omega} \int_r^R \frac{u - V(r)}{EV(r)}\, dr, \tag{6}$$

where R is the droplet radius as it emerges from the cloud; ρ is the water density; E is the capture coefficient; ω is the water content of the cloud; $V(r)$ is the speed at which droplets of radius r fall, and u is the ascending current speed in the cloud.

Substituting (3) and (6) in (5), and taking into account that the specific radioactivity of droplets of radius R_0 in our model is equal to the specific radioactivity of the cloud water at height z_0 from which the raindrop in the cloud starts to fall, we can derive the solution of this equation in the form

$$C(R) = \frac{3C_{0z}}{R^3} \int_{R_0}^R r^2 \exp\left[\frac{4\rho\sigma_0}{u\omega} \int_r^R \frac{u - V(r)}{EV(r)}\, dr\right] dr +$$

$$+ C_{0z}\left(\frac{R_0}{R}\right)^3 \exp\left[\frac{4\rho\sigma_0}{u\omega} \int_{R_0}^R \frac{u - V(r)}{EV(r)}\, dr\right]. \tag{7}$$

In calculations employing this formula we used Shishkin's formula /13/ for the capture coefficient:

$$E\,(r, r_*) = \left[1 - \frac{ar}{4r_*^2\,(r^2 - r_*^2)}\right]^2, \tag{8}$$

where r_* is the radius of the cloud-borne droplet, and $a = 3 \cdot 10^{-9}\, cm^3$. For the speed of droplet fall we used the following empirical formula (developed by us), which agrees satisfactorily with experimental data:

$$V(r) = 912\, r^{-(0.25 + 0.40\log r)}, \quad 0.01 \leqslant r \leqslant 3\ mm, \tag{9}$$

where r is in cm and $V(r)$ in cm/sec.

The value of R_0 was determined from the condition of equal velocities, $V(R_0) = u$. An experimental investigation into the dependence of the specific radioactivity of raindrops on their radius has been conducted to the best of our knowledge only in /21/ as regards artificial radioactivity. In all only four experimental points were obtained, which are clearly insufficient for any study of the relationship of interest to us. Accordingly, we conducted special measurements for a detailed study of the connection between the concentration of the products of nuclear weapons tests in raindrops and the size of these droplets /1/.

The measurements were conducted in summer 1967 in the Northern Caucasus in the region of Mt. Kuba-Taba. Heavy rains of global origin were investigated. Samples were taken from the middle part of the precipitation zone, whose displacement was recorded by VGI radar. Samples were not taken from the surrounding zones, in order to avoid the influence of partial evaporation of raindrops and the possibility of "end" effects associated with blowing of the subcloud space by advective currents. Contr in the absence of droplet evaporation was performed by continuous measure ments of the relative humidity f of ground level air and periodic launchings of VGI radiosondes equipped with special shielding against droplet penetration. An example is given of measurements during a single rain on 23 June 1967. The radar measurements established that during the rain the lower boundary of the clouds lay at an altitude of roughly 1.6 km above sea level, while the upper boundary was situated at 3—4 km. The humidity was measured 8 min, 20 min and 4 hours 17 min after the beginning of the rain and is presented on Figure 2. The figure shows that, after the beginni of the rain, there is established very rapidly in the atmosphere, everywhere from ground level to the lower boundary of the clouds, a water vapor satura tion pressure under which no raindrop evaporation takes place.

Rain samples were taken in 7-m^2 polyethylene cuvettes. The radioactiv products were subsequently extracted from the water by means of ion-exchange resin, which was then incinerated in a muffle furnace. The radio activity of the samples was determined under an end β-counter. Simultaneously with the sampling, the size spectrum of the raindrops was recorded by means of filter paper rubbed with a dye composition. From the size of the imprints, converted to the true droplet size, we determined their radius R_m, corresponding to the droplets making the maximum contribution to the precipitation falling during the sampling. The mean sampling time for the determination of the rain radioactivity was of the order of 10 min, during which the raindrop spectrum was recorded from three to five times. The number of measured droplets was of the order of 10^3. In subsequent calculations, we used those cases during which the droplet size spectrum remained practically constant during the collection of rainwater.

The measurement results are illustrated on Figure 3b; the circles represent the data of /21/, obtained by means of an installation separating raindrops by size into four fractions. For comparison, Figure 3a gives the data of /11/, obtained from the natural α-radioactivity of the individual droplets. For convenience, the values of the specific radioactivity were normalized in both cases with respect to the value corresponding to the minimum radius R_m. Solid lines on Figure 3b represent theoretical curves calculated by formula (7) for different values of the washout coefficient and typical meteorological parameters $\omega = 0.5 \, g/m^3$ and $u = 10 \, cm/sec$ /12/. Comparison of the theoretical curves with experimental data shows that the best agreement is obtained for a washout coefficient $\sigma_0 = 10^{-3} \, sec^{-1}$. In the calculations, we neglected variations in the specific radioactivity of raindr during their fall from the cloud to the ground resulting from the capture of

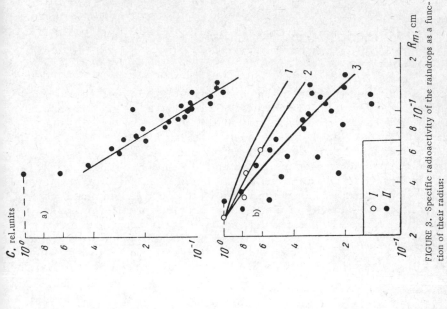

FIGURE 3. Specific radioactivity of the raindrops as a function of their radius:

a) natural α-activity /11/; b) artificial β-activity; I) data of /21/; II) our measurements; 1) $\sigma_0 = 10^{-4}$ sec^{-1}; 2) $\sigma_0 = 2 \cdot 10^{-4}$ sec^{-1}; 3) $\sigma_0 = 10^{-3}$ sec^{-1}.

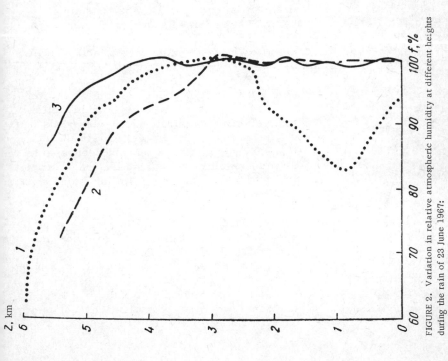

FIGURE 2. Variation in relative atmospheric humidity at different heights during the rain of 23 June 1967:

1) 8 min after the beginning of the rain; 2) 20 min; 3) 4 hours 17 min.

radioactive dust particles, since this effect is negligible /4/. This value of σ_0 agrees satisfactorily with the values obtained by other methods /5/.

3. DETERMINATION OF THE SIZE DISTRIBUTION OF THE SPECIFIC RADIOACTIVITY OF CLOUD-BORNE DROPLETS

The radioactivation of fine cloud-borne droplets has so far been poorly and incompletely studied. To the best of our knowledge, no data have been published on the form of the size distribution function of the artificial radioactivity of the cloud-borne droplets. Direct methods for constructing such a function seem at present to be fairly complicated, so accordingly we attempted an indirect procedure, based on the relationship between the specific radioactivity of raindrops and their size. In selecting the form of the required function we based ourselves on the only experimental data /7/ about the natural α-activity of cloud-borne droplets of different sizes, presented on Figure 4. The droplet radioactivity is expressed as the number of α-tracks per 1 g water. The experimental points lie satisfactori on a straight line drawn on a log—log scale, i.e., C and r are linked by the relationsh

$$C = C_{0r} r^{-b}. \qquad (10)$$

In the given case $b = 3$. The scarcity of available experimental material, and the fact that it corresponds to natural α-activity, does not allow us to substantiate the acceptability of formula (10) for the case of artificial β-activ ity. However, the form of functional relationship (10) will be correct to some extent for artificial radioactivity as well, and it follows from elementary physical considerations that $0 \leqslant b \leqslant 3$, since with droplet growth its total long-lived radioactivity cannot decrease.

In examining the radioactivation of droplets we shall start from the following, more rigorou assumptions.

1. Each cloud-borne droplet moves at its own speed, equal to the difference between the speed of the ascending air current and the gravitational speed of the droplet.

2. The cloud-borne droplets grow continuously during their ascent.

3. The combined action of the droplet growth mechanism and its radioactivation leads to a specific radioactivity size distribution of type (10

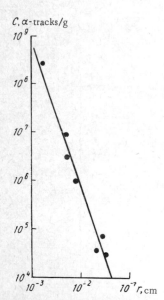

FIGURE 4. Natural specific radioactivity of cloud-borne droplets as a function of their size.

4. The radioactivity of large cloud-borne droplets, transformed into raindrops, increases due to the contribution of the radioactivity of captured fine droplets, as shown above in section 2.

5. We neglect as before the growth in the radioactivity of the raindrops caused by the washout of radioactive dust from the subcloud space.

An ascent of fine water droplets takes place in the cloud under the action of vertical ascending currents. With their ascent these droplets grow in size by the condensation of water vapor on them and their coagulation. Thus, a dynamic vertical distribution of droplets of different sizes is established in the cloud, fine droplets being located at the cloud bottom and the droplet size increasing with height. Since radioactive air masses enter the cloud from below, the most intense radioactivation occurs in its lower part. With the further ascent of cloud-borne droplets their specific radioactivity is diluted as a result of the condensation on them of cloud moisture, and therefore in the upper part of the cloud the large droplets have a lower specific radioactivity than the fine droplets at the cloud base, i.e., in formula (10) $b > 0$. The raindrops grow due to their coalescence with cloud-borne droplets; the higher the level from which the raindrops started their fall, the larger the size that they attain. Hence, the fine raindrops grow mainly at the expense of the relatively fine cloud-borne droplets at the lower part of the cloud, and therefore possess higher specific radio-activity than the large ones, as indeed is observed in practice.

We shall follow the growth of a cloud-borne particle during its transformation into a raindrop until it falls from the cloud. The growth rate of its total radioactivity during the capture of other cloud-borne droplets can be written in the form

$$\frac{dA(R)}{dt} = \int_{r_{min}}^{r_{max}} E(R,r)\,\pi\,(R+r)^2\,n(r)\,(V-v)\,A(r)\,dr, \tag{11}$$

where r is the radius of the smallest cloud-borne droplets coagulating with droplets of radius R; $A(r)$ and $A(R)$ are their total radioactivity; $n(r)$ is the size distribution function of the cloud-borne droplets; $(V-v)$ is the difference between the speeds of fall of the large and small droplets; r_{min} and r_{max} are respectively the minimum and maximum radii of cloud-borne droplets coagulating with droplets of radius R. As known, during the fall of a large droplet of radius R in a medium of polydisperse droplets the finest particles will flow together with the air stream. Larger droplets, starting with radius r_{min}, can overcome by inertia the resistance of the medium and fall on a droplet of radius R. However, the capture efficiency of the largest droplets, whose size is commensurate with radius R, decreases again, since these droplets fall with similar velocities and their relative speed is not large. Thus, starting with some r_{max}, the capture of these particles becomes impossible.

We shall use the analytical expression for r_{min} and r_{max} cited in /13/, yielding values fairly close to the exact values found by Hocking /19/ by a numerical method:

$$r_{min} = \frac{R}{\sqrt{2}} \sqrt{1 - \sqrt{1 - \left(\frac{a}{R}\right)^3}},$$

$$r_{max} = \frac{R}{\sqrt{2}} \sqrt{1 + \sqrt{1 - \left(\frac{a}{R}\right)^3}}. \tag{12}$$

The Khrgian-Mazin function /12/ will be used to describe the raindrop size distribution:

$$n(r) = \left(\frac{5}{2}\right)^5 \frac{\omega}{\pi \rho r_m^6} r^2 \exp\left(-\frac{5}{r_m} r\right), \tag{13}$$

where r_m is the droplet radius corresponding to the mass distribution mode.

With the aid of the Stokes formula, the difference between the speeds at which the droplets fall can be expressed in the form

$$V - v = \frac{2\rho g}{9\eta} (R^2 - r^2). \tag{14}$$

With allowance for (10), the general radioactivity of the raindrops can be written as

$$A(r) = \frac{3}{4} \pi \rho\, C_{0r}\, r^{3-b}. \tag{15}$$

Returning now to equation (11), and substituting in it the quantities expressed in (8) and (13)—(15) with integration limits (12), subsequent integration yields the following expression for the growth rate of droplet radioactivity at the ascending branch of its trajectory in the cloud:

$$\frac{dA}{dt} = B\left(\frac{r_m}{5}\right)^{2-b} \left\{ \frac{a^2 R^2}{2^4} [\gamma(2-b, y_1) - \gamma(2-b, y_0)] + \right.$$

$$+ \frac{aR^3}{2} \left(\frac{r_m}{5}\right)^2 [\gamma(4-b, y_1) - \gamma(4-b, y_0)] +$$

$$+ aR^2 \left(\frac{r_m}{5}\right)^3 [\gamma(5-b, y_1) - \gamma(5-b, y_0)] +$$

$$+ \left(\frac{aR}{2} - R^4\right) \left(\frac{r_m}{5}\right)^4 [\gamma(6-b, y_1) - \gamma(6-b, y_0)] -$$

$$- 2R^3 \left(\frac{r_m}{5}\right)^5 [\gamma(7-b, y_1) - \gamma(7-b, y_0)] + 2R \left(\frac{r_m}{5}\right)^7 [\gamma(9-b, y_1) -$$

$$- \gamma(9-b, y_0)] + \left(\frac{r_m}{5}\right)^8 [\gamma(10-b, y_1) - \gamma(10-b, y_0)] -$$

$$- \frac{a^2 R^3}{2^3} \left(\frac{r_m}{5}\right)^{b-2} I(b) \right\}. \tag{16}$$

Here $\gamma(x, y)$ is the incomplete gamma-function, while the following notation was introduced for brevity:

$$B = \frac{5^5}{2^2 \, 3^3} \frac{\pi \rho g \omega}{\eta r_m^6} C_{0r}; \qquad y_0 = \frac{5}{r_m} r_{min};$$

$$y_1 = \frac{5}{r_m} r_{max};$$

$$I(b) = \int_{r_{min}}^{r_{max}} r^{1-b} (R-r)^{-1} \exp\left(-\frac{5r}{r_m}\right) dr.$$

To calculate the variation in the total radioactivity of a droplet with its growth in size during its ascent with the ascending currents, we pass in (16) from differentiation with respect to t to differentiation with respect to R and employ the following analytical expression for dR/dt, given by Shishkin /14/:

$$\frac{dR}{dt} = (u-V)\frac{dR}{dz} = \frac{5^3}{2^8 \cdot 3^3}\frac{\omega q}{\eta} r_m^2 \left\{ \left(\frac{2}{5}\right)^4 \frac{R^2}{r_m^2} \times \right.$$

$$\times [\gamma(6,y_1) - \gamma(6,y_0)] + \left(\frac{2}{5}\right)^5 \frac{R}{r_m} [\gamma(7,y_1) - \gamma(7,y_0)] -$$

$$- \frac{2^5}{5^7}\frac{r_m}{R}[\gamma(9,y_1) - \gamma(9,y_0)] - \frac{2^4}{5^9}\frac{r_m^2}{R^2}[\gamma(10,y_1) - \gamma(10,y_0)] -$$

$$- \frac{2^3}{5^2}\frac{aR}{r_m^4}[\gamma(4,y_1) - \gamma(4,y_0)] - \frac{2^1}{5^3}\frac{a}{r_m^3}[\gamma(5,y_1) - \gamma(5,y_0)] -$$

$$- \frac{2^3}{5^4}\frac{a}{Rr_m^2}[\gamma(6,y_1) - \gamma(6,y_0)] - \frac{2\cdot5^2\, a^2 R^2}{r_m^8}\exp\left(-\frac{5R}{r_m}\right) \times$$

$$\times \left[\mathrm{Ei}\left(\frac{5R}{r_m} - y_1\right)\right] - \mathrm{Ei}\left(\frac{5R}{r_m} - y_0\right)\Big] + \frac{a^2}{r_m^6}\Big[\left(10\frac{R}{r_m} + 1 + y_1\right)e^{-y_1} -$$

$$\left. - \left(10\frac{R}{r_m} + 1 + y_0\right)e^{-y_0}\Big]\right\}. \tag{17}$$

This yields an analytical expression for $dA/dR = (dA/dt)(dt/dR)$. With this expression and the distribution of r_m with height in the cloud /2/ (Figure 5), formulas (16) and (17) enable us to compute numerically the change in droplet radioactivity on the ascending branch of its trajectory in the cloud until its fall speed becomes equal to the speed of the ascending current.

The subsequent change of specific radioactivity during its motion on the descending trajectory, when the condition $R > r_m$ is satisfied, can be calculated approximately, since the large falling droplet coagulates practically with all cloud-borne droplets because the capture coefficient becomes close to unity. Under these conditions the specific radioactivity of the droplets will be described by the following solution to equation (5):

$$C(R) = \frac{3}{R^3}\int_{R_0}^{R} \bar{C}_z R^2 dR + \left(\frac{R_0}{R}\right)^3 C(R_0). \tag{18}$$

Here $\bar{C}_z$ is the specific radioactivity of the cloud water at level z, averaged over the whole spectrum of cloud-borne droplets:

$$\bar{C}_z = \frac{\displaystyle\int_0^\infty A(r)\, n(r)\, dr}{\displaystyle\frac{4}{3}\pi\rho\int_0^\infty r^3 n(r)\, dr}. \tag{19}$$

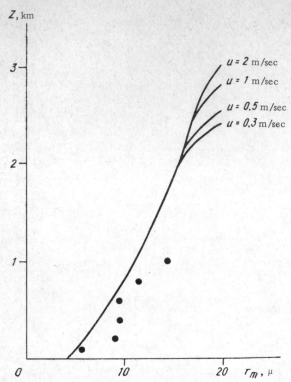

FIGURE 5. Variation in cloud-borne droplet size with height for different ascending current speeds /2/.

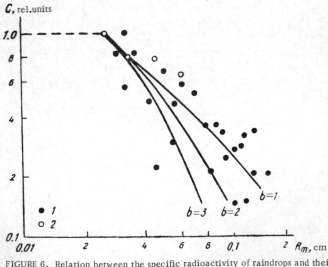

FIGURE 6. Relation between the specific radioactivity of raindrops and their size for different values of parameter b:

1) our measurements; 2) data of /21/.

With allowance for (15) and distribution (13), integration of (19) yields

$$\bar{C}_z = \frac{C_0}{120}\left(\frac{5}{r_m}\right)^b \Gamma (6 - b),\qquad\qquad (20)$$

where $\Gamma (x)$ is the gamma-function.

The calculation of the specific radioactivity of the raindrops was conducted by formulas (16)—(18), allowing for (20) with $b = 1, 2, 3$. It was found that the contribution of the radioactivity acquired by the ascending branch of the droplet trajectory to the specific radioactivity of the raindrops is not large. This is quite understandable, since the main increase in droplet mass occurs on the descending branch of its trajectory in the cloud.

The calculated specific radioactivity of the raindrops, normalized to the value corresponding to $R = 250\mu$, is presented on Figure 6. It follows that the agreement between experimental and calculated data is best when the exponent b in formula (10) equals unity.

Thus, with some approximation, the relation between the concentration of the products of nuclear weapons tests in cloud-borne droplets and their radius can be described by the inverse relationship $C \sim r^{-1}$.

4. VARIATION IN RAIN RADIOACTIVITY WITH TIME

During the fall of precipitation its radioactivity changes. Usually it decreases with time, but at times an increase in the concentration of fission products in the precipitation is observed at the end of the rain /15/. The decrease in rain radioactivity with time in the case of rain from strati is generally explained by the effect of the gradual depletion in the concentration of radioactive dust in the air in the course of the rain, and in the case of rain from cumuli, by the effect of the dilution of the radioactive water of the cloud by nonradioactive water, condensing on vapors entering the cloud /20/.

A different hypothesis has been advanced to explain the initial decay of the specific radioactivity of precipitation from cumuli /17/. At high altitudes there is an increase in the horizontal speed of the wind, which leads to the formation from the leeward side of the clouds of an overhanging "cap." The raindrops falling from this cap grow by coagulation with the droplets of the boundary part of the cloud, enriched by radioactivity due to their partial evaporation and the turbulent diffusion of radioactive contaminant from the air surrounding the cloud.

Such an explanation seems to us hardly probable. Cloud-borne droplets evaporate at distances of only about 100 m from the cloudiness boundary /15/, and diffusion trapping of the surrounding air is of the same order /8/. Starting from a mean cloud speed equal to ~ 20 km/hour (observed by us), we estimated that a zone of increased radioactivity concentration is observed in the precipitation for about 0.3 min, while in /17/ the time was given as 10—20 min.

Reliable control of the change of cloud masses and their transformation was conducted in hardly any of the studies devoted to the variation in precipitation radioactivity with time. Accordingly, we conducted such a control by means of VGI radar in summer 1967 in the region of Mt. Kuba-Taba while sampling precipitation by successive fractions from thick clouds of frontal origin.

According to our observations, during rain from unbroken cloud masses, a decrease in the specific radioactivity of shower precipitation was observed in the course of their fall in 10 out of 15 cases; in three cases the specific radioactivity decreased at the beginning and increased at the end of the shower, and in two cases a continuous increase in specific radioactivity was observed. It is characteristic that the latter five cases corresponded to rains from a cloud mass which disintegrated soon after its passage over the test grounds. Such a case is illustrated in Figure 7.

Radar observation of individual clouds showed that, at the moment of rain over the test grounds, the clouds had existed for no less than 5 hours, and that during the entire duration of cloud motion (~100 km) it had rained from them. Such a lengthy existence of precipitation must lead to the establishment of dynamic equilibrium between the entry of radioactivity in the cloud and its removal with the rain. Therefore, in this case the decrease in the specific radioactivity of the precipitation at the beginning of its fall over the observation station can no longer be explained by the dilution effect, as before /4, 20/.

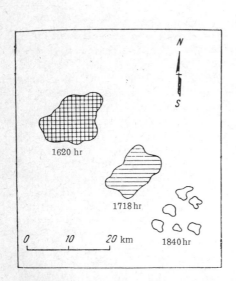

FIGURE 7. Successive positions of a rain-bearing cloud on 11 August 1967 over the test grounds according to radar data of the Northern Caucasus.

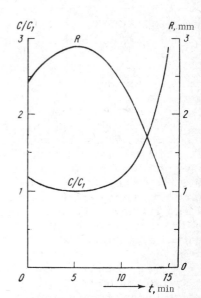

FIGURE 8. Variation in droplet radius R and precipitation radioactivity C/C_1 during a brief shower.

Our atmospheric humidity measurements during rain showed that relatively low humidity (60—90%) was observed at the beginning of a rain of frontal origin over the test grounds and that it decreased with height.

Therefore, at the beginning of the rain there could occur partial evaporation of the falling raindrops /6/ and the formation of increased concentrations of fission products in the rain. During rain there was observed a growth in the relative atmospheric humidity in the subcloud space, which must lead to a decrease in droplet evaporation and hence to a decrease in the specific radioactivity of the precipitation.

When the rains ceased over the test grounds (Figure 7), the growth in specific rain radioactivity at the end of its fall must be affected by the change in raindrop size. It is known /13/ that the spectrum of droplet sizes does not remain constant during a rain. At the beginning of a rain the droplet radius R_m increases up to some maximum value, in the middle of the rain the value of R_m remains constant, and at the end of the rain it starts to drop. If we approximate the experimental relationship (illustrated on Figure 6) between the specific radioactivity of raindrops and their radius by the formula

$$C \sim R_m^{-1}, \tag{21}$$

it is evident that at the end of the rain the decrease in droplet radius must lead to a growth in its specific radioactivity (Figure 8). The specific radioactivity curve was normalized here with respect to the value corresponding to the maximum droplet size.

The relative contribution of the described effect can exceed the contribution of the evaporation effect while the leading edge of the disintegrating cloud passes over the observation station. Then, already from the very beginning we will observe a continuous increase in the specific radioactivity of the precipitation with time. For example, in the case presented on Figure 7 the specific radioactivity was $0.8 \cdot 10^{-11}$ curie/liter for the first batch of precipitation, $1.1 \cdot 10^{-11}$ curie/liter for the second batch, and $4.3 \cdot 10^{-11}$ curie/liter for the third batch, collected at the end of the rain.

The authors are grateful to G. K. Sulakvelidze, director of the High-Altitude Geophysical Institute, and to the participants of the antihail expedition of the institute, for giving them permission to use the test grounds of the institute and for their help in the work.

BIBLIOGRAPHY

1. Avramenko, A.S. and K.P.Makhon'ko. O radioaktivnosti kapel' dozhdya (Radioactivity of Rain drops).—Izvestiya AN SSSR, Fizika Atmosfery i Okeana, Vol. 5, No. 6. 1969.
2. Barukova, Yu.A., I.I.Komaldina, T.S. Uchevatkina, and N.S.Shishkin. O kolichestve i intensivnosti osadkov iz konvektivnykh oblakov (Amount and Intensity of Precipitation from Convective Clouds).—Trudy GGO, No. 104. 1960.
3. Zimin, A.G. Mekhanizmy zakhvata i osazhdeniya atmosfernykh primesei oblakami i osadkami (Mechanisms of Capture and Deposition of Atmospheric Contaminants by Clouds and Precipitation).— In: Voprosy yadernoi meteorologii (Problems of Nuclear Meteorology). Moskva, Gosatomizdat. 1962.
4. Makhon'ko, K.P. Vymyvanie radioaktivnoi pyli iz atmosfery (Atmospheric Washout of Radioactive Dust).—Izvestiya AN SSSR, Seriya Geofizicheskaya, No. 4. 1964.
5. Makhon'ko, K.P. Samoochishchenie nizhnei troposfery ot radioaktivnoi pyli (obzor) (Radioactive Dust Scavenging in the Lower Troposphere (Survey)).—Izvestiya AN SSSR, Fizika Atmosfery i Okeana, Vol. 2, No. 5. 1966.

6. Mason, B. J. The Physics of Clouds.—Oxford. 1957.

7. Potsyus, V. Yu. Metodika izmereniya radioaktivnosti oblachnykh elementov al'fa-radiograficheskim metodom (Technique of Measuring the Radioactivity of Cloud Elements by the α-Radiographic Method).—Nauchnye Soobshcheniya Instituta Geologii i Geografii AN LitSSR, Vol. 10, No. 1. 1959.

8. Skatskii, V. I. O mekhanizme vovlecheniya v kuchevoe oblako okruzhayushchego vozdukha (Mechanism of Trapping Environmental Air in Cumuli).—Izvestiya AN SSSR, Fizika Atmosfery i Okeana, Vol. 2, No. 12. 1966.

9. Styro, B. I., E. Yu. Vebra, and K. K. Shopauskas. Determination of Natural Radionuclide Removal Rate on the Basis of a Radioactivity Profile of Cloud-Borne Droplets.—In: Atmospheric Scavenging of Radioisotopes. Israel Program for Scientific Translations, Jerusalem. 1970.

10. Styro, B. I., Yu. E. Vebra, and K. K. Shepauskas. Opredelenie nekotorykh parametrov udaleniya estestvennykh radioaktivnykh aerozolei iz vozdukha (Determination of Some Parameters Governing the Removal of Natural Radioactive Aerosols from the Atmosphere).—Izvestiya AN SSSR, Fizika Atmosfery i Okeana, Vol. 1, No. 12. 1965.

11. Styro, B. I. and B. K. Vebrene. O metodike izmereniya radioaktivnosti otdel'nykh chastits osadkov i nekotorye predvaritel'nye rezul'taty takikh issledovanii (On the Procedure of Measuring the Radioactivity of Different Precipitation Particles and Some Tentative Results of Such Investigations).—Izvestiya AN SSSR, Fizika Atmosfery i Okeana, Vol. 2, No. 10. 1966.

12. Khrgian, A. Kh. (editor). Fizika oblakov (Cloud Physics).—Gidrometeoizdat. 1961.

13. Shishkin, N. S. Oblaka, osadki i grozovoe elektrichestvo (Clouds, Precipitation and Thunderstorm Electricity).—Leningrad, Gidrometeoizdat. 1964.

14. Shishkin, N. S. Vliyanie vida raspredeleniya oblachnykh kapel' po razmeram na velichinu kapel' dozhdya (Influence of the Size Distribution of Cloud-Borne Droplets on the Size of Raindrops).—Trudy GGO, No. 54. 1955.

15. Shifrin, K. S. and Zh. K. Zolotova. Kinetika ispareniya kapli v radiatsionnom pole (Droplet Evaporation Kinetics in a Radiation Field).—Izvestiya AN SSSR, Fizika Atmosfery i Okeana, Vol. 2, No. 12. 1966.

16. Best, A. C. The Evaporation of Rain Drops.—Q. J. Roy. Met. Soc., Vol. 78, p. 336. 1952.

17. Bleeker, W. and W. N. Lablans. Some Remarks about the Scavenging of Radioactive Material from the Atmosphere by Precipitation.—Meteorol. Aspects of Atmospheric Radioactivity, WMO No. 169, p. 83; Technical Note, No. 68. 1965.

18. Cambray, R. S., E. M. Fisher, G. S. Spicer, C. G. Wallace, and T. I. Webber. Radioactive Fallout in Air and Rain: Results to the Middle of 1963.—AERE—R 4392. 1963.

19. Hocking, L. M. The Collision Efficiency of Small Drops.—Q. J. Roy. Met. Soc., Vol. 85, p. 363. 1959.

20. Makhon'ko, K. P. Simplified Theoretical Notion of Contaminant Removal by Precipitation from the Atmosphere.—Tellus, Vol. 19, p. 5. 1966.

21. Stierstadt, K. and H. G. Kadereit. Die Verteilung der künstlichen Radioaktivität und der Menge des festen Rückstands auf das Grössenspektrum der Regentropfen.—Meteorol. Rundschau, Vol. 14, p. 1. 1961.

UDC 551.510.7.001.5

DISTRIBUTION OF RAINDROPS WITH RESPECT TO SPECIFIC RADIOACTIVITY

B. I. Styro and B. K. Vebrene

The distribution of raindrops was investigated with respect to their specific radioactivity. The distribution curves of droplets are similar for a uniform distribution of the isotope and when it is introduced at some point in the cloud. The position of the maximum on the curve depends on the isotope quantity. The variation in the specific radioactivity of rain during its fall was also investigated. The first specific radioactivity maximum appears several minutes after the isotope is introduced in the cloud. The second, not so sharp maximum appears after 10–15 min. The very rapid (3–4 min) appearance of activated droplets at the earth's surface is associated with the accelerating effect of descending air currents.

We study in the present work the distribution of raindrops with respect to their specific radioactivity both for an almost uniform distribution of radioactive matter in the atmosphere (the case of natural radioactivity) and for the artificial introduction of an isotope at some point in the cloud.

Sampling followed a procedure described elsewhere /1/. The droplets were collected on a stainless steel plate or on a copper foil, and after drying were brought into contact with an A-2 emulsion. When investigating natural radioactivity, the exposure for determining short-lived products lasted for about 24 hours. In the case of artificial introduction of a Po^{210} isotope at one point of the cloud and the collection of radioactivity samples, the different droplets of the plate were brought into contact four days after the end of the collection period, in order to give the natural short-lived radioisotopes of the Rn, Tn and An series time to disintegrate. The exposure of these plates continued for 20 days. The background appearing in the plate as a result of the natural long-lived α-radioactivity does not exceed $1.3 \cdot 10^3$ α-tracks/g water. After exposure the emulsion was treated, and the zones in contact with droplet tracks were studied. After examination of the emulsion and counting of the number of α-tracks the droplets were sorted with respect to their specific radioactivity. Note that the corresponding droplet distributions were found to be the same in all cases (some are presented on Figures 1–3). A difference was observed only in the position of the maximum.

For short-lived isotopes of the decay products of radon this maximum was equal to $2.5 \cdot 10^3$ tracks/g water in both shower and thick clouds /2/. The curves obtained after the introduction of Po^{210} have maxima shifted toward higher specific radioactivities. Comparison of the different droplet distribution curves shows that the maximum increases with increasing amount of isotope introduced in the cloud. For example, it is seen from Figure 3a that the maximum is shifted toward higher radioactivities, and the following proportionality is observed: in the experiment corresponding to

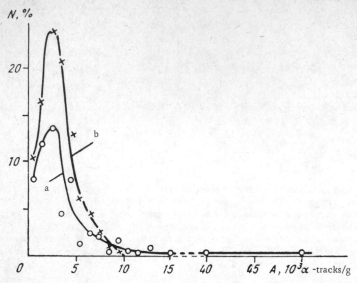

FIGURE 1. Droplet distribution with respect to specific radioactivity for natural precipitation from thick and shower clouds.

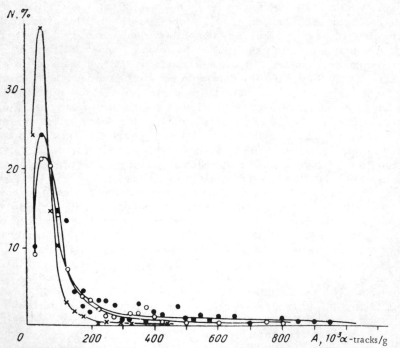

FIGURE 2. Droplet distributions according to the results of three observation stations for a cloud in which Po^{210} was introduced.

Figure 3a about five times more isotope was introduced, and the curve maximum is about five times larger than the maximum on Figure 3b. We always see evidence of a certain number of droplets with high specific radioactivity. This value in the case of natural radioactivity probably arises on "old" droplets, existing for a long time in the cloud or evaporated intensively during their fall. The possibility is not excluded that radioactive aerosols were captured by droplets in the subcloud layer. The large specific radioactivities of some droplets in which Po^{210} was introduced are explained by the capture of large conglomerates of Po^{210} (hot particles).

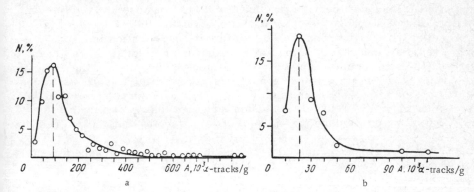

FIGURE 3. Distribution curves for different amounts of isotope introduced in two clouds. The amount introduced in one cloud (a) is five times larger than the amount introduced in the other cloud (b).

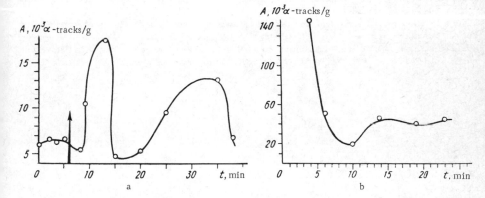

FIGURE 4. Variation in the specific radioactivity of rainwater with time:

a) isotope introduced in the cloud during rain; b) isotope introduced before the beginning of rain. The arrow indicates the time at which the rocket exploded.

The maxima of the droplet distribution with respect to the specific radioactivity for samples of the same rain, collected at different points, correspond to the same specific radioactivity value. Figure 2 is given as an example. Here the samples were collected at points roughly 1.5—3 km apart.

The maxima of radioactivity are situated around $50 \cdot 10^3$ tracks/g water.

Investigations into the specific radioactivity of raindrops with time show that before the introduction of a radioactive isotope in the cloud one can observe very low specific radioactivities, whereas the principal specific radioactivity maximum appears 3—7 min after the rocket explosion. After some time a second maximum appears (Figure 4). This points to the propagation of the isotope in the cloud in the direction opposing the main transfer or to processes associated with the interaction of the different "centers" in the cloud.

The appearance of a specific radioactivity maximum of Po^{210} in the precipitation does not mean as yet that Po^{210} was not observed earlier on the droplets. The presence of artificial polonium on large droplets is observed at times very soon (3—4 min) after its introduction in a cloud. Such a rapid appearance of polonium in raindrops collected on the ground points to the very intense capture of the isotope by droplets in the explosion zone and to very large descending currents, contributing to such a rapid appearance of activated droplets on the ground. The speed of vertical fall of droplets must be 10—20 m/sec. Such large speeds represent the sum of the speed of the descending air current and the droplet motion with respect to the air.

The tentative results obtained here are in need of further experimental corroboration.

BIBLIOGRAPHY

1. Styro, B.I. and B.K. Vebrene. O metodike izmereniya radioaktivnosti otdel'nykh chastits osadkov i nekotorye predvaritel'nye rezul'taty takikh issledovanii (On the Procedure for Measuring the Radioactivity of Individual Precipitation Particles and Some Tentative Results of Such Investigations).—Izvestiya AN SSSR, Fizika Atmosfery i Okeana, Vol. 2, p. 10. 1966.
2. Styro, B.I. and B.K. Vebrene. Radioactivity Distribution in Raindrops.—In: Atmospheric Scavenging of Radioisotopes. Israel Program for Scientific Translations, Jerusalem. 1970.

UDC 551.510.7

APPLICATION OF THE STOCHASTIC APPROACH TO THE PROBLEM OF THE RADIOACTIVITY OF RAINDROPS AND CLOUD-BORNE DROPS

A. S. Avramenko

An attempt is made to apply the stochastic approach to the problem of the radioactivity of raindrops and cloud-borne drops. A general system of equations is written with which to calculate the distribution function of the cloud-borne drops with respect to activity for the radioactive series of natural decay products in elemental state. A steady solution is given for the case when the concentrations of the preceding elements of the radioactive series can be neglected. The obtained distribution is used to derive a relationship between the number of nonradioactive raindrops and their size. The theoretical relationships and published experimental data are in satisfactory agreement.

The problem of the radioactivation of cloud-borne drops can be solved employing an approach which disregards the discreteness and probabilistic nature of the individual acts of capture. Telford /12/ showed that for the growth of cloud-borne drops such an approach is valid only in the case of considerable concentrations of coagulating elements. The discreteness of the distribution of elements in space and the probability of their capture by each other become important at concentrations of roughly $10^2\,\mathrm{cm}^{-3}$. Thus, in the model of the growth of cloud-borne drops allowance for these factors leads to results differing by an order of magnitude from those obtained by the Langmuir-Shishkin scheme, in which discreteness is not considered /9/.

We shall attempt a stochastic approach to the problem of the radioactivation of cloud-borne drops. Note that all the results obtained below will apply mainly to the decay products of radon in elemental state. It was shown by Wilkening /13/ that the latter condition is satisfied approximately at altitudes corresponding to the level of clouds.

Consider a unit air volume possessing natural radioactivity which rises from ground level and penetrates a cloud. We shall follow the decay products of some given natural radioactive series, such as the Rn^{222} series, and consider for simplicity the case of a monodisperse cloud with drop concentration N.

Let the cloud-borne drop possess j atoms of radioactive isotope i and let the concentration of such drops at time t be $N_{j,\,i}(t)$.

Correspondingly, the concentration of cloud-borne drops with $j-k$ radioactive atoms will be $N_{j-k,\,i}(t)$. Further, suppose $P_{k,\,i}$ is the probability that the cloud-borne drop captures k more radioactive atoms per unit time. The growth rate of drop concentration $N_{j,\,i}(t)$ resulting from the capture of k radioactive atoms by the drop already carrying $j-k$ atoms can be expressed in the form of the product $P_{k,i} N_{j-k,i}(t)$. When k radioactive atoms are captured by drops with j atoms, a decrease in the drop concentration $N_{j,i}(t)$ will occur at a rate $-P_{k,i} N_{j,i}(t)$ The total change of concentration $N_{j,i}(t)$ per unit time as a result of the capture of radioactive atoms by the drops can be obtained by summing these expressions over all possible values of k:

$$\sum_{k=1}^{j} P_{k,i} N_{j-k,i}(t) - \sum_{k=1}^{\infty} P_{k,i} N_{j,i}(t). \tag{1}$$

The drop concentration $N_{j,i}(t)$ changes also, owing to the radioactive decay of both the isotope i itself and its precursor $i-1$. If $B_{k,i}$ is the probability of decay on the drop per unit time of k radioactive atoms of isotope i, the growth rate of concentration $N_{j,i}$ due to the decay of k radioactive atoms on drops with $j+k$ atoms is given by the product $B_{k,i} N_{j+k,i}(t)$. During the decay of k radioactive atoms on drops with j atoms, the concentration $N_{j,i}(t)$ will decrease at a rate $B_{k,i} N_{j,i}(t)$. The total change of concentration $N_{j,i}(t)$ per unit time as a result of the decay of isotope i is found by summing these expressions with respect to k:

$$\sum_{k=1}^{\infty} B_{k,i} N_{j+k,i}(t) - \sum_{k=1}^{j} B_{k,i} N_{j,i}(t). \tag{2}$$

If $B_{j,i-1}$ is the probability of decay on the drop per unit time of j radioactive atoms of the mother isotope $i-1$, the rate of growth of concentration $N_{j,i}(t)$ because of the decay of isotope $i-1$ will be $B_{j,i-1} N_{k,i-1}(t)$, where $N_{k,i-1}(t)$ is the concentration of drops associated with isotope $i-1$. The total change of $N_{j,i}(t)$ as a result of the last factor is found by summing this product over values $k \geqslant j$:

$$\sum_{k>j}^{\infty} B_{j,i-1} N_{k,i-1}(t). \tag{3}$$

The change of $N_{j,i}(t)$ can be expressed finally by the following system of equations:

$$\frac{d N_{j,i}(t)}{dt} = \sum_{k=1}^{j} P_{k,i} N_{j-k,i}(t) - \sum_{k=1}^{\infty} P_{k,i} N_{j,i}(t) +$$

$$+ \sum_{k=1}^{\infty} B_{k,i} N_{j+k,i}(t) - \sum_{k=1}^{j} B_{k,i} N_{j,i}(t) + \sum_{k>j}^{\infty} B_{j,i-1} N_{k,i-1}(t)$$

$$\left. \frac{d N_{0,i}(t)}{dt} = - \sum_{k=1}^{\infty} P_{k,i} N_{0,i}(t) + \sum_{k=1}^{\infty} B_{k,i} N_{k,i}(t) - \right\} \tag{4}$$

$$- \sum_{k=1}^{\infty} B_{k,i-1} N_{k,i-1}(t).$$

If we neglect terms containing the probability of decay or capture of two and more atoms simultaneously, the latter equations assume the form

$$
\begin{aligned}
\frac{dN_{j,i}(t)}{dt} &= P_{1,i} N_{j-1,i}(t) - P_{1,i} N_{j,i}(t) + \\
&+ B_{1,i} N_{j+1,i}(t) - B_{1,i} N_{j,i}(t) + A_j(t); \\
\frac{dN_{0,i}(t)}{dt} &= -P_{1,i} N_{0,i}(t) + B_{1,i} N_{1,i}(t) - \\
&- \sum_{k=1}^{\infty} B_{1,i-1} N_{k,i-1}(t),
\end{aligned}
\tag{5}
$$

where

$$
A_1 = \sum_{k=1}^{\infty} B_{1,i-1} N_{k,i-1}(t); \quad A_{i>1} = 0.
$$

The value of $P_{1,i}$ can be found on the basis of the following considerations. The change in the concentration of radioactive atoms per unit air volume in time dt as a result of the capture of atoms by the drops will be proportional to the product of the concentration of atoms by the concentration of drops N:

$$
dn_i = -Kn_i N dt, \tag{6}
$$

where K is the coagulation constant. At the same time, this change can be expressed as follows in terms of $P_{k,i}$:

$$
dn_i = -\sum_{k=1}^{\infty} k P_{k,i} N dt. \tag{7}
$$

On the basis of equations (6) and (7) and the above assumption regarding the neglect of the possibilities of capture by cloud-borne drops of two and more radioactive atoms in time dt, we then obtain

$$
P_{1,i} = Kn_i. \tag{8}
$$

The probability of capture of one atom in a drop with k radioactive atoms can be found from the following considerations.

In time dt, dm_i atoms decay on a drop with k radioactive atoms of isotope i:

$$
dm_i = -\lambda_i k dt, \tag{9}
$$

where λ_i is the decay constant. The number of decaying atoms can also be written in terms of $B_{k,i}$ in the form

$$
dm_i = -\sum_{i=1}^{k} k B_{k,i} dt. \tag{10}
$$

139

On the basis of equations (9) and (10) and the above assumption that the probabilities of decay in time dt of two or more atoms can be neglected, we obtain

$$B_{1,i} = \lambda_i. \tag{11}$$

The radioactivity of the individual raindrops is usually measured by means of thick-layer nuclear photographic emulsions and, in the main, two decay products of radon, Pb^{214} (RaB) and Bi^{214} (RaC), are recorded. Indeed, the short-lived isotope Po^{218} (RaA), which precedes lead-214, usually decays completely in the time taken to prepare captured drops for radiography on the nuclear photographic emulsion, and the resulting number of Pb^{214} atoms is usually smaller by an order of magnitude than that already present, and can be neglected. The radioactive gas Rn^{222} is washed out relatively poorly by precipitation /11/, and as a result is not recorded by the nuclear emulsion.

When a mixture of radioactive isotopes consisting of k_2 atoms of Pb^{214} and k_3 atoms of Bi^{214} is maintained for 1 day in contact with the nuclear emulsion, $k_2 + k_3$ α-tracks are formed. Since the half-decay periods of Pb^{214} and Bi^{214} are quite close to each other (26.8 and 19.7 min), the mixture of these isotopes can be replaced by a single isotope with effective decay constant /1,3/

$$\lambda = 3\left(\frac{2}{\lambda_2} + \frac{1}{\lambda_3}\right)^{-1} \approx 4.72 \cdot 10^{-4}\, \text{sec}^{-1} \tag{12}$$

and concentration equal to the sum of the concentrations of Pb^{214} and Bi^{214}. The corresponding value of the half-decay period is $T = 24.5$ min. Here, λ_2 and λ_3 are the decay constants of Pb^{214} and Bi^{214}, respectively. Using (8), (11) and (12), we can rewrite system of equations (5) in the following form:

$$\left. \begin{aligned} \frac{d N_j(t)}{dt} &= K n N_{j-1}(t) - \\ &- (\lambda + K n) N_j(t) + \lambda N_{j+1}(t), \\ \frac{d N_0(t)}{dt} &= - K n N_0(t) + \lambda N_1(t). \end{aligned} \right\} \tag{13}$$

This system is analogous to the general system of equations of processes of death and propagation, studied in detail by Feller /8/. It possesses a solution when the series

$$\sum_{j=1}^{\infty} \left(\frac{\lambda}{K n}\right)^j \tag{14}$$

diverges and the series

$$\sum_{j=1}^{\infty} \left(\frac{Kn}{\lambda} \right)^j \tag{15}$$

converges, i.e., when $\frac{Kn}{\lambda} < 1$.

We shall find the values of $N_j(t)$ to which the radioactive atoms—drops system tends after a sufficiently long time. To that end we must solve the following system of algebraic equations derived from (13) by substituting $dN_j(t)/dt = 0$ and replacing $N_j(t)$ by N_j:

$$\left. \begin{array}{l} Kn N_{j-1} - (\lambda + Kn) N_j + \lambda N_{j+1} = 0, \\ \quad - Kn N_0 + \lambda N_1 = 0. \end{array} \right\} \tag{16}$$

If, for brevity, we set

$$- Kn N_j + \lambda N_{j+1} = Z_j$$
$$(j = 0, 1, 2, \ldots)$$

and express (16) in the form

$$\left. \begin{array}{l} Z_{j-1} - Z_j = 0 \\ Z_0 = 0 \quad (j = 0, 1\,2, \ldots), \end{array} \right\} \tag{17}$$

we see that $Z_j = 0$ for all j, i.e.,

$$Kn N_j - \lambda N_{j+1} = 0 \quad (j = 0, 1, 2 \ldots). \tag{18}$$

The solution of (18) for N_j is

$$N_j = \frac{Kn}{\lambda} N_{j-1} = N_0 \left(\frac{Kn}{\lambda} \right)^j. \tag{19}$$

Using (19), the condition $\sum_{j=0}^{\infty} N_j = N$ enables us to obtain

$$N_0 = \left[1 + \sum_{j=1}^{\infty} \left(\frac{Kn}{\lambda} \right)^j \right]^{-1} N. \tag{20}$$

Substitution of (20) in (19) finally yields

$$N_j = N \left(\frac{Kn}{\lambda} \right) \left[1 + \sum_{j=1}^{\infty} \left(\frac{Kn}{\lambda} \right)^j \right]^{-1}. \tag{21}$$

Since $Kn/\lambda < 1$, the terms of the geometrical progression can be summed to give

$$N_j = N\left(1 - \frac{Kn}{\lambda}\right)\left(\frac{Kn}{\lambda}\right)^j.$$ (22)

Substituting $j = 0$ in (22), we obtain the formula for the frequency of the appearance of nonradioactive cloud-borne drops:

$$\frac{N_0}{N} = 1 - \frac{Kn}{\lambda}.$$ (23)

When measuring the radioactivity of a large number of cloud-borne drops, the frequency, according to Mises' probability notion /4/, will differ little from the probability, i.e., $P_0 \approx N_0/N$.

A direct experimental check of formula (22) is very difficult, since the procedure for determining the radioactivity of individual cloud-borne drops has been poorly developed so far and does not enable us to obtain experimental material having sufficient statistical reliability. Accordingly, using the distribution (22) of the radioactivity of cloud-borne drops, we shall convert to quantities which are easier to determine in practice. Such quantities are the specific radioactivity of the cloud water and the fraction of nonradioactive raindrops.

A. Specific radioactivity of cloud water. The number of radioactive atoms on cloud-borne drops per unit air volume can be written in the form

$$A = \sum_{j=1}^{\infty} j N_j.$$ (24)

On the other hand, this quantity is given by the expression

$$A = \frac{C\omega}{\lambda},$$ (25)

where C is the specific radioactivity of cloud water, ω is the cloud water content, and λ is the effective radioactive decay constant. Equating the right sides of (24) and (25) yields

$$C = \frac{\lambda}{\omega} \sum_{j=1}^{\infty} j N_j.$$ (26)

Next, substituting the value of N_j from (22) and summing, we obtain

$$C = \frac{KnN}{\omega}.$$ (27)

We pass from the concentration of atoms n to the specific air radioactivity q, expressed in curies per unit volume. If we assume that the short-lived decay products of radon are in equilibrium and are captured by the drops with equal efficiency, we can set $q = \lambda n$. The specific radioactivity of cloud water then becomes

$$C = \frac{KN}{\lambda \omega} q. \tag{28}$$

This expression can be used to calculate the coagulation constants of cloud-borne drops with radioactive aerosol.

B. **Fraction of nonradioactive raindrops.** Raindrops grow mainly through coagulation with cloud-borne drops. Schematically, we can divide the mass m of one raindrop of radius R into v cloud-borne drops with mean mass m_0 and radius r. The probability that our system of v drops will not possess radioactivity is then written (according to the law of multiplication of probabilities) in the following form:

$$P_0 = \left(1 - \frac{Kn}{\lambda}\right)^v. \tag{29}$$

Substitution of $v = \frac{m}{m_0} = \left(\frac{R}{r}\right)^3$ and $P_0 \approx \frac{N_0}{N}$ in (29) yields the frequency of appearance of nonradioactive raindrops as a function of their radius:

$$\frac{N_0}{N} = \left(1 - \frac{Kn}{\lambda}\right)^{\left(\frac{R}{r}\right)^3}. \tag{30}$$

Since $K \sim 10^{-6}\,\mathrm{cm^3/sec}$ /7/, $\lambda \sim 10^{-4}\,\mathrm{sec^{-1}}$ and $n = \frac{q}{\lambda} \sim 10^{-2}\,\mathrm{sec^{-3}}$, we have $\frac{Kn}{\lambda} \ll 1$ and equation (3) can be represented by the following straight line in $\log\left(-\log \frac{N_0}{N}\right)$, $\log R$ coordinates:

$$\log\left(-\log\frac{N_0}{N}\right) = 3\log R + B, \tag{31}$$

where

$$B = \log\frac{Kn\log e}{\lambda r^3}.$$

The washout of radioactive particles in the subcloud layer of the atmosphere can be neglected /11/. Accordingly we make use of experimental data from /6/ pertaining to the dependence of the frequency of appearance of nonradioactive raindrops on their radius, obtained on the ground by the α-radiography of drop imprints on filter paper and polished steel plates. These data are represented on Figure 1 by dots. The theoretical relationship calculated by formula (31) for values of the free term $B = 3.8$ (line 1) and $B = 3.0$ (line 2) was plotted on the same figure. The experimental points are seen to lie between the theoretical lines. The values of B given above can be used to estimate the constants of coagulation of the cloud-borne drops with the radioactive aerosols. To that end n is given in terms of q.

According to the above assumption that the concentrations of Po^{218} atoms in the raindrop samples used for radiography can be neglected, and assuming radioactive equilibrium between the short-lived decay products, we obtain

$$n = \frac{2}{3} \frac{q}{\lambda},$$ (32)

where λ is given by (12).

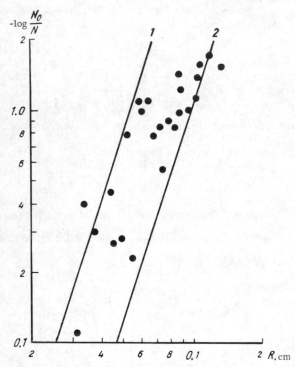

FIGURE 1. Frequency of appearance of nonradioactive raindrops as a function of their radius.

If (32) is substituted in the free term of equation (31), we obtain the expression for finding K in the form

$$\log K = (3 - 3.8) - \log\left(\frac{2\log e}{3} \frac{q}{\lambda^2 r^3}\right).$$ (33)

Substitution of the values $\lambda = 4.7 \cdot 10^{-4}$ sec^{-1}, $q \approx 10^{-16}$ curie/cm^3 /5/ and $r \approx 15\mu$ (size of the cloud-borne drops at which their intense coagulation

144

growth starts /10/) yields values of K in the range $(0.7-4.4) \cdot 10^{-6} \, \text{cm}^3/\text{sec}$. These values of the constants of coagulation of the short-lived decay products of Rn^{222} with cloud-borne drops coincide satisfactorily with the values obtained by other methods /7, 11/.

BIBLIOGRAPHY

1. B r e s l e r, V. Radioaktivnye elementy (Radioactive Elements). — Moskva, Gostekhteorizdat. 1949.
2. G n e d e n k o, B. V. Kurs teorii veroyatnostei (A Course in the Theory of Probability). — Moskva, Izd. "Nauka." 1965.
3. M a l a k h o v, S. G. and P. G. C h e r n y s h e v a. O sezonnykh izmeneniyakh kontsentratsii radona i torona v prizemnom sloe atmosfery (On the Seasonal Variation in the Concentration of Radon and Thoron in the Ground Layer of the Atmosphere). — In: Radioaktivnye izotopy v atmosfere i ikh ispol'zovanie v meteorologii (Radioactive Isotopes in the Atmosphere and their Utilization in Meteorology). Moskva, Atomizdat. 1965.
4. Von Mises, R. Probability and Statistics. [Russian translation, 1930.]
5. S t y r o, B. I. Voprosy yadernoi meteorologii (Problems of Nuclear Meteorology). — Vilnius, Izd. AN LitSSR. 1959.
6. S t y r o, B. I. and B. K. V e b r e n e. O metodike izmereniya radioaktivnosti otdel'nykh chastits osadkov i nekotorye predvaritel'nye rezul'taty takikh issledovanii (Procedure for Measuring the Radioactivity of Individual Precipitation Particles and Some Preliminary Results of Such Investigations). — Izvestiya AN SSSR, Fizika Atmosfery i Okeana, Vol. 2, No. 10. 1966.
7. S t y r o, B. I. , Yu. E. V e b r a, and K. K. S h o p a u s k a s. Opredelenie nekotorykh parametrov udaleniya estestvennykh radioaktivnykh aerozolei iz vozdukha (Determination of Some Parameters Pertaining to the Removal of Natural Radioactive Aerosols from the Atmosphere). — Izvestiya AN SSSR, Fizika Atmosfery i Okeana, Vol. 1, No. 12. 1965.
8. F e l l e r, W. The Theory of Stochastic Processes. — Uspekhi Matematicheskikh Nauk, No. 5. [Russian translation, 1938.]
9. C h o u - H s ü - C h i. O vliyanii elektricheskikh zaryadov na koagulyatsiyu oblachnykh kapel' v teplykh oblakakh (Effect of Electric Charges on the Coagulation of Cloud-Borne Drops in Warm Clouds). Author's Summary of Thesis for the Degree of Candidate of Physicomathematical Sciences. Moskva. 1961.
10. S h i s h k i n, N. S. Oblaka, osadki i grozovoe elektrichestvo (Clouds, Precipitation and Thunderstorm Electricity). — Leningrad, Gidrometeoizdat. 1964.
11. M a k h o n'k o, K. P. Simplified Theoretical Notion of Contaminant Removal by Precipitation from the Atmosphere. — Tellus, Vol. 19, No. 3. 1967.
12. T e l f o r d, J. W. A New Aspect of Coalescence Theory. — J. Met., Vol. 12, No. 5. 1955.
13. W i l k e n i n g, M. H. Variation of Natural Radioactivity in the Atmosphere with Altitude. — Trans. Am. Geophys. Un., Vol. 37, No. 2. 1956.

UDC 551.510.7

COMPARISON OF THE CHARACTERISTICS OF HYGROSCOPIC AND NONHYGROSCOPIC AEROSOL WASHOUT BY CLOUD-BORNE DROPS

I. I. Burtsev and L. V. Burtseva

Washout by cloud-borne drops of aerosol of size $0.1-0.5\,\mu$ is examined as a function of its hygroscopicity. Radioactive hygroscopic $P_2^{32}O_5$ and nonhygroscopic $Sr^{89}CO_3$ aerosols were investigated and their washout characteristics compared. It is shown on the basis of an experimental comparison of the characteristics of the capture of aerosol of the same disperse group, but with different physical properties, that the hygroscopicity of the aerosol substantially affects its behavior in a cloud medium. The capture efficiency of hygroscopic aerosol is twice that of nonhygroscopic aerosol.

Meteorological problems, such as the development of frontal activity, the circulation of the atmosphere and the mechanism of atmospheric scavenging, have been studied recently with the aid of radioactive aerosol masses of both natural and artificial origin. In particular, a procedure for introducing radioactive aerosol in a cloud and obtaining information about its subsequent behavior was developed /1/ for investigating the process of aerosol washout by cloud-borne drops (under full-scale and laboratory conditions) and also for explaining a number of problems associated with the prevention or production of hail from thick cumulus.

Aerosols are defined as systems in which the particles can be in solid or liquid state /8/. The dispersity of the aerosol determines a number of very important physical properties, such as the medium resistance, rates of evaporation and cooling, coagulation constants. Therefore, the dispersity of the aerosols must be known when studying meteorological problems with their aid. If the aerosols belong to the same disperse system, they must possess identical physical properties and must obey the same physical laws.

However, atmospheric aerosols (those of both natural origin and introduced artificially in the atmosphere) include hygroscopic and nonhygroscopic aerosols. The aerosol cloud from hygroscopic particles can contain solid, semiliquid or liquid particles depending on the medium humidity. The physical state of the particles necessarily affects the aerosol behavior in the cloud medium. McDonald /11/ examined theoretically the influence of aerosol wettability on their capture by drops, and concluded that unwettable particles and drops coagulate with a lower efficiency than wettable ones.

We attempted to clarify experimentally the degree of influence of hygroscopicity on the behavior of aerosols with equal dispersity.

We used in our study two radioactive substances, $P_2^{32}O_5$ (hygroscopic) and $Sr^{89}CO_3$ (nonhygroscopic), and under laboratory conditions determined corresponding characteristics of aerosol capture (washout coefficient λ and coefficient K of particle coagulation with drops) by cloud-borne drops.

The experiments were conducted in a chamber where the radioactive aerosol was generated by burning the substance in a voltaic arc, after which a cloud of fog drops was created.

The procedure as well as the measuring equipment were described in detail elsewhere /2–4/. The particle spectrum was obtained by electron-microscope microphotography of aerosol samples taken by a thermoprecipitator. The aerosol was generated at a relative air humidity of 90–95%, and the hygroscopic particle size was determined with allowance for partial evaporation (zones of lower contrast) during their heating in an electron beam.

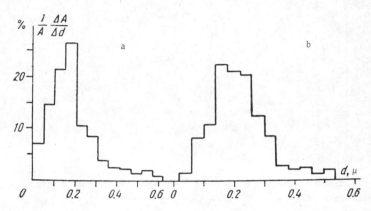

FIGURE 1. Distribution of β-activity by particle size:

a) $P_2^{32}O_5$; b) $Sr^{89}CO_3$.

Figure 1 presents the β-activity distribution by particle size on the assumption that the particle activity is proportional to the cube of the radius. Curve a (Figure 1) corresponds to the spectrum of P_2O_5 particles, curve b (Figure 1) to $SrCO_3$. It is seen from curve a that the radioactivity is maximum for particles of size 0.15–0.2μ, and that the entire spectrum lies between 0.5 and $5 \cdot 10^{-5}$ cm, which implies that the P_2O_5 aerosol belongs to the group of aerosols with mean dispersity /2/.

We must take into account that the P_2O_5 formed during the burning of phosphorus is very hygroscopic, and therefore the size spectrum of the β-activity distribution characterizes the P_2O_5 aerosol at maximum moisture content, i. e., in its state when introduced into natural clouds.

The distribution curve of β-activity by particle size for $SrCO_3$ (Figure 1, curve 3) was obtained in the same way as for P_2O_5. The dispersity of the P_2O_5 and $SrCO_3$ aerosols is seen to be roughly the same, which enables us to compare the behavior of aerosols differing in their hygroscopicity alone.

The microstructure of the fog formed in the chamber is shown in Figure 2. The diameter of maximum-frequency drops is 4–6μ. The mean water content $w = 3$ g/m^3, the drop concentration $N = (1–3.5) \cdot 10^3$ cm^{-3}, and the concentration of aerosol particles $n = 10^5–10^6$ cm^{-3}.

During the experiment measurements were conducted of the concentration of radioactive substances in the drops for different times of their residence and concentration in the air, both prior to the formation of the drops and after their precipitation. These experimental data enabled us to determine λ and K, assuming that the medium inside the chamber simulates some cloud volume in which the capture of particles by the drops and their subsequent deposition lead to the removal of aerosol from the considered air column. The particle concentration changes according to the laws of first-order kinetics.

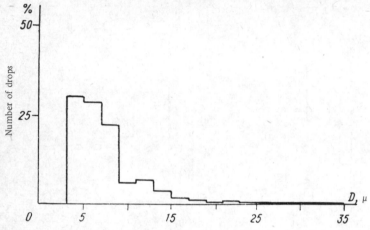

FIGURE 2. Microstructure of the fog formed in the chamber.

The decrease in radioactive aerosol concentration n with time can be described by the equation

$$\frac{dn}{dt} = -\lambda n. \tag{1}$$

If the radioactivity concentrations in the air before the formation of the drops (q_0) and after their deposition (q) are assumed proportional to the aerosol concentrations, the solution of equation (1) for $\lambda =$ const is

$$q = q_0 e^{-\lambda t}. \tag{2}$$

Equation (2) yields the washout coefficient λ, characterizing the amount of aerosol washed out per unit time from unit cloud volume.

The mean "lifetime" of the aerosol, i.e., the time during which the number of particles decreases e times, was determined by the formula

$$\tau = \frac{1}{\lambda}.$$

The coagulation coefficient of the aerosol with the drops was calculated on the assumption that each contact of a drop with a particle leads to their coalescence, and that the decrease of radioactivity concentration in the chamber air volume results from the coagulation of radioactive particles with cloud-borne drops according to the Smoluchowsky law (we assume for simplicity that the drops and particles are monodispersive). The variation in radioactive particle concentration in the chamber air is given by

$$\frac{dn}{dt} = -K\,n\,N. \tag{3}$$

But the number N of drops per unit volume changes in the course of the experiment as a result of deposition, evaporation, and other processes. Investigations showed that the change of parameter N can be described by the empirical formula

$$N = N_0\,e^{-bt}, \tag{4}$$

where N_0 is the drop concentration at the initial time and b is an empirical coefficient.

Integrating (3) allowing for (4), and taking the time-averaged value of K outside the integral, we obtain

$$K = \frac{b\ln\dfrac{n_0}{n}}{N_0\,(1 - e^{-bt})}. \tag{5}$$

The results of the experimental determination of λ, K, and τ for hygroscopic and nonhygroscopic aerosols for different fog water contents are tabulated in Table 1, which shows that the washout efficiency for hygroscopic particles is twice that for insoluble particles.

TABLE 1. Constants of the washout of radioactive aerosol by fine cloud-borne drops

Water content w, g/m^3	λ, 10^{-4} sec^{-1}		K, 10^{-7} cm^3/sec		τ, 10^4 sec	
	$P_2^{32}O_5$	$Sr^{89}CO_3$	$P_2^{32}O_5$	$Sr^{89}CO_3$	$P_2^{32}O_5$	$Sr^{89}CO_3$
0.65	4.8	2.2	2.0	0.94	0.21	0.45
1.86	6.2	3.7	2.0	0.54	0.16	0.27
2.50	7.5	3.3	2.7	0.36	0.13	0.30
3.35	8.5	4.2	4.7	0.54	0.12	0.23
4.6	10.5	5.4	7.2	0.29	0.095	0.185
5.7	11.8	4.8	7.8	0.22	0.084	0.21

On the average, the following results were derived for clouds with a water content of $2-4$ g/m^3: for $Sr^{89}CO_3$, $\lambda = 4.3\cdot10^{-4}$ sec^{-1}, $K = 0.5\cdot10^{-7}$ cm^3/sec and $\tau = 3\cdot10^3$ sec; for $P_2^{32}O_5$, $\lambda = 9\cdot10^{-4}$ sec, $K = 4.8\cdot10^{-7}$ cm^3/sec and $\tau = 1\cdot10^3$ sec.

These experimental results corroborate that the hygroscopicity considerably affects the aerosol properties.

Since the equipment enabled us to create a cloud with water content between 0.5 and 6 g/m^3, it was possible to estimate the dependence of the washout coefficient on water content for two types of aerosol.

It is seen from Table 1 that the increase in water content from 0.65 to 5.7 g/m³ is accompanied by a relative increase in λ by a factor of two for both hygroscopic and nonhygroscopic aerosols, i.e., increased cloud water content is accompanied by its increased capacity to wash out substances, independently of their physicochemical properties.

The change in drop activity with their increased lifetime in the aerosol cloud is presented in Figure 3. For the $P_2^{32}O_5$ aerosol the curve lies much higher, and indicates the large growth in the content of this substance in drops with their increased lifetime in the aerosol cloud. This growth is much smaller for $Sr^{89}CO_3$.

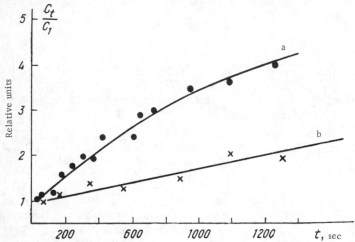

FIGURE 3. Variation in drop activity with their increased lifetime in the aerosol cloud: a) $P_2^{32}O_5$; b) $Sr^{89}CO_3$.

Since the aerosol obtained during the sublimation of P^{32} is hygroscopic, we can assume that the capture of radioactive aerosol by the particles occurs mainly as a result of vapor condensation on the particles in the form of condensation nuclei. But there exists in the chamber a surplus of aerosol particles, since $n/N \sim 10^3$. Therefore the growth of the specific activity of the drops with time indicates that the process of particle activation continues after their formation.

The physical conditions of the experiment for $P_2^{32}O_5$ and $Sr^{89}CO_3$ were absolutely identical, and for nonhygroscopic aerosols we ought to observe the same increase in aerosol concentration in the drops as for hygroscopic aerosol. However, the experiment showed that for the phosphorus aerosol there operates an additional mechanism of drop activation besides those which are identical for $P_2^{32}O_5$ and $Sr^{89}CO_3$.

The dissolution of hygroscopic matter in the drop evidently has a considerable effect. It is known that admixtures of salts and acids lower the saturation vapor pressure above the water surface. This creates an additional flux of aerosol to the drop, so increasing the solution concentration and leading to an even greater drop in the vapor pressure above the drop and to increased aerosol flux to the drop. This conclusion is corroborated by an analysis of the values of the coagulation coefficient.

It was found that for $P_2^{32}O_5$ the value of K is proportional to the drop surface (Figure 4). If there exists above this drop a lowered vapor pressure, the increase in the amount of aerosol coagulating with the drop will be proportional to the drop surface.

For nonhygroscopic aerosol such a phenomenon is not observed, as is clear from Figure 4.

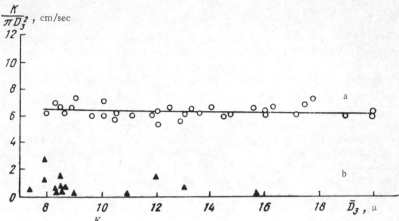

FIGURE 4. Quantity $\dfrac{K}{\pi D_3^2}$ as a function of the mean-cubic diameter of cloud-borne drops in the chamber for particles of $P_2^{32}O_5$ (a) and $Sr^{89}CO_3$ (b) aerosols.

On the basis of an experimental comparison of the capture characteristics of the same disperse group but with different physical properties, we can say that the hygroscopicity of the aerosol substantially affects the behavior of these aerosols in a cloud environment: hygroscopic aerosols are captured more effectively by cloud-borne drops than by nonhygroscopic ones.

We shall compare the experimental and theoretical values of K and λ. Numerous theoretical investigations /5–7/ have established that the main capture mechanism of aerosol particles of size about 0.1μ by small cloud-borne drops is diffusion. Usually, three types of diffusion capture are considered /7/: a) diffusion in an immobile environment; b) convective diffusion, which takes place in the case of a moving drop, when it continually receives a fresh admixture of relatively high concentration; c) diffusion allowing for electrostatic interaction.

Calculations for the first two types of diffusion capture showed that the brownian and convective diffusion plays a negligible part in processes of radioactive aerosol capture by cloud-borne drops.

We shall consider the influence of electrostatic interaction between drops and particles on the washout constant. The particle charge is taken as $q = 4.8 \cdot 10^{-10}$ CGSE, and that of the drop charge $Q = 10R^{-3}$ /6, 9, 10/. We shall employ the following drop distribution in the chamber /9/:

$$F(R) = \frac{\beta^3}{2} R^2 e^{-\beta R},$$

where $\beta = 2/R_m$, R_m being the radius of the maximum-frequency drop. We shall calculate K_{br} for neutral and charged particles /9/:

$$K_{br}^{n} = \frac{kT}{3\eta}\left(3C_r + 3\frac{C_r}{\eta}R_m + \frac{2r}{R_m} + 2\right),\qquad(6)$$

$$K_{br}^{el} = \frac{1.6\cdot10^{-13}}{\eta}\left(\frac{3C_r}{r\beta} + C_r\right),\qquad(7)$$

where $C_r = 1 + \dfrac{Al}{r}$ is the correction to the Stokes law, r is the radius of the aerosol particles, η is the air viscosity, and k is the Boltzmann constant.

We give in Table 2 the theoretical values of the coagulation constant and washout coefficient $\lambda = KN$ calculated by formulas (6) and (7) and obtained experimentally. The following parametric values were used in the calculations: $r = 0.1\mu$, $R_m = 2-3\mu$, $A \approx 0.9$, $l = 0.94\cdot10^{-5}$ cm, $\eta = 1.8\cdot10^{-4}$ g/cm$\cdot$sec.

It is seen from Table 2 that the experimental values of λ and K for the nonhygroscopic $Sr^{89}CO_3$ aerosol are in better agreement with the theoretically calculated K_{br}^{el} and λ_{br}^{el} values than for $P_2^{32}O_5$, which exceed considerably the calculated values.

Thus, whereas the characteristics of the capture of soluble radioactive particles by cloud-borne drops can be explained by their hygroscopic properties (a lowering of the vapor pressure above the drops in the presence of hygroscopic substances) and the part played by the particles as centers of condensation, the mechanism of capture of nonhygroscopic aerosols cannot be understood without allowing for the electrostatic interaction between drops and particles.

TABLE 2. Experimental and calculated values of the washout coefficient $\lambda(10^{-4}\,\text{sec}^{-1})$ and coagulation constant $K(10^{-7}\text{cm}^3/\text{sec})$

R_m, μ	$P_2^{32}O_5$		$Sr^{89}CO_3$		Calculated values			
	K	λ	K	λ	K_{br}^{n}	K_{br}^{el}	λ_{br}^{n}	λ_{br}^{el}
2	1.6	6.0	0.6	3.1	0.04	0.12	0.20	0.6
3	2.0	6.4	0.3	0.6	0.07	0.14	0.35	0.7

BIBLIOGRAPHY

1. Burtsev, I.I., L.V. Burtseva, and S.G. Malakhov. Washout Characteristics of a [32]P Aerosol Injected into a Cloud.— In: Atmospheric Scavenging of Radioisotopes. Israel Program for Scientific Translations, Jerusalem. 1970.

2. Burtsev, I.I. and L.V. Burtseva. Issledovaniya protsessa zakhvata aerozolei v oblake metodom mechenykh atomov (Study of Aerosol Capture in a Cloud by the Use of Labeled Atoms).— Trudy VGI, No.3(5). 1966.

3. Burtsev, I.I. and L.V. Burtseva. K voprosu o vymyvanii oblachnymi kaplyami radioaktivnogo aerozola po dannym opytov v kamere (Radioactive Aerosol Washout by Cloud-Borne Drops, According to the Data of Experiments in a Chamber).— Trudy VGI, No.8. 1968.

4. Burtsev, I.I. and L.V. Burtseva. Issledovanie vymyvaniya negigroskopicheskikh chastits oblachnymi kaplyami (Nonhygroscopic Particle Washout by Cloud-Borne Drops).— Trudy VGI, No.8. 1968.

5. Byutner, E.K. Effektivnyi koeffitsient zakhvata chastits aerozolya dozhdevymi i oblachnymi kaplyami (Effective Coefficient of Aerosol Particle Capture by Raindrops and Cloud-Borne Drops).— Trudy LGMI, No.15. 1963.

6. Zimin, A.G. Mekhanizm zakhvata i osazhdeniya atmosfernykh primesei oblakami i osadkami (Mechanisms for the Capture and Deposition of Atmospheric Contaminant by Clouds and Precipitation).— In: Voprosy yadernoi meterologii (Problems of Nuclear Meterology). Moskva, Atomizdat. 1962.

7. Levich, V.G. Fiziko-khimicheskaya gidrodinamika (Physicochemical Hydrodynamics).— Moskva, Fizmatizdat. 1959.

8. Fuchs, N.A. The Mechanics of Aerosols. — Oxford, Pergamon Press. 1964.

9. Byutner, E.G. and F.A.Gisina. Effektivnyi koeffitsient zakhvata chastits aerozolya dozhdevymi i oblachnymi kaplyami (Effective Coefficient of Aerosol Particle Capture by Raindrops and Cloud-Borne Drops).— Trudy LGMI, No.15. 1963.

10. Frenkel', Ya.I. Teoriya yavlenii atmosfernogo elektrichestva (Theory of Atmospheric Electricity Phenomena).—Moskva, Gostekhizdat. 1949.

11. McDonald, J.E. Rain Washout of Partially Wettable Insoluble Particles.— J. Geophys. Res., Vol.68, No.17. 1963.

UDC 551.510.7

ATMOSPHERIC WASHOUT OF RADIOACTIVE CONTAMINANT IN THE MOUNTAINS OF CENTRAL CAUCASUS

A. S. Avramenko and K. P. Makhon'ko

The coefficient σ of radioactive dust washout from the subcloud layer of the atmosphere was determined by measuring the contaminant concentration in precipitation at two different altitudes in 1968–1969 in mountains. The mean value of σ for the products of nuclear bursts in steady rain was $3 \cdot 10^{-5} \sec^{-1}$; for showers σ is roughly twice as large, and for snows five times as large. Measurements during steady rain for upslope and downslope winds enabled us to estimate the mean speed of the ascending air currents, found to be ~ 0.6 m/sec. With increase in precipitation intensity I the value of σ decreases rapidly at first, passes through a minimum when $I \sim 1$ mm/hr, and then increases. It is shown that vertical air currents affect the obtained relationship.

When measuring σ for short-lived decay products of radon, samples were taken simultaneously at two altitudes, a radiotelephone being used to ensure simultaneity. Due to the brief sampling time of rapidly decaying samples, the influence of fluctuations in the concentration of natural radioactivity in precipitation (C) and in air (q) and fluctuations in precipitation intensity was so large that it was not possible to determine σ for rains; for snow $\sigma \sim 9 \cdot 10^{-5} \sec^{-1}$ with a 95% error. Similarly, we were unable to detect from the results of 313 observations a time-dependence of the specific radioactivity of precipitation (C) against the background of the large fluctuations in the measured quantity. In spite of the large scatter of the individual values of C, it was possible to observe a decrease in C with increasing I. A study of the polar diagrams of q and C showed that the ground concentration of short-lived decay products of radon is affected by exhalation mainly within a radius of several kilometers, while the concentration in precipitation is affected within a radius of tens of kilometers.

The aim of this study is to investigate the washout of aerosol contaminant from the atmosphere in mountain conditions. It is known that similar investigations were conducted in the Bavarian Alps /22/, at Hokkaido /21/, in the Caucasus /1, 2, 8, 15/ and at Tyan'-Shan /19, 20/.

We continued these investigations in 1968–1969 in the mountains of Central Caucasus, and measured simultaneously the concentrations of natural and artificial radioactivity in the air and in precipitation at two points situated 1,200 m apart along the horizontal but located at different altitudes: 2,200 m above sea level at the Azau valley and 3,100 m at the Terskol peak.

1. SAMPLING AND TREATMENT METHODS

Atmospheric dust was sampled by means of filtering installations of 1,900 m^3/hr output on an FPP-15—1.5 filter /4/. Samples of atmospheric precipitation were collected in cuvettes of total area 7.5 m^2, covered by acid-treated polyethylene to avoid the sorption of isotopes.

To analyze the precipitation for content of short-lived natural radio-activity, the water was evaporated by drops on a metallic target. The duration of sample preparation, from its collection until the beginning of counting under an MST-17 end counter, was 10–15 min. The natural radioactivity of the atmospheric dust was determined by direct measurement of the filter radioactivity by means of an SBT-10 counter. It was assumed that radon and its short-lived decay products are in equilibrium.

To determine the content of artificial radioactivity in the samples, the water was passed through an ion-exchange column filled with KU-2 cationite and EDE-10P anionite. The ion-exchange resin was then reduced to ashes in a muffle furnace, and its radioactivity measured under an end counter. Calibration was conducted with respect to $Sr^{90} + Y^{90}$.

2. ATMOSPHERIC WASHOUT OF ARTIFICIAL RADIOACTIVITY

The concentration of artificial radioactivity in air and in precipitation was measured simultaneously at the Terskol peak and the Azau valley, in order to study the washout of aerosol contaminant from the subcloud layer of the atmosphere. The relatively small distance between observation points enabled us to capture precipitation from practically the same part of the cloud. Simultaneously, on the Terskol peak, we recorded the wind direction by an M-12 anemograph with respect to eight compass points.

According to Makhon'ko /9/, the washout coefficient σ of an aerosol contaminant of concentration q from the subcloud atmospheric layer of height H is related to the specific radioactivity of the precipitation C by the following formula:

$$C = \frac{H}{I}\,\sigma q, \tag{1}$$

where I is the precipitation intensity. Applying this equality to the upper and lower layers we can derive an expression for the washout coefficient:

$$\sigma = \frac{(C_1 - C_2)\, I_1 I_2}{\overline{q}_{01}(H_0 - H_1)\, I_2 - \overline{q}_{02}(H_0 - H_2)\, I_1}, \tag{2}$$

where H_0 is the height of the cloud level; $\overline{q}_{01}$ and $\overline{q}_{02}$ are the mean concentrations in the corresponding air layers.

The measurements established that in the cases considered by us the values of I and q were roughly constant in height, which points to the absence of evaporation of the falling raindrops and to the fact that the observations were conducted in the same air mass. We can therefore simplify formula (2) to the form

$$\sigma = \frac{I \Delta C}{\overline{q}\, \Delta H}, \tag{3}$$

where ΔC is the difference between the concentrations of nuclear test products in precipitation collected at the upper and lower levels; ΔH is the difference in height between them; $\bar{I}$ is the mean precipitation intensity; $\bar{q}$ is the mean concentration of radioactivity in the air.

The measurements showed that, in steady rain, the mean washout coefficient is $\sigma = 3 \cdot 10^{-5}\,\text{sec}^{-1}$; in showers it is twice as large on the average, and for snow five times as large (individual values are up to eight times as large). It is known /11, 19/ that the coefficient is somewhat larger in mountains than in the plain. We formulated earlier the hypothesis /11/ that the reason for this is that vertical air currents exist in mountain conditions. The mountain—plain circulation, clearly expressed in clear weather, is disturbed during the fall of precipitation. Even in their absence plain winds ar absent in cloudy weather, and only nighttime mountain winds remain /18/. As a result the difference between the values of σ obtained at night and by day was 15–20% in all /2/.

We attempted to clarify the part played by vertical air currents, by following the dependence of σ on wind direction. We selected for the analysi precipitation falls of the same type — steady rains. The wind direction hardly ever remains constant in the course of a given rainfall. The probability that the mean value of σ_n for the n-th rain corresponds to the i-th wind direction will be taken as proportional to the frequency of this direction in the measurement period, and denoted by P_{in}. If different values of σ_n are observed for different wind roses, we can find the mean washout coefficient $\bar{\sigma}_i$ for the i-th wind direction. To that end, for the given wind direction we sum the product $\sigma_n P_{in}$ over all m rains and divide the result by the sum of the corresponding probabilities:

$$\bar{\sigma}_i = \sum_{n=1}^{m} \sigma_n P_{ni} \left(\sum_{n=1}^{m} P_{ni} \right)^{-1}. \tag{4}$$

The frequency of the given wind direction during the measurement period was defined as the ratio of the number of marks on the anemograph tape corresponding to that direction, to the total number of marks at all compass points.

TABLE 1. Washout coefficient $\sigma(10^{-5}\,\text{sec}^{-1})$ for different wind directions and precipitation intensities

$\bar{I}$, mm/hr	Wind direction i								$\bar{\sigma}\,(\bar{I})$
	N	NE	E	SE	S	SW	W	NW	
0.1–0.2	3.61	1.30	1.30	9.85	10.26	8.23	6.95	1.30	5.35
0.3–0.4	2.20	2.68	1.07	3.12	4.74	4.49	3.47	3.20	3.12
0.7–0.8	0.68	0.97	1.50	1.86	1.60	0.90	0.79	0.87	1.15
0.9–1.1	0.73	0.43	0.51	1.12	0.45	0.84	0.79	0.62	0.69
1.2–1.5	2.61	3.12	3.33	3.80	4.04	3.73	3.42	1.75	3.22
1.7–1.9	2.83	2.68	3.85	3.43	4.20	3.39	3.21	3.70	3.41
2.2–2.7	1.62	3.36	3.57	3.39	4.66	4.46	2.66	1.96	3.21
3.5–4.9	4.15	1.82	2.64	5.92	5.61	4.96	4.52	2.66	4.04
Average	2.30	2.04	2.22	4.06	4.50	3.86	3.22	2.00	3.02

Table 1 gives the results of determining (by formula (4)) the washout coefficient of the products of nuclear tests from the subcloud layer of the atmosphere for precipitation of different intensity and for different wind directions. For southerly winds, σ attains a maximum value, equal to $4.5 \cdot 10^{-5} \sec^{-1}$, while for winds in the opposite direction the value of σ decreases by more than a factor of two. In the latter case the winds blow from El'brus to the Azau valley, while SE, S and SW winds blow from the valley and the air rises along the slope of the Terskol peak. The actual three-dimensional motion of the air currents in this case is naturally fairly complex, but its main features can be expressed by the simplified two-dimensional model in Figure 1.

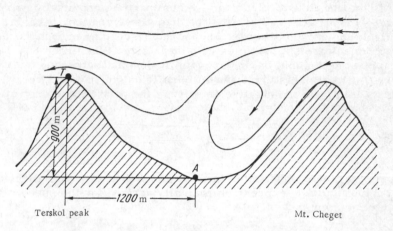

FIGURE 1. Proposed simplified circulation model for wind across the Azau valley. Observation points: T – Terskol peak, A – Azau valley.

The studies of Selezneva /14/ and Vorontsov /3/ conducted in that region established that practically the whole air layer between the peak and the valley is subjected to vertical motions. The additional specific radioactivity of the precipitation appearing in the presence of ascending currents is due to the increased air volume flowing past the raindrops. It follows from formula (3) that the change in the specific radioactivity of the raindrops ΔC during their fall between the sampling levels is proportional to σ, from which we obtain

$$\frac{\Delta C_+}{\Delta C_-} = \frac{\sigma_+}{\sigma_-}. \tag{5}$$

Here the plus and minus signs denote, respectively, ascending and descending currents.

On the other hand, substituting in (3)

$$\sigma_+ = E_+ \pi \bar{R}^2 (v + u_+) N,$$
$$I_+ = \frac{4}{3} \pi \bar{R}^3 (v - u_+) N \tag{6}$$

157

for ascending currents and

$$\sigma_- = E_- \pi \overline{R}^2 (v - u_-) N,$$
$$I_- = \frac{4}{3} \pi \overline{R}^3 (v + u_-) N$$

(7)

for descending currents, we derive the relationship

$$\frac{\Delta C_+}{\Delta C_-} = \frac{E_+ (v + u_+)(v + u_-)}{E_-(v - u_-)(v - u_+)}.$$

(8)

Here E is the coefficient of radioactive dust particle capture by raindrops of radius R falling at speed v; N is the drop concentration; u_+, u_- are respectively the speeds of the ascending and descending currents. For radioactive nuclear-test particles with mean size of the order of 0.1μ, the main capture mechanism is convective diffusion and, according to /15/, $E \sim \sqrt{D/u_\infty R}$, where D is the diffusion coefficient of radioactive particles, while u_∞ is the relative velocity of the particle and drop at infinity It follows that

$$\frac{E_+}{E_-} = \sqrt{\frac{v - u_-}{v + u_+}}.$$

(9)

If (5) and (9) are now substituted in (8) and in a first approximation we set $u_+ \approx u_- \approx u$, the following expression is finally derived for the speed of the vertical air currents:

$$u = v \frac{a - 1}{a + 1},$$

(10)

where $a = (\sigma_+/\sigma_-)^{2/3}$.

The mean precipitation intensity in our case was $\sim 1.4 \, \text{mm/hr}$, to which corresponds a mean drop radius $R = 0.3 \, \text{mm}$ /6/ and a corresponding speed of fall $v \sim 250 \, \text{cm/sec}$ /12/. The value $\sigma_+ = 4 \cdot 10^{-5} \, \text{sec}^{-1}$ is taken from Table 1 as mean value for southeast, south and southwest wind directions, and the value $\sigma_- = 2 \cdot 10^{-5} \, \text{sec}^{-1}$ as mean value for the northwest, north and northeast directions. The mean value of the speed of the ascending currents calculated by formula (8), is then $u \approx 0.6 \, \text{m/sec}$.

We return to the examination of Table 1. The right-side column of Table 1 gives values of the washout coefficient σ for different intensities of steady rain, averaged over all directions. With increased intensity, the value of σ decreases rapidly at first, passes through a minimum when $I \sim 1 \, \text{mm/hr}$, and then starts to increase slowly. This pattern approximates the earlier-observed dependence of σ on I on the Caucasus mountains /2/ and Tyan'-Shan /19/, where the dependence of σ on I was explained by the change in the flow of raindrops vN and the capture coefficient E with increase in rain intensity I. We shall show that the presence of vertical currents in the subcloud layer of the atmosphere also affects this relationship.

Indeed, it follows from (6) and (7) that in the presence of ascending currents the washout coefficient can be expressed in the form

$$\sigma_+ = \frac{3}{4} \cdot \frac{\overline{R^2}}{\overline{R^3}} \cdot \frac{\sqrt{v(v + u_+)}}{v - u_+} E I_+,$$

(11)

158

where E is the capture coefficient in still air, while in the presence of descending currents

$$\sigma_- = \frac{3}{4} \frac{\overline{R^2}}{\overline{R^3}} \frac{\sqrt{v(v-u_-)}}{v+u_-} EI_-. \tag{12}$$

When the precipitation intensity decreases, the raindrop radius also decreases, leading to a decrease in their speed of fall v. As soon as the values of v, u_+ and u_- become comparable, coefficient σ_+ starts to grow rapidly as v approaches u_+, and coefficient $\sigma_- \to 0$ for $v \to u_-$ (see (11) and (12)). Thus, when averaging a large number of cases for low precipitation intensities I we observe with a decrease in I an increase in the averaged washout coefficient σ, accompanied by some scatter of individual experimental values of the washout coefficient in this range of values of I.

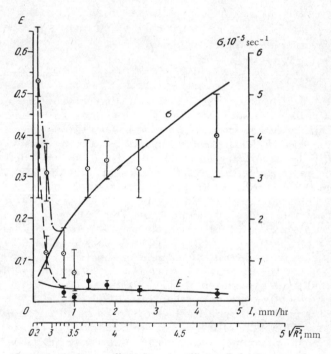

FIGURE 2. Washout coefficient σ and coefficient E of radioactive dust particle capture by raindrops as a function of rain intensity I and mean-square drop radius $\sqrt{\overline{R^2}}$.

These features of the dependence of σ on I must also affect the behavior of the coefficient E of radioactive dust particle capture by raindrops. In order to pass from σ to E we can use formulas (11) and (12). If we neglect vertical currents, these formulas yield

$$E = \frac{4}{3} \frac{\overline{R^3}}{\overline{R^2}} \frac{\sigma}{I}. \tag{13}$$

159

The ratio $\overline{R^3}/\overline{R^2}$ can be expressed analytically in terms of I by using the raindrop-size distribution function of Polyakov and Shifrin /13/

$$f(R) = A(2R)^2 \exp(-2\gamma R), \tag{14}$$

where A is a constant. Then, adopting the value $\gamma = 4.87 \cdot I^{0.2}\,\text{mm}^{-1}$ (I in mm/hr), determined experimentally in /6/, we obtain $\overline{R^3}/\overline{R^2} = 0.515 \cdot I^{0.2}\,\text{mm}$. Substitution of this value in (13) yields the dependence of E on I (dashed curve on Figure 2). The vertical lines near the experimental points represent the standard errors. The values of the mean-square drop radius, corresponding to the given intensity and calculated by formula (14), are marked on the abscissa axis. The solid curve represents the theoretical curve /5/

$$E = \frac{a_1}{\sqrt{u_\infty R}}, \tag{15}$$

where u_∞ is given by the empirical formula

$$u_\infty = 912\,R^{-0.25-0.40\log R}. \tag{16}$$

Since theoretical difficulties prevent us from guaranteeing the accuracy of the theoretically calculated constant a_1, this value was estimated experimentally by trial and error until curve (15) passed through the experimental points. For $a_1 = 0.115$ the theoretical curve (as seen from Figure 2) is in agreement with the experimental values of E for $I > 0.7\,\text{mm/hr}$. For lower values of I the capture coefficient increases sharply with decreasing I and diverges from the theoretical curve. It is in this region that the part played by ascending air currents increases.

The experimental values of σ from Table 1 have been marked for comparison on Figure 2, while the unbroken curve represents the theoretical relationship $\sigma(I)$, plotted by formula (13) allowing for (14)—(16). As in the preceding case, satisfactory agreement is observed between the experimental data and the theoretical curve for $I > 0.7\,\text{mm/hr}$, while with decreasing intensity the experimental curve begins to rise steeply and diverge from the monotonically decreasing theoretical curve.

It is noteworthy that for small values of $I \sim 1\,\text{mm/hr}$ the relation between R and I possesses low reliability, due to the considerable experimental difficulties. Accordingly, our calculations for this range are to be regarded as qualitative estimates.

3. ATMOSPHERIC WASHOUT OF NATURAL RADIOACTIVITY

The natural radioactivity of precipitation at the Terskol peak and in the Azau valley was measured already in 1956 and 1957 by Solodikhina /8, 15/. However, almost all the measurements on the peak and in the valley were not conducted simultaneously; this throws doubt on our conclusion regarding the existence of a washout effect. Doubts as to the existence of a washout effect of natural radioactivity from the subcloud layer of the atmosphere were formulated earlier by Styro /16/.

TABLE 2. Frequency (%) of the washout coefficient of short-lived natural radioactivity for different types of precipitation

$\sigma, 10^{-5} sec^{-1}$	Positive values				Negative values			
	rain		snow		rain		snow	
	steady	shower	steady	shower	steady	shower	steady	shower
0−1	16	5	23	14	18	8	12	3
1−2	9	4	6	10	9	4	5	13
2−3	4	4	5	7	3	−	3	7
3−4	4	13	6	7	2	−	3	7
4−5	−	−	5	3	1	4	2	7
5−6	2	−	2	−	3	−	−	−
6−7	2	−	2	−	2	4	−	−
7−8	1	−	2	3	2	4	2	3
8−9	2	−	5	−	1	8	−	−
9−10	−	4	−	−	1	4	−	3
> 10	6	17	10	3	12	17	7	10
Total	46	47	66	47	54	53	34	53
Number of cases	62	11	26	14	72	13	13	16

During the summer and autumn months of 1968 and 1969 we sampled simultaneously precipitation and air on the peak and in the valley, simultaneity being ensured by means of radiotelephone communication between these points. The washout coefficient of the short-lived decay products of radon was calculated by formula (3) for the different types of precipitation. It was found that the concentration of natural radioactivity in the precipitation collected in the valley can be both smaller and larger than that observed on the peak. Therefore, the washout coefficient can assume both positive and negative values. Table 2 tabulates the frequency of the different values of σ for different types of precipitation, expressed in percent of the total number of cases of the given type of precipitation. It is seen that only in steady snowfalls are negative values of σ encountered half as often as positive values. For all other types of precipitation, negative and positive values occur with roughly the same frequency.

The above pattern is explained by the relatively short sample-collection duration (~ 1 min), which cannot be increased considerably due to the rapid decay of the short-lived daughter products of radon. The short sample-collection duration leads to a sharp increase in the influence of fluctuations in natural radioactivity concentration in precipitation and in air, and also to fluctuations in precipitation intensity. This leads to such a great increase in measurement error that it becomes impossible to determine the washout coefficient in this manner. For example, according to /7/, minute-long measurements of precipitation intensity in the Azau valley indicate that the fluctuations in this quantity differ from the mean value by as much as a factor of 10. Some notion of the fluctuations in the specific radioactivity of precipitation is given by Figure 3, which presents the distribution function of this quantity divided by the specific radioactivity C_0 observed at the beginning of the rain. The variance of this (near-lognormal) curve is equal to unity, the total number of experimental points being 313. We can also conclude from Figure 3 that the mean concentration of short-lived decay products of radon in precipitation does not change during their fall. This follows from the agreement between the maximum of the distribution of C/C_0 and the ordinate axis, since the precipitation samples were collected roughly uniformly throughout the duration of their fall. Attempts at a direct plotting of the dependence of C on time for the individual rains show that such a relationship cannot be detected against the background of the large fluctuations in the measured quantity; this corroborates Styro's earlier conclusions /16/ on the basis of a relatively small amount of experimental data. In the case of steady snow, when the washout effect is large, the frequency of positive values of σ starts to exceed that of negative values. This enables us to assess the value of σ at $9 \cdot 10^{-5}\,\text{sec}^{-1}$. The standard error of this magnitude, found as the arithmetic mean of the results of 39 measurements, is 95%. Thus the effect of natural radioactivity washout from the subcloud layer of the atmosphere nevertheless exists, and further efforts are needed in order to develop a procedure for its measurement.

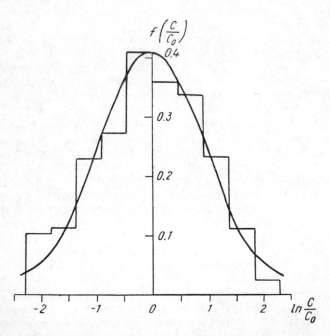

FIGURE 3. Distribution function of short-lived decay products of radon by concentration in precipitation. The histogram represents experimental data, and the solid curve the lognormal distribution.

4. NATURAL RADIOACTIVITY OF PRECIPITATION AND AIR AS A FUNCTION OF WIND DIRECTION

Parallel measurements of wind direction and the radioactivity of air and precipitation, conducted while studying washout in 1968–1969 on the Terskol peak, enabled us to obtain the dependence of the concentration of short-lived decay products of radon in precipitation and in air on wind direction. The collection of individual rain samples lasted about 1 minute, but since the drop radioactivation takes place mainly in the cloud and the duration of that process is of the order of 1 hour /10, 11, 16/, we selected for analysis the wind direction during the last hour.

The mean specific rain radioactivity $\overline{C}_i$ was calculated for the i-th wind direction by the following formula (notation as in (4)):

$$\overline{C}_i = \sum_{n=1}^{m} C_n P_{ni} \left(\sum_{n=1}^{m} P_{ni} \right)^{-1}. \qquad (17)$$

In the calculations, the initial data were grouped by similar values of the precipitation intensity I. The results of processing the data on the radioactivity of 130 samples of steady rain are presented in Table 3. The natural radioactivity of the precipitation for winds from the west, northwest and north is noticeably lower than for winds of opposite direction. This pattern is explained by the fact that the zone of glaciers with lower exhalation is located on that side. This zone begins several kilometers from the Terskol peak. If the mean speed of motion of the precipitation zone is taken as $10 \, \text{km/hr}$ /17/ and the lifetime of the cloud-borne drops as $\sim 1 \, \text{hour}$, the precipitation falling at the observation point for winds from the west, northwest and north is found to be formed roughly in the central part of the El'brus glacier, where the air is impoverished of short-lived decay products of radon.

TABLE 3. Dependence of the concentration of short-lived decay products of radon in steady rain $C \, (10^{-11} \, \text{curie/cm}^3)$ on wind direction and precipitation intensity

I, mm/hr	Wind direction, i								$C (I)$
	N	NW	W	SW	S	SE	E	NE	
0.05–0.07	2.58	2.52	2.92	3.38	4.50	4.47	4.01	3.23	3.5
0.1	2.31	2.14	2.55	2.98	4.34	4.57	4.64	3.70	3.4
0.2	2.80	2.80	4.47	5.71	6.19	4.97	2.80	2.80	4.1
0.3	3.23	1.11	2.64	4.12	3.39	4.40	4.14	4.92	3.5
0.4	1.40	0.83	0.68	1.65	2.42	2.81	2.98	2.73	1.9
0.5	2.06	2.27	1.15	2.38	4.99	7.26	7.58	4.11	4
0.6	3.31	3.26	4.69	2.51	4.59	5.05	2.61	3.00	3.6
0.7	2.30	0.78	1.05	2.29	3.04	2.95	3.17	1.96	2.2
0.8	0.74	0.81	2.17	4.50	4.04	3.88	3.97	3.21	2.9
0.9	1.06	1.54	3.00	3.20	6.00	4.85	5.00	4.45	3.6
1–1.5	2.58	1.29	0.82	1.62	2.85	4.95	5.90	5.65	3.2
1.6–2	1.68	1.63	1.30	2.25	3.81	4.49	4.28	2.34	2.7
2.1–3	2.15	1.79	1.82	1.50	0.91	2.17	1.85	1.49	1.7
3.1–3.7	0.7	0.43	0.58	0.78	1.58	2.30	2.85	2.23	1.4
5.1–6.2	1.68	0.80	0.81	1.96	4.56	5.29	3.69	3.18	2.7
9.2–10.5	2.15	2.69	2.18	1.85	1.55	1.56	1.56	1.72	1.9
Average	2.0	1.7	2.0	2.7	3.7	4.1	3.8	3.2	2.9

Similarly, we studied the concentration of short-lived decay products of radon in the ground air at the Terskol peak. In all 135 air samples were subjected to statistical processing. The sampling duration was no less than two hours. The wind direction was taken into account for the last two hours before the end of sampling, since the natural radioactivity of earlier portions of filtered air up to the time of measurement had already practically decayed.

The decrease in the concentration of natural radioactivity in air for winds from the northwest did not exceed 20%, compared with winds from a southeastern direction. This is explained by the rapid restoration of the deficit of short-lived decay products of radon in the ground air during its motion from the boundary of the glacier zone to the Terskol peak above the snow-free slopes of El'brus.

Thus, the concentration of short-lived decay products of radon in the ground layer is mainly affected by exhalation within a radius of several kilometers, while the concentration in precipitation is affected within a radius of tens of kilometers.

The last column of Table 3 gives the calculated mean concentration of natural radioactivity in precipitation for different intensities. From Figure 4, on which these experimental data have been plotted, we see that in spite of the large scatter of individual values of C they are arranged satisfactorily on a straight line on a log-log plot. The corresponding empirical formula has the form

$$C = 0.43 \, I^{-0.13}, \quad 10^{-11} \, \text{curie/cm}^3, \tag{18}$$

where I is expressed in mm/hr. Thus, our data corroborate the decrease in the concentration of natural radioactivity in precipitation with its increasing intensity, as observed in /15/ on the basis of a limited amount of data obtained on the Terskol peak.

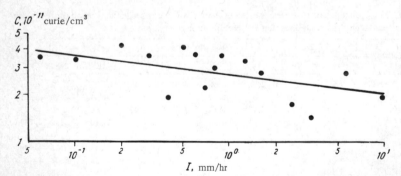

FIGURE 4. Concentration of natural radioactivity in steady rain as a function of its intensity.

The authors express their gratitude to the administration of the High-Altitude Geophysical Institute on whose territory these studies were conducted, and to the staff of the Institute for their help.

BIBLIOGRAPHY

1. B u r t s e v , I.I. O vymyvanii osadkami iskusstvennykh radioaktivnykh aerozolei iz atmosfery (On the Precipitation Washout of Artificial Radioactive Aerosols from the Atmosphere).— In: Radioaktivnye izotopy v atmosfere i ikh ispol'zovanie v meteorologii (Radioactive Isotopes in the Atmosphere and their Utilization in Meteorology). Moskva, Atomizdat. 1965.

2. B u r t s e v , I.I. and S.G.M a l a k h o v. Vymyvanie osadkami produktov deleniya iz podoblachnogo sloya atmosfery (Precipitation Washout of Fission Products from the Subcloud Layer of the Atmosphere).— Izvestiya AN SSSR, Fizika Atmosfery i Okeana, Vol.4, No.3. 1968.

3. V o r o n t s o v , P.A. Aerologicheskie issledovaniya pogranichnogo sloya atmosfery (Aerological Study of the Boundary Layer of the Atmosphere).— Leningrad, Gidrometeoizdat. 1960.

4. D a v y d o v , E.N., S.G.M a l a k h o v, K.P.M a k h o n ' k o, and S.T.M a s h k o v. Fil'truyushchie ustanovki dlya opredeleniya kontsentratsii radioaktivnoi pyli v prizemnoi atmosfere (Filtering Units for the Determination of Radioactive Dust Concentrations Near the Ground).— Trudy IEM, No.2. 1969.

5. Z i m i n , A.G. Mekhanizmy zakhvata i osazhdeniya atmosfernykh primesei oblakami i osadkami (Mechanisms of Capture and Deposition of Atmospheric Contaminant by Clouds and Precipitation).— In: Voprosy yadernoi meteorologii (Problems of Nuclear Meteorology). Moskva, Gosatomizdat. 1962.

6. L i t v i n o v , I.V. O funktsii raspredeleniya chastits zhidkikh osadkov (Raindrop Distribution Function).— Izvestiya AN SSSR, Seriya Geofizicheskaya, No.6. 1957.

7. L i t v i n o v , I.V. Metodicheskie voprosy izucheniya spektral'nogo raspredeleniya chastits osadkov (Methodological Questions in the Study of the Spectral Distribution of Raindrops).— Trudy El'brusskoi Vysokogornoi Ekspeditsii, Vol.2. 1961.

8. M a l a k h o v , S.G. and L.D.S o l o d i k h i n a. O vymyvanii dozhdem produktov raspada radona iz atmosfery (Rain Washout of Decay Products of Radon from the Atmosphere).— In: Voprosy yadernoi meteorologii (Problems of Nuclear Meteorology). Moskva, Gosatomizdat. 1962.

9. M a k h o n ' k o , K.P. Vymyvanie radioaktivnoi pyli iz atmosfery (Washout of Radioactive Dust from the Atmosphere).— Izvestiya AN SSSR, Seriya Geofizicheskaya, No.4. 1964.

10. M a k h o n ' k o , K.P. Opredelenie parametrov vymyvaniya produktov deleniya iz atmosfery (Determination of Parameters of Fission Product Washout from the Atmosphere).— Izvestiya AN SSSR, Seriya Geofizicheskaya, No.9. 1964.

11. M a k h o n ' k o , K.P. Samoochishchenie nizhnei troposfery ot radioaktivnoi pyli (Radioactive Dust Scavenging in the Lower Troposphere).— Izvestiya AN SSSR, Fizika Atmosfery i Okeana, Vol.2, No.5. 1966.

12. M a s o n , B.J. The Physics of Clouds. Oxford. 1957.

13. P o l y a k o v a , E.A. and K.S.S h i f r i n. Mikrostruktura i prozrachnost' dozhdei (Microstructure and Transmission of Rain).— Trudy GGO, No.42(104). 1953.

14. S e l e z n e v a , E.S. Mestnye periodicheskie vetry v gorakh (Local Periodic Winds in Mountains).— Izvestiya AN SSSR, Seriya Geofizicheskaya i Geograficheskaya, Nos.4—5. 1939.

15. S o l o d i k h i n a , L.D. O estestvennoi radioaktivnosti atmosfernykh osadkov (Natural Radioactivity of Atmospheric Precipitation).— Izvestiya AN SSSR, Seriya Geofizicheskaya, No.2. 1959.

16. S t y r o , B.I. Voprosy yadernoi meteorologii (Problems of Nuclear Meteorology).— Vilnius, Izd. AN LitSSR. 1959.

17. S u l a k v e l i d z e , G.K. Rainstorms and Hail.— Israel Program for Scientific Translations, Jerusalem. 1969.

18. K h r g i a n , A.Kh. Aerologicheskoe issledovanie gorno-dolinnykh vetrov (Aerological Study of Mountain and Valley Winds).— Trudy TsAO, No.2. 1947.

19. T s e v e l e v , M.A., P.I.C h a l o v, and K.P.M a k h o n ' k o. Izuchenie zakonomernostei vymyvaniya radioaktivnykh produktov deleniya v gorakh i predgor'yakh (Study on Patterns of Radioactive Fission Product Washout in Mountains and Foothills).— Trudy IEM, No.5. 1969.

20. C h a l o v , P.I. and M.A.T s e v e l e v. O vymyvanii radioaktivnykh aerozolei atmosfernymi osadkami v podoblachnom sloe (Washout of Radioactive Aerosols by Atmospheric Precipitation in the Subcloud Layer).— Izvestiya AN SSSR, Fizika Atmosfery i Okeana, Vol.2, No.2. 1966.

21. I t a g a k i , K. and S.K o e n u m a. Altitude Distribution of Fallout Contained in Rain and Snow.— J. Geophys. Res., Vol.67, No.3927. 1962.

22. R e i t e r , R. Felder, Ströme und Aerosole in der unteren Troposphäre. Darmstadt. 1964.

165

UDC 551.510.71

UTILIZATION OF NATURAL RADIOACTIVE SUBSTANCES IN THE STUDY OF TURBULENT EXCHANGE AND ATMOSPHERIC SCAVENGING BY MEANS OF GROUND MEASUREMENTS

V. N. Bakulin, E. E. Sen'ko, B. G. Starikov,
and V. A. Trufakin

On the basis of round-the-clock measurements of the exhalation of thoron and the concentrations of thoron and Pb^{212}(ThB) at heights of 1 and 5 m, we obtained mean values of the growth rate of the turbulence coefficient with height in a summer anticyclone, equal to 5–10 cm/sec by day and about 3 cm/sec at night. It is shown that these data enable one to evaluate the mean value of the turbulence coefficient in the lower km layer of the troposphere with the aid of ground measurements. It is shown that, unlike thoron and Pb^{212}(ThB), radon cannot be considered as existing in quasi-steady conditions, and we must use nonsteady models of its behavior in the atmosphere.

Near the earth, the ratio between the decay products of radon is a good indicator of the time variation in the turbulent exchange. Maximum perturbations of equilibrium in the radon series are observed in the morning and evening, during the establishment and destruction of the night inversions.

It is noteworthy that in the morning hours one can observe many specific features in the height distribution of radioactive substances, explained by the mechanisms of the inversion destruction process.

Data are given about the washout coefficients of radioactive aerosols by precipitation on the basis of Pb^{212}(ThB), radon and Pb^{210}(RaD) concentration measurements.

INTRODUCTION

Radioactive emanations and their decay products are widely used at present as permanent natural tracers in the study of turbulent diffusion and transfer processes. However, the quantitative interpretation of the space and time variation in the concentration of radioactive substances encounters mathematical difficulties pertaining to the nonsteady models of their propagation.

Therefore, in every case it is necessary to first investigate the applicability of simpler steady solutions to the differential equation governing radioactive emanations and daughter products in the atmosphere:

$$\frac{\partial q_i}{\partial t} = \frac{1}{\rho} \frac{\partial}{\partial z} \left(K_z \rho \frac{\partial q_i}{\partial z} \right) - \lambda_i q_i + \lambda_{i-1} q_{i-1}.$$

This can be done by comparing the corresponding nonsteady solution to the given equation (if known) with the steady models or, as suggested by Belekhova and Karol' /5/, by examining the possibility of neglecting the nonsteady term

$$L = \frac{1}{q} \frac{\partial q_i}{\partial t} \simeq \frac{2|q_2 - q_1|}{(q_1 + q_2)(t_2 - t_1)}$$

determined for the given time interval from experimental data and characterizing the variability in the concentration of the corresponding isotope compared with the decay constant λ_i. Since vertical soundings of the atmospheric distribution of natural radioactive substances are very expensive and are practically nowhere conducted systematically, it is of interest to examine information about exchange and transfer processes in the lower troposphere, obtainable from ground measurements.

PROCEDURE OF THE EXPERIMENT

Measurements of the concentrations of thoron and its decay products were conducted round the clock at heights of 1 and 5 m by means of two 360-liter decay chambers (described in /9/), with a percolation rate of 180 liters/min. The filter diameters were 9 cm and the exposure time 3 hr. The ThB concentration was determined from the β-activity of the first filter 5 hours after the end of the percolation, and that of thoron from the activity of the second filter. In addition, the thoron exhalation was measured simultaneously by an installation combining a Pearson collector and the discharge chamber /9, 14/.

The radon concentrations were determined at a height of 1 m by adsorption on cooled activated coal from a 300-liter sample.

The short-lived decay products of radon were collected on FPP-15 cellulose filters at a linear speed of 20–50 cm/sec at heights of 1, 11 and 20 m every one or two hours round the clock. After 20 minutes of air collection the α-activity decay curve was recorded in the course of one hour.

For the separate determination of the Po^{218} (RaA), Pb^{214} (RaB) and Bi^{214} (RaC) concentrations in air from the decay curve, we developed a special procedure, representing an analytical analog of Malakhov's graphic method /3/.

A filtering installation of output $1,500 \text{ m}^3/\text{hr}$ was used in the determination of the Pb^{210} (RaD) concentration. The air samples averaged for two days were subjected to standard radiochemical treatment /4/ with subsequent β-activity counting.

Besides, the wind speed at a height of 1 m (v_1) and the temperature gradient Δt° at heights of 0.5 and 2 m were measured systematically, making it possible to calculate the turbulence coefficient at a height of 1 m for convective conditions by the formula /8/

$$K = 0.0305 \, v_1 \left(1 + 15.4 \, \frac{\Delta t}{v_1^2} \right),$$

while for indifferent stratification or for inversion conditions in the presence of wind we used the Rossby formula

$$K = 0.38^2 \, \frac{v_1^2}{\ln \left[(z + z_0)/z_0 \right]} \, (z + z_0).$$

RESULTS OF MEASUREMENTS

For thoron (Rn^{220}) $\lambda = 1.272 \cdot 10^{-2} \sec^{-1}$. This is much larger than the nonsteady term L, which according to our data has at heights of 1 and 5 m a maximum value in the morning and evening (up to $0.8 \cdot 10^{-4} \sec^{-1}$) and a somewhat smaller value during the day and night. It follows from the nonsteady solution to the equation of radioactive emanation propagation that steady distributions are established after a time of the order of the half-decay period of the radioactive tracer. Hence, from the standpoint of an investigation into diurnal fluctuations in the intensity of turbulent exchange, thoron is undoubtedly under quasi-steady conditions. The possibilities offered by thoron, whose vertical distribution reflects the instantaneous profile of the turbulence coefficient, are not used widely, since air must be collected for hours in order to determine its concentration /2, 10−12/.

In view of the short half-decay period ($\tau = 54 \sec$), thoron is not observed above several tens of meters from its source (earth) and its vertical distribution is determined only from the profile of the turbulence coefficient in a boundary layer several tens of meters thick. In this layer the coefficient of vertical turbulent mixing is usually considered in a first approximation as growing linearly with height: $K_z = K_0 + Kz$ where K_0 is the turbulence coefficient at ground level and K the growth rate of the turbulence coefficient with altitude. In the calculations we assumed K_0 equal to the coefficient of molecular diffusion.

In our experiments we measured simultaneously thoron concentrations S_1 and S_5 at heights of 1 and 5 m, and also its exhalation E, which makes it possible to determine K in three ways (from $\dfrac{S_1}{S_5}$, $\dfrac{S_1}{E}$ and $\dfrac{S_5}{E}$). The methods of K determination are known /2, 5/.

The three estimates give similar results, indicating that this model of the turbulence coefficient profile is indeed correct. The mean value of K obtained under summer anticyclone conditions was found to be 5−10 cm/sec by day and about 3 cm/sec at night. The value of K was determined simultaneously from the wind speed and temperature gradient. Within the accuracy limits it coincided with the data obtained using thoron, and only in the morning hours during the inversion destruction was it three to four times higher than the value of K determined from the thoron profile.

For Pb^{212} (ThB) $\lambda = 1.816 \cdot 10^{-5} \sec^{-1}$. The nonsteady term L by day and night is as a rule not larger than $1.4 \cdot 10^{-6} \sec^{-1}$, and in the morning and evening hours not larger than $0.8 \cdot 10^{-4} \sec^{-1}$. It follows from the solution to the nonsteady equation of Pb^{212} propagation /7/ that near the earth half of the steady concentration of Pb^{212} is established in three hours. Hence, when collecting air samples during a period of 2−3 hours, the Pb^{212} concentration differs by no more than a factor of two from the steady concentration, and for day and night conditions can be considered in a first approximation as subjected to quasi-steady conditions.

According to the calculations, the vertical distribution of Pb^{212} depends little on the boundary layer, and is determined by the mean value of the turbulence coefficient in the ground layer up to several hundred meters /1, 5/. Therefore, knowing the concentration of thoron and Pb^{212} at heights of 1 and 5 m, we could calculate to within 50% the value of this mean turbulence coefficient in the lower tropospheric layer, roughly one kilometer thick.

This value of K for diurnal conditions of the summer anticyclone was found to be between 10 and $40\,\mathrm{m^2/sec}$, and at night between 1 and $4\,\mathrm{m^2/sec}$. It is thus possible to estimate the value of the turbulence coefficient in the ground layer from simultaneous ground measurements of Th and Pb^{212} at two altitudes.

When determining the washout coefficient of radioactive aerosols from the decrease in Pb^{212} concentration near the ground during precipitation, we must remember that, according to the obtained data, Th exhalation during rainfall decreases very rapidly and is practically interrupted. The decrease in Pb^{212} concentration near the ground is caused not only by the washout, but also by the decay and by its diffusion flux upward. Calculations showed that utilization of the exponential law of Pb^{212} washout leads to an overestimated washout coefficient by a factor of 1.5 to 4. Reliable determination of the washout coefficient $\sigma(\mathrm{sec^{-1}})$ from Pb^{212} is possible only when σ is not smaller than its decay constant. Allowance for these effects in the case of storm rains yielded values of σ between $2\cdot10^{-5}$ and $4\cdot10^{-5}\,\mathrm{sec^{-1}}$ /2/.

For radon $(\mathrm{Rn^{222}})$ $\lambda = 2.097\cdot10^{-6}\,\mathrm{sec^{-1}}$. The nonsteady term L at heights of up to several km is as a rule no smaller than $3\cdot10^{-5}\,\mathrm{sec^{-1}}$, so that radon or the total concentration in air of its decay products can be used for estimating the turbulence parameters from the steady distribution only in very rare cases, when we analyze all possible errors associated with the influence of advection, the diurnal cycle of turbulent exchange, the passage of fronts, ascending currents, and clouds.

Nearest to the actual values will be estimates of the turbulence parameters obtained with the aid of published nonsteady solutions to the diffusion equation /1, 7, 13/.

However, such estimates are possible only with the aid of aircraft sounding results, while ground measurements of the exhalation and concentration of radon alone cannot yield quantitative information about the structure and the time cycle of the turbulence.

According to our data, a good indicator in the ground layer of the time cycle of the turbulence coefficient and the rate of radon entry in the atmosphere is the ratio between the short-lived decay products of radon.

Figure 1 presents characteristic diurnal cycles of the radon decay product concentrations and their ratios. Maximum disturbance of the equilibrium is observed in the evening hours (beginning of the inversion).

On some days at about 1400—1500 hrs one can see another maximum of the disturbance of equilibrium, observed also from the change in Po^{218} (RaA) concentration. This maximum corresponds in our opinion to a decrease in the convective component of turbulence during the development of cloudiness.

Figure 2 represents the averaged diurnal variation of the radon decay product concentration at heights of 1, 10, 20 m in the summer anticyclones of 1966—1967.

Of particular interest is the growth in the concentration of the decay products of radon with height in the morning hours, noted by other investigators as well. There exist three possible explanations of this effect: variation in filter efficiency with height, increased flux of radioactive aerosols to the ground as a result of their dry deposition, and height-limited

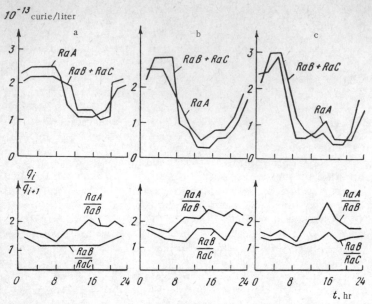

FIGURE 1. Averaged diurnal cycle of thoron decay product concentrations and their ratios at a height of 1 m in 1965:

a) winter, field; b) June, forest; c) June, field.

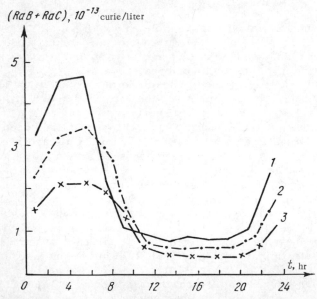

FIGURE 2. Averaged diurnal cycle of RaB + RaC concentration at various heights:

1) 1 m; 2) 10 m; 3) 20 m.

vertical air displacements leading to periodical breaks upward by several meters of ground air parcels enriched by fresh radon. We regard the latter explanation as most probable, especially as this effect is also observed from changes in radon concentration /14/ in the morning hours during the destruction of ground inversions.

Attempts to determine the washout coefficient from measurements of the ratio between the radon decay products at ground level showed that it is too small compared with their decay constants, so that the influence of washout is completely masked by the fluctuations in the degree of disturbance of equilibrium in the radon series as a result of the turbulent mixing always accompanying precipitation.

For Pb^{210} (RaD) $\lambda = 1.57 \cdot 10^{-9} sec^{-1}$. The nonsteady term L, according to our data, is about $3 \cdot 10^{-6} sec^{-1}$, so that one cannot utilize steady models for Pb^{210}.

It was found that in periods without precipitation the ratio of the mean-daily concentration of radon to the mean concentration of Pb^{210} for two days is very stable. In winter and summer it lies in the range $n = (1-2) \cdot 10^4$, which gives the mean coefficient of Pb^{210} washout from the troposphere, according to Karol's calculations /6/, as

$$\sigma = (0.5 - 1.5)10^{-5} sec^{-1}$$

Analysis of 19 cases with daily precipitation amounts r not smaller than 5 mm, under the assumption of an exponential washout law $q = q_0 e^{-r\delta}$, yielded a mean coefficient of Pb^{210} washout by precipitation $\delta = (5 \pm 2) \times 10^{-3} mm^{-1}$. Unfortunately, the period of air collection for the determination of the Pb^{210} concentration exceeds severalfold the duration of the precipitation, and it is impossible to estimate what part of the drop in Pb^{210} concentration at ground level belongs to the precipitation itself, and what part to the increase in the direct ("dry") deposition of aerosols on wet earth, grass and trees after the rain.

For an annual precipitation of 600 mm we obtain a mean washout coefficient by precipitation $\sigma = 10^{-7} sec^{-1}$, which is much smaller than the total washout coefficient in the lower troposphere.

BIBLIOGRAPHY

1. B a k u l i n , V.N. Vliyanie sutochnogo khoda koeffitsienta turbulentnogo obmena na kontsentratsii Rn, Tn, An i produktov ikh raspada v atmosfere (Effect of the Diurnal Variation in the Turbulent Exchange Coefficient on the Concentrations of Rn, Tn, and An and their Decay Products in the Atmosphere).— Izvestiya AN SSSR, Fizika Atmosfery i Okeana, Vol.3, No.2. 1967.

2. B a k u l i n , V.N. and E.E.S e n ' k o. Opredelenie parametrov turbulentnosti po vertikal'nomu raspredeleniyu Tn i ThB v prizemnom sloe (Determination of Turbulence Parameters from the Vertical Distribution of Tn and ThB in the Ground Layer).— Izvestiya AN SSSR, Fizika Atmosfery i Okeana, Vol.4, No.10. 1968.

3. B a k u l i n , V.N. and B.G.S t a r i k o v. Razdel'noe opredelenie v vozdukhe kontsentratsii Rn, RaA, RaB i RaC po krivoi spada α-aktivnosti fil'tra (Separate Determination of Rn, RaA, RaB, and RaC Concentrations in Air from the α-Activity Decay Curve of a Filter). — In this collection.

4. B a r a n o v , V.I. and V.D.V i l e n s k i i. Opredelenie dolgozhivushchikh β-izluchatelei v atmosfernykh vypadeniyakh (Determination of Long-lived β-Emitters in Atmospheric Fallout). — Radiokhimiya, Vol. 4, No. 4. 1962.

5. B e l e k h o v a , N.G. and I.L.K a r o l '. K teorii rasprostraneniya radioaktivnykh emanatsii v prizemnom sloe atmosfery (Theory of Radioactive Emanation Propagation in the Ground Layer of the Atmosphere).— Izvestiya AN SSSR, Fizika Atmosfery i Okeana, Vol.3, No.7. 1967.

6. K a r o l ', I.L. Otsenka srednei skorosti udaleniya estestvennykh radioaktivnykh aerozolei iz atmosfery oblakami i osadkami (Estimation of the Mean Removal Rate of Natural Radioactive Aerosols from the Atmosphere by Clouds and Precipitation).— Izvestiya AN SSSR, Seriya Geofizicheskaya, No.11. 1963.

7. M a l a k h o v , S.G. and V.N.B a k u l i n. Vliyanie kolebanii ekskhalyatsii radona i torona na izmenenie kontsentratsii etikh emanatsii i ikh dochernikh produktov v atmosfere (Effect of Variations in Radon and Thoron Exhalation on the Concentration Changes of these Emanations and their Daughter Products in the Atmosphere).— Izvestiya AN SSSR, Fizika Atmosfery i Okeana, Vol.3, No.7. 1967.

8. R a s t o r g u e v a , G.P. O raschetakh koeffitsienta turbulentnogo obmena po gradientnym dannym (Computation of the Turbulent Exchange Coefficient from Gradient Data).— Trudy GGO, No.158. 1964.

9. S e n ' k o, E.E. Ekskhalyatsiya torona i soderzhanie ego v atmosfere (Exhalation of Thoron and its Abundance in the Atmosphere).— Izvestiya AN SSSR, Fizika Atmosfery i Okeana, Vol.3, No.9. 1967.

10. G r o z i e r, W.D. and N.B i l e s. Measurements of Radon-220 (Thoron) in the Atmosphere below 50 cm.— J. Geophys. Res., Vol.71, No.20. 1966.

11. I s r a e l, G.M. Thoron (Rn-220) Measurements in the Atmosphere and their Application in Meteorology.— Tellus, Vol.17, No.3. 1965.

12. J a c o b i, W. Der Thorongehalt der bodennahen Luftschicht.— Atomkernenergie, Vol.10, Nos.11—12. 1965.

13. M a l a k h o v, S.G., V.N.B a k u l i n, G.V.D m i t r i e v a, L.V.K i r i c h e n k o, T.I.S s i s s i g i n a, and B.G.S t a r i k o v. Diurnal Variations of Radon and Thoron Decay Product Concentrations in the Surface Layer of the Atmosphere and their Washout by Precipitations. — Tellus, Vol.18, Nos.2—3, pp.643—654. 1966.

14. P e a r s o n, I.E. Natural Environmental Radioactivity from Radon-222.— Public Health Service Publication, No.999-PH-26. 1967.

UDC 551.577.7

SOME FEATURES OF ATMOSPHERIC CLEANSING BY GROUND CONDENSATION

B. I. Styro and N. P. Dargene

Simultaneous measurements were conducted of the radioactivity of air and dew samples formed on the upper and lower surfaces of a polyethylene film spread on closely cut grass. The dew samples were collected in two ways: 1) several identical films were spread simultaneously on the grass surface, the sample from the first film being taken immediately after the formation of the dew with subsequent sampling at hourly intervals throughout the night; 2) a single polyethylene film on the selected area was changed hourly and the radioactivity of the dew formed on it determined. The dew samples collected by the two methods were called "old" and "new" dew, respectively. The short-lived α-radioactivity of the dew due to the decay of $_{84}Po^{218}$, $_{82}Pb^{214}$ and $_{83}Bi^{214}$ was determined. For old dew they lie in the range $(0.1-24.5) \cdot 10^{-11}$ curie/mliter, and for the new dew in the range $(0.1-26) \cdot 10^{-11}$ curie/mliter. The parameter of radioactivity removal from the air during the fall of dew is $(0.02-1) \cdot 10^{-4} sec^{-1}$ for old dew and $(0.3-1) \cdot 10^{-4} sec^{-1}$ for new dew. A parabolic relationship was obtained between the specific radioactivity of new dew and the specific radioactivity of the air, which points to the growth in washout intensity with increasing air radioactivity. The specific radioactivity and the coefficient of nonradioactive removal of radioactive substances by old dew was studied as a function of the amount of fallen dew. It was concluded that atmospheric cleansing occurs mainly: 1) through direct condensation of water vapor on radioactive aerosols; 2) under the influence of electric interactions between the aerosol particles and the dewdrops.

INTRODUCTION

In 1910 Negro /6/ established that dew is radioactive, and Holzapfel, Delafield and Cox /5/ detected that artificially obtained dew has a higher radioactivity. Subsequently Manolov /3/ obtained data on the long-lived β-radioactivity of the dew, which was found to equal $0.19 \cdot 10^{-9}$ curie/liter, and after four months remained as high as $0.14 \cdot 10^{-9}$ curie/liter. Comparison of the radioactivity of the air and dew led to the conclusion that the different types of hydrocondensates are substantial deactivators of the ground layer of the atmosphere.

2. EXPERIMENT

The dew samples were collected by us on a polyethylene film spread on closely cropped grass. A condensate appeared simultaneously on the film and on the uncovered grass. Dew was deposited on both the upper and lower sides of the film. Dew samples were collected in two ways. First, several identical films were spread simultaneously on the grass surface. The first sample was taken immediately after the formation of the dew, the second one an hour later, the third after another hour, and so on throughout the night. Second, on the selected area the polyethylene film was changed every hour, and the radioactivity of the dew formed on it was determined.

Below we shall call the first samples "old" dew, and the samples taken by the second procedure "new" dew.

The collected liquid was evaporated on a polished steel plate to which was applied a lacquer (5 g benzene, 0.4 g polystyrene, 0.1 g paraffin) ring restricting the evaporation area.

In addition to the dew samples, samples of the air radioactivity were taken by passing it through an LFS-1 filter at a linear rate of $2-3$ m/sec in the course of 10 min with a capture efficiency of 70%. The dew and air samples were brought in contact with A-2 nuclear emulsions. The exposure time was 4 hours, which made it possible to measure the radioactivity of the short-lived decay products of radon. In a number of experiments the radioactivity was measured by means of an RV-4 radiometer.

The preparation of nuclear emulsions for work and their photographic processing were conducted by the method described in /2/. The original thickness of the emulsions was restored by soaking them for two hours in a 20% solution of glycerin at 21°C. The α-tracks were counted under an MBI-3 microscope with 630-fold magnification.

3. PROCESSING OF EXPERIMENTAL RESULTS

Since the air radioactivity samples were taken on the ground, we assumed that radioactive equilibrium is not achieved between Rn and its decay products. When processing measurements of the activity of short-lived radon decay products in the air we obtained data on the isotopic composition by plotting experimental curves and comparing them with theoretical curves.

The following assumptions were made when calculating the value of the short-lived dew radioactivity:

1) We assumed radioactive equilibrium between the short-lived decay products of radon, since relatively small dew samples gave a large scatter in the determination of the radioactive decay curves. Vaporization of large dew samples necessitated considerable time, while we had to conduct the measurements during the first 15 min, when the decay curve varies most rapidly.

2) We selected time $T = 0$ at the beginning of dew formation.

3) It was assumed that the change of dew radioactivity during its exposure occurs both as a result of the capture of radioactive aerosols from the air at a rate averaged over the exposure time, and as a result of the radioactive decay of the substances captured by the dew.

4) During sampling, sample preparation, and when it is brought into contact with the nuclear emulsion, the concentration of radioactive substances varies, only due to radioactive transformation.

Denoting by N_A, N_B and N_C the concentrations of $_{84}Po^{218}$, $_{82}Pb^{214}$ and $_{83}Bi^{214}$ respectively at time t in the dew sample, and by $N_{A,o}$, $N_{B,o}$ and $N_{C,o}$ the number of atoms of $_{84}Po^{218}$, $_{82}Pb^{214}$ and $_{83}Bi^{214}$ captured by one milliliter dew in time T, we can write the variation in the concentration of radioactive substances in the dew as follows:

$$dN_A = \frac{N_{A,0}}{T}\,dt - \lambda_A N_A\,dt,$$

$$dN_B = \frac{N_{B,0}}{T}\,dt - \lambda_B N_B\,dt + \lambda_A N_A\,dt, \qquad (1)$$

$$dN_C = \frac{N_{C,0}}{T}\,dt - \lambda_C N_C\,dt + \lambda_B N_B\,dt.$$

Integration of the equations from time 0 to T (T is the time from the beginning of dew formation until the dew sample is collected) yields expressions for the concentrations of $_{84}\text{Po}^{218}$, $_{82}\text{Pb}^{214}$ and $_{83}\text{Bi}^{214}$ in the dew at time T:

$$N_A = \frac{N_{A,0}}{T\lambda_A}(1 - e^{-\lambda_A T}),$$

$$N_B = \frac{N_{A,0} + N_{B,0}}{T\lambda_B}(1 - e^{-\lambda_B T}) - \frac{N_{A,0}}{(\lambda_B - \lambda_A)\,T}(e^{-\lambda_A T} - e^{-\lambda_B T}),$$

$$N_C = \frac{N_{A,0} + N_{B,0} + N_{C,0}}{\lambda_C T}(1 - e^{-\lambda_C T}) - \frac{N_{A,0} + N_{B,0}}{T(\lambda_C - \lambda_B)} \times$$

$$\times (e^{-\lambda_B T} - e^{-\lambda_C T}) - \frac{N_{A,0}}{T(\lambda_B - \lambda_A)}\left[\frac{1}{\lambda_C - \lambda_A}(e^{-\lambda_A T} - e^{-\lambda_C T}) - \right.$$

$$\left. - \frac{1}{\lambda_C - \lambda_B}(e^{-\lambda_B T} - e^{-\lambda_C T})\right]. \qquad (2)$$

Some time τ is spent in preparing the sample and bringing it in contact with the nuclear emulsion. Therefore, at the beginning of the exposure the following concentrations of $_{84}\text{Po}^{218}$, $_{82}\text{Pb}^{214}$ and $_{83}\text{Bi}^{214}$ will exist in the sample:

$$N_A(\tau) = N_A e^{-\lambda_A \tau},$$

$$N_B(\tau) = N_B e^{-\lambda_B \tau} + N_A \frac{\lambda_A}{\lambda_B - \lambda_A}(e^{-\lambda_A \tau} - e^{-\lambda_B \tau}),$$

$$N_C(\tau) = N_C e^{-\lambda_C \tau} + N_B \frac{\lambda_B}{\lambda_C - \lambda_B}(e^{-\lambda_B \tau} - e^{-\lambda_C \tau}) +$$

$$+ N_A \lambda_A \lambda_B\left[\frac{e^{-\lambda_A \tau}}{(\lambda_C - \lambda_A)(\lambda_B - \lambda_A)} + \frac{e^{-\lambda_B \tau}}{(\lambda_C - \lambda_B)(\lambda_A - \lambda_B)} + \right. \qquad (3)$$

$$\left. + \frac{e^{-\lambda_C \tau}}{(\lambda_A - \lambda_C)(\lambda_B - \lambda_C)}\right].$$

The exposure time was sufficient for the full decay of the short-lived decay products of radon. Hence the total number of α-tracks on the nuclear plate will be

$$P = \frac{2N_A(\tau) + N_B(\tau) + N_C(\tau)}{2}. \qquad (4)$$

Substituting (2) in (3) and then in (4), and allowing for the assumption of radioactive equilibrium between the short-lived decay products of radon in the dew at the moment of sample collection, we obtain

$$P = \frac{N_{A,0}\lambda_A}{2T}\left\{\frac{1}{\lambda_A^2}\left[1+\frac{\lambda_B\lambda_C}{(\lambda_C-\lambda_A)(\lambda_B-\lambda_A)}\right](1-e^{-\lambda_A T})e^{-\lambda_A \tau}-\right.$$

$$-\frac{\lambda_A\lambda_C}{\lambda_B^2(\lambda_A-\lambda_B)(\lambda_C-\lambda_B)}(1-e^{-\lambda_B T})e^{-\lambda_B \tau}+$$

$$\left.+\frac{\lambda_A\lambda_B}{\lambda_C^2(\lambda_A-\lambda_C)(\lambda_B-\lambda_C)}(1-e^{-\lambda_C T})e^{-\lambda_C \tau}\right\}. \tag{5}$$

The total α-radioactivity of the dew as a result of $_{84}Po^{218}$, $_{82}Pb^{214}$ and $_{83}Bi^{214}$ will be

$$R = 4\lambda_A N_{A,0}, \text{disintegrations/mliter}\cdot\text{sec} = 4.095\cdot 10^{-13} N_{A,0}, \text{curie/mliter}.$$

4. DISCUSSION OF THE RESULTS

Dew acquires radioactivity during condensation phenomena as a result of the air radioactivity, but we do not know which layer of ground air participates in the formation of the dew and the proportion of the moisture removed in the form of dew from the given air volume. We were faced with the problem of determining the parameter of nonradioactive removal Λ and solved it subject to the following assumptions:

1) The dew consists of monodisperse drops.

2) Radioactive aerosols of different dispersity are captured with equal efficiency.

3) The constant of nonradioactive removal Λ is independent of time, and its value is analogous to the radioactivity decay constant.

4) The whole moisture excess appearing as a result of the decrease in temperature is removed in the form of dew.

Under conditions of dew formation the absolute air humidity is near to 100%. If temperature data are available, we can calculate the absolute humidity of the air. The difference between the absolute humidities at the moments of sample collection and dew formation was assumed to equal the amount of moisture removed as dew from $1\,m^3$ air.

If M_A, M_B and M_C denote the number of atoms of $_{84}Po^{218}$, $_{83}Pb^{214}$ and $_{83}Bi^{214}$ in the water removed from $1\,m^3$ ($M_A=kN_{A,0}$, $M_B=kN_{B,0}$, $M_C=kN_{C,0}$, where k is the amount of moisture removed from $1\,m^3$, in mliters), and N_1, N_2 and N_3 denote the number of atoms of $_{84}Po^{218}$, $_{82}Pb^{214}$ and $_{83}Bi^{214}$ in $1\,m^3$ air, then

$$\left.\begin{aligned}dM_A &= \Lambda N_1 dt - \lambda_A M_A dt,\\dM_B &= \Lambda N_2 dt - \lambda_B M_B dt + \lambda_A M_A dt,\\dM_C &= \Lambda N_3 dt - \lambda_C M_C dt + \lambda_B M_B dt.\end{aligned}\right\} \tag{6}$$

Integration gives equations describing the concentrations of $_{84}Po^{218}$, $_{82}Pb^{214}$ and $_{83}Bi^{214}$ in the dew at time T:

$$\left.\begin{aligned}M_A &= \frac{\Lambda}{\lambda_A}(1-e^{-\lambda_A T})N_1,\\M_B &= \frac{\Lambda}{\lambda_B}\left[(1-e^{-\lambda_B T})N_2+\left(1+\frac{\lambda_A e^{-\lambda_B T}-\lambda_B e^{-\lambda_A T}}{\lambda_B-\lambda_A}\right)N_1\right];\end{aligned}\right\} \tag{7}$$

$$M_C = \frac{\Lambda}{\lambda_C} \left\{ (1 - e^{-\lambda_C T}) N_3 + \left(1 + \frac{\lambda_B e^{-\lambda_C T} - \lambda_C e^{-\lambda_B T}}{\lambda_C - \lambda_B} \right) N_2 + \right.$$
$$\left. + \left[1 - \frac{\lambda_A \lambda_B e^{-\lambda_C T}}{(\lambda_C - \lambda_B)(\lambda_C - \lambda_A)} + \frac{\lambda_C}{\lambda_B - \lambda_A} \left(\frac{\lambda_A e^{-\lambda_B T}}{\lambda_C - \lambda_B} - \frac{\lambda_B e^{-\lambda_A T}}{\lambda_C - \lambda_A} \right) \right] N_1 \right\}. \tag{7}$$

Summation of equations (7) yields parameter Λ from the resulting equation. By substituting numerical values, we find the following expressions for determining the parameter of nonradioactive removal of radioactive aerosols from the air by dew:

1) one hour after the beginning of dew formation

$$\Lambda = \frac{(M_A + M_B + M_C) \, 10^{-3}}{3.361 N_1 + 2.629 N_2 + 1.544 N_3},$$

2) two hours after the beginning of dew formation

$$\Lambda = \frac{(M_A + M_B + M_C) \, 10^{-3}}{4.176 N_1 + 2.936 N_2 + 1.734 N_3},$$

3) three and more hours after the beginning of dew formation

$$\Lambda = \frac{(M_A + M_B + M_C) \, 10^{-3}}{4.341 N_1 + 4.078 N_2 + 1.759 N_3}.$$

Table 1 tabulates values of the specific radioactivity of the air, the upper old (u.o) and new (u.n) dew, i. e., the dew formed on the upper surface of the polyethylene, as well as the parameters of nonradioactive removal.

In the search for mechanisms of atmospheric cleansing by ground condensation, we plotted a curve of the specific radioactivity of new dew as a function of the specific radioactivity of the air, employing the averaging of much data and the least squares method. The parabolic curve shows that the specific radioactivity of the dew (Figure 1) increases with increasing specific radioactivity of the air.

Goldsmith, Delafield and Cox /4/ indicate four processes by means of which particles in the atmosphere are captured by cloud-borne droplets:

1) Diffusion capture, resulting from the random motion of aerosol particles with respect to the cloud-borne droplets.

2) Capture under the influence of turbulent diffusion.

3) Direct condensation of drops on radioactive particles.

4) Diffusiophoresis, i. e., the phenomenon of carrying-away of aerosol particles by water vapor molecules diffusing between them.

Besides the factors listed, the capture by cloud-borne droplets of radioactive aerosols is also possible by electric interactions /1/.

The processes listed above also take place during the capture of aerosol particles by dewdrops. In order to clarify which is the dominant mechanism, we plotted a curve of the specific radioactivity of old dew as a function of its quantity, expressed in mm (Figures 2a and b). The straight line obtained by averaging many measurements shows that the specific dew radioactivity changes during the night, possessing a maximum at the beginning of its formation. During the formation of dew there apparently takes place an intense capture of radioactive substances by direct condensation on radioactive particles. This is corroborated by the fact that the specific radioactivity of the new dew is always higher than the specific radioactivity of the old dew.

TABLE 1. Parameters of the removal of natural radioactivity from ground air by dew

Sampling time, hrs	$R.$ 10^{-13} curie/liter	$R_{u.o},$ 10^{-11} curie/liter	$\Lambda_{u.o},$ 10^{-4} sec^{-1}	$R_{u.n},$ 10^{-11} curie/liter	$\Lambda_{u.n},$ 10^{-4} sec^{-1}
26 June 1968					
2300–2400	2.3	1.1	0.8		
2400–0100	4.4	1.0	0.8	1.8	0.5±0.0
0100–0200	4.6	0.6	0.4	3.9	0.6±0.1
0200–0300	4.1	0.5	0.4	2.4	0.4±0.1
0300–0400	4.1	0.3	0.4	3.3	0.6±0.1
0400–0500	3.6	0.1	0.2	2.2	0.4±0.1
Mean					0.5±0.1
18 July 1968					
2300–2400	5.5	2.0	0.3		
2400–0100	11.4	2.8	0.2	14.2	0.9±0.2
0100–0200	17.0	3.5	0.1	18.8	0.8±0.1
0200–0300	20.1	2.5	0.06	24.3	0.8±0.1
0300–0400	24.5	1.7	0.04	21.5	0.6±0.1
0400–0500	24.3	1.7	0.03	21.0	0.6±0.1
0500–0600	20.7	1.2	0.03	19.0	0.6±0.1
Mean					0.7±0.1
7 August 1968					
2200–2300	4.8	3.5	0.9		
2300–2400	9.7	2.8	0.8	3.1	0.2±0.02
2400–0100	8.2	2.7	0.8	3.5	0.3±0.06
0100–0200	10.7	2.1	0.5	2.7	0.2±0.04
0200–0300	11.9	1.7	0.3	3.1	0.2±0.04
0300–0400	9.9	1.3	0.3	2.8	0.2±0.04
0400–0500	8.7	1.1	0.2	3.6	0.3±0.06
Mean					0.2±0.04

Figures 3a and b, illustrating the dependence of the parameter of nonradioactive removal of radioactive substances for old dew, both upper and lower, on the amount of fallen dew at the moment of its formation, also points to intense cleansing of the atmosphere. The constancy of the coefficient of nonradioactive removal for new dew can be explained by the fact that the drops of new dew increase during each hour roughly to the same value in the course of a given night; this can be seen from the amount of collected dew.

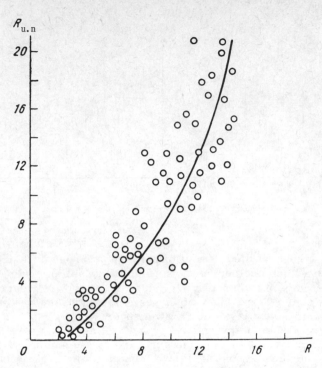

FIGURE 1. Plot of specific radioactivity of upper new dew $R_{u.n}$ as a function of specific radioactivity of the air R (in relative units).

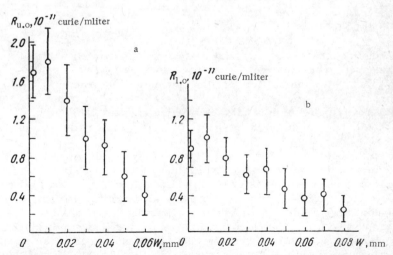

FIGURE 2. Specific radioactivity as a function of the amount of formed dew: a) upper old $R_{u.o}$; b) lower old $R_{l.o}$.

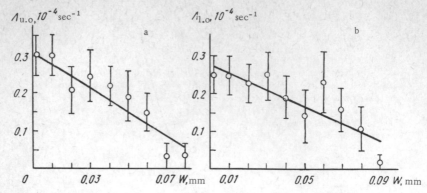

FIGURE 3. Parameter of nonradioactive removal as a function of the amount of formed dew:

a) upper old $\Lambda_{u.o}$; b) lower old $\Lambda_{l.o}$.

Having in mind that the washout of particles through diffusiophoresis represents less than one per cent for each condensation cycle /4/, and assuming that only one condensation cycle of dew growth occurs during the night, we can conclude that diffusiophoresis does not play a substantial role in cleansing the ground layer of the atmosphere.

Finally, we calculated the amount of dew falling on the average in the course of a night over $1\,km^2$ ground surface, and the amount of radioactive substances removed with the dew. We found that the radioactivity removed during a night from $1\,km^2$ ground is on the average $6 \cdot 10^{-4}$ curie. This points to the very substantial role played by dew in cleansing the ground layer of the atmosphere.

5. CONCLUSIONS

1. Values of the α-radioactivity of dew caused by short-lived radon decay products were obtained. For old dew they lie in the range $(0.1-24.5) \cdot 10^{-11}$ curie/mliter and for new dew in the range $(0.1-26) \cdot 10^{-11}$ curie/mliter.

2. The parameter of nonradioactive removal was calculated. For old dew it lies in the range $(0.02-1) \cdot 10^{-4}\,sec^{-1}$ and for new dew in the range $(0.3-1) \cdot 10^{-4}\,sec^{-1}$.

3. A parabolic relationship was derived between the specific radioactivity of new dew and the specific radioactivity of the air. This points to a growth in washout intensity with the growth in air radioactivity.

4. Examination of the curves of the specific activity and the coefficient of nonradioactive removal of radioactive substances of old dew as a function of the amount of fallen dew leads to the conclusion that atmospheric cleansing results mainly from the direct condensation of water vapor on radioactive aerosols.

BIBLIOGRAPHY

1. S t y r o , B.I. Samoochischchenie atmosfery ot radioaktivnykh veshchestv (Atmospheric Scavenging of
   Radioactive Substances).— Leningrad, Gidrometeoizdat. 1968.
2. S t y r o , B.I., E.Yu.V e b r a, B.K.V e b r e n e, and K.K.S h o p a u s k a s. Primenenie al'fa- radiografii pri
   izuchenii slabykh radioaktivnykh atmosfernykh ob"ektov (Application of Alpha-Radiography in
   Studying Weak Radioactive Atmospheric Objects).— Tezisy doklada na konferentsii v Karadage po
   metodikam izmereniya slabykh aktivnostei. 1969.
3. M a n o l o v , L. Kondenzatsionite yavleniya kato dezaktivatori na prizemnya v"zdushne sloi ot radioaktivna
   produkti (Condensation Phenomena as Deactivators of Radioactive Products at the Ground Air Layer).—
   Izvestiya na Fizicheskaya Institut s ANEB, Vol.14, pp.39—44. 1968.
4. G o l d s m i t h , P., H.J. D e l a f i e l d, and L.C.C o x. The Role of Diffusiophoresis in the Scavenging of
   Radioactive Particles from the Atmosphere).— Q.Roy. R.Met. Soc., Vol. 89, No. 43. 1963.
5. H o l z a p f e l , L., H.C a u e r, and R.R e i t e r. Über den Nachweis erhöhter Radioaktivität in Aerosol-
   kondensaten.— Naturwissenschaften, Vol.45, No.7. 1958.
6. N e g r o , C. Über die Radioaktivität des Taues.— Phys. Z., Vol.1, No.189. 1910.

UDC 551.594.1:551.577

RELATION BETWEEN ATMOSPHERIC PRECIPITATION WASHOUT OF RADIOACTIVITY AND NONACTIVE IONS

L. I. Piskunov and S. I. Tarasov

A correlation in the form of a power relationship is assumed between the atmospheric washout of radioactive and nonactive contaminants. We selected as the latter chlorides and sulfates, differing from the others in that their background ratio in atmospheric precipitation for the continental part of European USSR is stable. For a tropospheric background radioactivity, the constancy of the relation in atmospheric precipitation of the radioactivity q with respect to the chlorides m and the sulfates n follows from their identical washout laws. On the basis of the logarithmic equilibrium constants

$$P_1 \log = \left[\frac{(q+c_1)^{\frac{1}{b_1}}}{m} \right] = \text{const},$$

$$P_2 \log = \left[\frac{(q+c_2)^{\frac{1}{b_2}}}{n} \right] = \text{const}$$

(b_1, b_2, c_1 and c_2 are empirical parameters) it is possible to derive an approximate evaluation of the radioactive state of the atmosphere. To determine constants P_1 and P_2 one requires observations with sufficient statistics subject to the conditions of the background concentration of the contaminants. It is assumed that the absence of a correlation between dust washed out from the atmosphere, radioactive components, and the background concentration of nonactive ions can serve as an indicator of anomalous phenomena.

The atmosphere is a medium of the global migration of radioactive aerosols. Atmospheric scavenging is a continuous process, occurring mainly as a result of the action of atmospheric precipitation /24, 26, 27/ The most important aspects of the washout of radioactive contaminants from atmospheric air can be determined by examining this effect on the basis of the natural radioactivity /7, 10, 22, 25/, the fission products /1–3, 8, 11, 12, 16, 27, 38, 31, 32/, and also in the complex of the latter with non-active ions /13, 15, 30/. The investigations were summarized in a survey by Makhon'ko /14/ and in Styro's book /24/.

It was established in the first place that atmospheric precipitation captures contaminants mainly in the cloud layer, and to a smaller extent in the subcloud layer /1, 2, 11, 15, 16, 24, 25/. Shower clouds and snow possess the highest washout capacity /16, 22, 27, 30, 31/. In different geographical regions, and also as a function of the season and meteorological factors, radioactivity washout takes place with various intensities /9, 16, 18, 30/, fresh fission products being washed out more efficiently /11, 12, 15/.

Some studies draw attention to an increase in the specific radioactivity of precipitation with decreasing height above sea level /10, 22/ and attempt to explain this effect by the pollution of ground level air /29/. This fact finds corroboration in the form of the relationship between the activity of precipitation and the contamination observed in urban regions /5/. The opinion of some authors, that there is no correlation between air activity, fallout and amount of precipitation /3, 6, 23/, is contradicted by many theoretical calculations and observations. Apparently, the existing discrepancies in the various points of view are mainly due to random or anomalous factors. We must also keep in mind that the processes of radioactive aerosol washout have been insufficiently studied /3, 16, 26/. These considerations apply also in a first approximation to the questions of atmospheric scavenging of nonactive contaminants, since we can assume that an identical or very similar washout mechanism operates in this case /13, 15, 23, 30/.

In elementary form the washout effect can be represented by an exponential relation /15, 24/. Statistical processing of meteorological data showed that the washout of such widely disseminated anions as chlorides and sulfates satisfies a similar relationship /21/. It follows that the concentration of radioactive substances, chlorides and sulfates in precipitation decreases with an increase in the amount of precipitation according to an exponential law with different exponents. Therefore, some stochastic relation must exist between the indicated components of atmospheric precipitation.

It has been established /20/ that for atmospheric precipitation under typical meteorological conditions the following regression equation holds between the chlorides m and sulfates n:

$$m + c = An^b, \qquad (1)$$

where A, b and c are some parameters determined from many observations. Equation (1) can be used to calculate the logarithmic equilibrium constant /21/:

$$K = \log \left[\frac{(m+c)^{\frac{1}{b}}}{n} \right] = \text{const.} \qquad (2)$$

Relation (2) indicates a difference between the washout of chlorides and sulfates, the former being washed out more intensively than the latter ($K > 1$), as already observed qualitatively /13/. Therefore, the washout of chlorides and sulfates can be expressed in the form

$$l(h) = m_0 \exp(-\beta_1 h) + n_0 \exp(-\beta_2 h), \qquad (3)$$

where $l(h)$ is the total concentration of chlorides and sulfates during the fallout of precipitation h; m_0 and n_0 are the concentrations of chlorides and sulfates at the initial time; β_1 and β_2 are the washout coefficients ($\beta_1 > \beta_2$). Since the washout of many fission products, radon and its decay products (q), and atmospheric dust (Q) can be approximated by an exponent with different intensity exponents α_i and γ_i, allowing for (3) we may write

$$\Sigma q_i + \Sigma l_i + \Sigma Q_i = b + \Sigma q_{0i} \exp(-\alpha_i h) + \Sigma l_{0i} \exp(-\beta_i h) + \\ + \Sigma Q_{0i} \exp(-\gamma_i h), \qquad (4)$$

where all the components of the i contaminants are expressed in weight concentration; b is a constant.

In view of the independence of the terms of (4) and their general relation with the amount of precipitation, it seems possible to form pairs of statistical series and derive formulas similar to regression equation (1). For the radioactivity of precipitation and their concentration of chloride and sulfate ions we obtain

$$\left.\begin{aligned} q + c_1 &= A_1 m^{b_1} \\ q + c_2 &= A_2 n^{b_2} \end{aligned}\right\} \tag{5}$$

whence the logarithmic equilibrium constants are derived in the form

$$\left.\begin{aligned} P_1 &= \log\left[\frac{(q+c_1)^{\frac{1}{b_1}}}{m}\right] = \text{const.} \\ P_2 &= \log\left[\frac{(q+c_2)^{\frac{1}{b_2}}}{n}\right] = \text{const.} \end{aligned}\right\} \tag{6}$$

Regression equations (1) and (5) follow from the background ratios of the contaminants in atmospheric air and the typical meteorological situation during the fallout of precipitation, or more exactly from the equilibrium conditions.*

In the case of anomalies, i.e., for values of K, P_1 and P_2 outside the confidence limits, the aerosol washout relations will be somewhat different, and will correspond apparently to the observations which did not indicate any correlation between q_i, l_i and Q_i. This fact is easily established by using the numerical value of constant K, which is sufficiently stable with respect to the background concentrations m and n.

Thus, for European USSR we obtained the empirical formulas

$$m + 3.8 = 4.1 n^{0.076},$$
$$m + 3.8 = 4.1 n^{0.1177},$$

the second of which corresponds to regions with shifted chloride-sulfate equilibrium (southern European USSR, Central Urals). The logarithmic equilibrium constant K for the Central Urals was found to be 5.2 according to observations of the Vysokaya Dubrava meteorological station /4/. The confidence limits are defined by the ellipse $\frac{\psi^2}{\sigma_\psi^2} + \frac{\rho^2}{\sigma_\rho^2} = \chi_\rho^2$ /19/, where $\sigma_\psi = 0.39$, $\sigma_\rho = 4.11$, $\chi_{0.95} = 0.103$. The geometrical center of the ellipse was taken as the point on the regression line with abscissa $n = \bar{n}$.

Thus, when estimating the radioactivity state in the atmosphere we can use measurements of q, m and n in precipitation. Constants K, P_1, P_2 are calculated by formulas (2) and (6) and compared with their values under normal conditions. The correspondence between the values of K and the divergence between P_1 and P_2 (allowing for the confidence limits) must point to the existence of anomalous radioactivity in the atmosphere. Constants P_1 and P_2 must be known beforehand from background observations with the aid of sufficient statistics.

---

* The onset of an equilibrium state of the fission products in the period after 1963 has been stressed in many papers /17, 29/.

CONCLUSIONS

1. Under certain conditions a correlation can exist between the radioactivity and the nonactive ions (chlorides, sulfates) in atmospheric precipitation.

2. The obtained characteristics of an indirect connection between radioactivity and nonactive ions are simple and independent of the amount of precipitation. The determination of the empirical parameters entering the equilibrium constants is possible if sufficient statistical observation data are available under conditions of normal (background) contaminant content in atmospheric air.

3. It is desirable to conduct a statistical analysis of simultaneous measurements of specific radioactivity and the concentration of chlorides and sulfates in atmospheric precipitation, allowing for the influence of random factors and anomalous phenomena in the atmosphere. Such a formulation of the problem can be of practical interest.

BIBLIOGRAPHY

1. Burtsev, I.I. O vymyvanii osadkami iskusstvennykh radioaktivnykh aerozolei iz atmosfery (Washout of Artificial Radioactive Aerosols from the Atmosphere by Precipitation).— In: Radioaktivnye izotopy v atmosfere i ikh ispol'zovanie v meteorologii (Radioactive Isotopes in the Atmosphere and their Utilization in Meteorology). Moskva, Atomizdat. 1965.

2. Burtsev, I.I. and S.G.Malakhov. Vymyvanie osadkami produktov deleniya iz podoblachnogo sloya atmosfery (Washout of Fission Products from the Subcloud Layer of the Atmosphere by Precipitation).— Izvestiya AN SSSR, Fizika Atmosfery i Okeana, Vol.4, No.3. 1968.

3. Dmitrieva, G.V. O vliyanii atmosfernykh osadkov na radioaktivnost' prizemnogo sloya atmosfery (Effect of Atmospheric Precipitation on the Radioactivity of the Ground Layer of the Atmosphere).— In: Voprosy yadernoi meteorologii (Problems of Nuclear Meteorology). Moskva, Gosatomizdat. 1962.

4. Drozdova, V.M., O.P.Petrenchuk, E.S.Selezneva, and P.F.Svistov. Khimicheskii sostav atmosfernykh osadkov na Evropeiskoi territorii SSSR (Chemical Composition of Atmospheric Precipitation over European USSR).— Leningrad, Gidrometeoizdat. 1964.

5. Dubrovina, Z.V. Nekotorye dannye o zavisimosti plotnosti vypadeniya radioaktivnykh veshchestv ot zapylennosti atmosfernogo vozdukha (Some Data about the Relation of the Fallout Density of Radioactive Substances to the Pollution of Atmospheric Air).— Gigiena i Sanitariya, No.5. 1962.

6. Zorin, V.I. and E.I.Kabishcher. Vliyanie atmosfernykh osadkov na vypadenie radioaktivnykh veshchestv iz atmosfery (Effect of Atmospheric Precipitation on the Atmospheric Fallout of Radioactive Substances). Gigiena i Sanitariya, No.11. 1965.

7. Karol', I.L. and V.D.Vilenskii. Otsenka parametrov vertikal'nogo obmena i srednei skorosti udaleniya aerozolei oblakami i osadkami v nizhnei chasti atmosfery po dannym o estestvennoi radioaktivnosti prizemnogo vozdukha (Estimation of Parameters of Vertical Exchange and Mean Removal Rate of Aerosols by Clouds and Precipitation in the Lower Atmosphere from Data on the Natural Radioactivity of Ground Level Air).— In: Radioaktivnye izotopy v atmosfere i ikh ispol'zovanie v meteorologii (Radioactive Isotopes in the Atmosphere and their Utilization in Meteorology). Moskva, Atomizdat. 1965.

8. Koroda, P. et al. Produkty deleniya v atmosfere i dozhde (Fission Products in the Atmosphere and Rain).— In: Radioaktivnye vypadeniya ot yadernykh vzryvov (Radioactive Fallout from Nuclear Bursts).— Izd. "Mir." 1968.

9. Lavrenchik, V.N. Global'noe vypadenie produktov yadernykh vzryvov (Global Fallout of the Products of Nuclear Bursts).— Moskva, Atomizdat. 1965.

10. Malakhov, S.G. and L.D.Solodikhina. O vymyvanii dozhdem produktov raspada radona iz atmosfery (Rain Washout of Radon Decay Products from the Atmosphere).— In: Voprosy yadernoi meteorologii (Problems of Nuclear Meteorology). Moskva, Gosatomizdat. 1962.

11. M a k h o n ' k o, K.P. Vymyvanie radioaktivnoi pyli iz atmosfery (Atmospheric Washout of Radioactive Dust).— Izvestiya AN SSSR, Seriya Geofizicheskaya, No.4. 1964.

12. M a k h o n ' k o, K.P. Opredelenie parametrov vymyvaniya produktov deleniya iz atmosfery (Determination of the Atmospheric Washout Parameters of Fission Products).— Izvestiya AN SSSR, Seriya Geofizicheskaya, No.9. 1964.

13. M a k h o n ' k o, K.P. Vymyvanie radioaktivnykh izotopov, khimicheskikh elementov i ikh soedinenii iz atmosfery (Washout of Radioactive Isotopes, Chemical Elements and their Compounds from the Atmosphere).— Doklad na simpoziume po voprosam issledovaniya samoochishcheniya atmosfery ot radioaktivnykh zagryaznenii. Palanga, LitSSR. 1966.

14. M a k h o n ' k o, K.P. Samoochishchenie nizhnei troposfery ot radioaktivnoi pyli (Lower Tropospheric Scavenging of Radioactive Dust).— Izvestiya AN SSSR, Fizika Atmosfery i Okeana, Vol.2, No.5. 1966.

15. M a k h o n ' k o, K.P. Elementarnye teoreticheskie predstavleniya o vymyvanii primesi osadkami iz atmosfery (Elementary Theoretical Concepts in the Atmospheric Washout of Contaminants by Precipitation).— Trudy IPG, No.8. 1967.

16. M a k h o n ' k o, K.P. and G.V.D m i t r i e v a. Sposobnost' razlichnykh tipov osadkov k vymyvaniyu produktov deleniya iz atmosfery i kharakteristiki vymyvaniya (Capacity of Different Types of Precipitation to Wash Out Fission Products from the Atmosphere and Washout Characteristics).— Izvestiya AN SSSR, Fizika Atmosfery i Okeana, Vol.2, No.3. 1966.

17. M a k h o n ' k o, K.P., S.G.M a l a k h o v, and M.P.N e k h o r o s h e v a. Vymyvanie iz atmosfery produktov deleniya (Washout of Fission Products from the Atmosphere).— In: Radioaktivnye izotopy v atmosfere i ikh ispol'zovanie v meteorologii (Radioactive Isotopes in the Atmosphere and their Utilization in Meteorology). Moskva, Atomizdat. 1965.

18. F e d o r o v, E.K. (editor). Meteorologiya i Atomnaya Energiya (Meteorology and Atomic Energy). [Russian translations, 1959.]

19. N a l i m o v, V.V. Primenenie matematicheskoi statistiki pri analize veshchestva (Utilization of Mathematical Statistics in the Analysis of Substances).— Moskva, Fizmatgiz. 1960.

20. P i s k u n o v, L.I. Korrelyatsiya khlor-i sul'fationov v prirodnykh vodakh (Correlation between Chloride and Sulfate Ions in Natural Waters).— DAN SSSR, Vol.176, No.5. 1967.

21. P i s k u n o v, L.I. and E.F.K u p e r m a n. Ob otsenke zagryaznennosti atmosfernogo vozdukha po khlorid-sul'fatnomu pokazatelyu atmosfernykh osadkov (Estimation of Atmospheric Air Pollution from the Chloride-Sulfate Index of Precipitation).— Materialy IV nauchno-prakticheskoi konferentsii Sverdlovskoi oblastnoi i gorodskoi sanitarno-epidemiologicheskikh stantsii. Sverdlovsk. 1969.

22. S o l o d i k h i n a, L.D. Ob estestvennoi radioaktivnosti atmosfernykh osadkov (Natural Radioactivity of Atmospheric Precipitation).— Izvestiya AN SSSR, Seriya Geofizicheskaya, No.2. 1959.

23. S t y r o, B.I. Soveshchanie po voprosam issledovaniya samoochishcheniya atmosfery ot radioaktivnykh zagryaznenii (Conference on the Problem of Studying Atmospheric Scavenging of Radioactive Contaminants).— Izvestiya AN SSSR, Fizika Atmosfery i Okeana, Vol.2, No.12. 1966.

24. S t y r o, B.I. Samoochishchenie atmosfery ot radioaktivnykh zagryaznenii (Atmospheric Scavenging of Radioactive Contaminants).— Leningrad, Gidrometeoizdat. 1968.

25. S t y r o, B.I., Yu.E.V e b r a, and K.K.S h o p a u s k a s. Opredelenie nekotorykh parametrov udaleniya estestvennykh aerozolei iz vozdukha (Determination of Various Parameters of the Removal of Natural Radioactive Aerosols from Air).— Izvestiya AN SSSR, Fizika Atmosfery i Okeana, Vol.1, No.12. 1965.

26. F a c e y, L. Radioactive Precipitation and Fallout. [Russian translation, 1964.]

27. K h i n t s p e t e r, M. Elementy atmosfernykh osadkov kak nositeli informatsii o radioaktivnykh chastitsakh v atmosfere (Elements of Atmospheric Precipitation as Carriers of Information about Radioactive Particles in the Atmosphere).— In: Radioaktivnye chastitsy v atmosfere (Radioactive Particles in the Atmosphere). Moskva, Gosatomizdat. 1963.

28. C h a l o v, P.I. and M.A.T s e v e l e v. O vymyvanii radioaktivnykh aerozolei atmosfernymi osadkami v podoblachnom sloe (Washout of Radioactive Aerosols by Atmospheric Precipitation in the Subcloud Layer).— Izvestiya AN SSSR, Fizika Atmosfery i Okeana, Vol.2, No.2. 1966.

29. S h e m ' i - Z a d e, A. Korrelyatsiya mezhdu kontsentratsiyami radioaktivnykh aerozolei estestvennogo i oskolochnogo proiskhozhdeniya v prizemnom sloe atmosfery (Correlation between the Concentrations of Radioactive Aerosols of Natural and Fragmentary Origin in the Ground Layer of the Atmosphere).— Atomnaya Energiya, Vol. 22, No. 1. 1967.

30. J u n g e, C.E. Air Chemistry and Radioactivity.— New York, Academic Press. 1963.

31. H i c k s, B.B. Nucleation and the Wet Removal of Fallout.— J. Appl. Meteorol., Vol.5, No.2. 1966.

32. L i b b y, W.E. Radioactive Fallout.— Proc. Natn. Acad. Sci. U.S.A., Vol.44, No.8. 1958.

V. NATURAL RADIOACTIVITY OF THE ATMOSPHERE

UDC 539.163:546.296

ACCOUNTING FOR SOME NONSTEADY PROCESSES IN RECORDING NATURAL AIR RADIOACTIVITY

V. N. Bakulin and V. P. Matulyavichyus

The accumulation of radon disintegration products is studied theoretically for recorders with fixed and mobile filters, for constant and linearly increasing concentration of these products in air, taking into account the relation between their concentrations. It is demonstrated that neglecting the equilibrium in the radon series can lead to an error several times greater when determining the concentration of radon and its disintegration products in air from measurements of the activity of recorder filters. A formula is proposed for determining constant concentrations of Rn and its disintegration products in air by various suction methods in relation to the degree of equilibrium in the radon series. The optimum filtration time for a recorder with a mobile filter is shown to be at most 1.5 — 2 hrs; longer times do not practically increase the sensitivity of the setup, but increase the recorder's time constant and render more difficult determination of the actual time variation in the concentration of radioactive substances.

A method is suggested for determining the relationship between radon disintegration products measured by two counters, one positioned in the path of the recorder film. Very reliable data can thus be obtained for an α-recorder, at minimum spacing between the two counters.

The increased use of automatic recorders of natural air radioactivity /2—5/ calls for a more detailed investigation of certain nonsteady processes to be allowed for when assessing the variation in time of radon daughter products and in the quantitative analysis of recorded data.

Consider the equation of filter accumulation of radon decay products, which account for most of the air activity:

$$\frac{dq_i}{dt} = \lambda_{i-1} q_{i-1} - \lambda_i q_i + Q_i w, \tag{1}$$

where λ_i (in sec^{-1}) are the disintegration constants (λ_1— RaA, λ_2— RaB, λ_3— RaC), Q_i (in atom/cm^3) are the atom concentrations in the air, q_i (in atoms) is the number of atoms of radon daughter products on the filter, and w (in cm^3/sec) is the bulk air suction rate.

If the initial activity of the filter is nil, the solution to equation (1) for different types of recorders determining the number of atoms in the different links of the radioactive chain that accumulated on the filter during the exposure time Θ is

$$q_1(\Theta) = \frac{Q_1 w}{\lambda_1} f(\lambda_1, \Theta), \tag{2a}$$

$$q_2(\Theta)=\frac{(Q_1+Q_2)\,w}{\lambda_2}\,f(\lambda_2,\Theta)+\frac{Q_1\,w}{\lambda_2-\lambda_1}[f(\lambda_1,\Theta)-f(\lambda_2,\Theta)],\qquad(2b)$$

$$q_3(\Theta)=\frac{(Q_1+Q_2+Q_3)\,w}{\lambda_3}\,f(\lambda_3,\Theta)+\frac{(Q_1+Q_2)w}{\lambda_3-\lambda_2}[f(\lambda_2,\Theta)-f(\lambda_3,\Theta)]+$$

$$+\frac{Q_1\,w\,\lambda_2}{\lambda_1-\lambda_2}\left\{\frac{1}{\lambda_3-\lambda_1}[f(\lambda_3,\Theta)-f(\lambda_1,\Theta)]-\frac{f(\lambda_3,\Theta)-f(\lambda_2,\Theta)}{\lambda_3-\lambda_2}\right\}.\qquad(2c)$$

The form of function $f(\lambda_i,\Theta)$ depends on the recorder type and the time of variation of the radioactive substance concentration in the air.

1. For a fixed filter at an air activity that is constant in time Θ,

$$f^*(\lambda_i,\Theta)=1-e^{-\lambda_i\Theta}\ .$$

2. For a fixed filter at an air activity that increases linearly from zero to Q_i over the duration Θ of the process,

$$f^{**}(\lambda_i,\Theta)=1-\frac{1-e^{-\lambda_i\Theta}}{\lambda_i\Theta}\ .$$

3. For a filter moving at speed v and crossing a rectangular activation window of width b in time $\Theta=\dfrac{b}{v}$, at constant air activity, the form of function $f(\lambda_i\,\Theta)$ is the same as in case 2.

4. For a mobile filter at an air activity that increases linearly from zero to Q_i during time $\Theta=\dfrac{b}{v}$ in which the filter passes by the rectangular activation filter,

$$f^{***}(\lambda_i,\Theta)=\frac{1}{2}-\frac{1}{\lambda_i\Theta}\left(1-\frac{1-e^{-\lambda_i\Theta}}{\lambda_i\Theta}\right).$$

In these cases, the number of radioactive atoms accumulating on the filter in an interval of time $0\leqslant t\leqslant\Theta$ is given by

$$1.\ q_i(t)=q_i^*(t),$$

$$2.\ q_i(t)=q_i^{**}(t),$$

$$3.\ q_i(t)=\frac{t}{\Theta}\,q_i^{**}(t)+\frac{\Theta-t}{\Theta}\,q_i^*(t),$$

$$4.\ q_i(t)=\frac{t}{\Theta}\,q_i^{***}(t)+\frac{\Theta-t}{\Theta}\,q_i^{**}(t),\qquad(3)$$

where $q_i^*(t)$, $q_i^{**}(t)$ and $q_i^{***}(t)$ are expressions of form (2) with corresponding values of $f(\lambda_i,\Theta)$ at time t.

The number of atoms remaining on a fixed filter after the air suction ceases is, for $t \geqslant \Theta$,

$$1. \quad q_i(t) = q_i^*(t) - q_i^*(\Theta),$$
$$2. \quad q_i(t) = q_i^{**}(t) - q_i^{**}(\Theta). \tag{4}$$

The filter activity C_α and C_β (in disintegrations per second) at any moment t is

$$C_\alpha(t) = \lambda_1 q_1(t) + \lambda_3 q_3(t),$$

$$C_\beta(t) = \lambda_2 q_2(t) + \lambda_3 q_3(t). \tag{5}$$

Consider the possibilities offered by a recorder for determining the absolute concentrations of radon or its daughter products in air.

It follows from formulas $(2)-(5)$ that the maximum activity C_{max} accumulated by the filter of a β-activity recorder over a long enough time Θ is

$$C_{\beta \, max} = w(2Q_1 + 2Q_2 + Q_3), \tag{6}$$

and for an α-activity recorder

$$C_{\alpha \, max} = w(2Q_1 + Q_2 + Q_3). \tag{7}$$

Consequently, the β-activity of any filter is not proportional to the total RaB + RaC concentration in air, and the α-activity of a filter is not proportional to RaA + RaC. Both activities are fairly complicated functions of Q_1, Q_2 and Q_3, i. e., they depend on the ratio between the products of radon disintegration. Besides, the contribution of any link of the radon disintegration chain to the filter activity varies according to the activation time Θ.

According to Bakulin and Starikov /1/, the ratios $\lambda_1 Q_1/\lambda_2 Q_2$ and $\lambda_2 Q_2/\lambda_3 Q_3$ under natural conditions are always nearly equal and their value generally lies between 1.2 and 2.

Calculations have shown that, if $\dfrac{C_{max}}{\omega}$ is taken as a conventional unit,

the curves $C_{rel}(\Theta)$ of filter activity vs. time agree to within 10% for $\Theta \geqslant 10$ min and $\lambda_2 Q_2/\lambda_3 Q_3 \leqslant 3$.

We shall denote by $B = \dfrac{C_{max}}{\omega C_{air}}$ the ratio of the maximum filter activity

C_{max} to air activity C_{air} at unit volumetric rate of filtration w.

Figure 1 presents the variation of B as a function of $\lambda_2 Q_2/\lambda_3 Q_3$ and $\lambda_1 Q_1/\lambda_2 Q_2$. Curves 1 and 2 pertain to the ratio of filter α- and β-activity to the corresponding total activity of the air, and curves 1a and 2a to the ratio of the same filter activities to the radon concentration in the atmosphere. These ratios vary widely in relation to the degree of equilibrium in the radon series. Neglecting an equilibrium disturbance can thus lead to a several times greater error in the evaluation of the radon concentration taken equal to the RaA concentration, and of its disintegration products in the air from recorded data.

189

If the relationship between the radon disintegration products has been determined by some method, the air activity can be calculated from the follc ing formula for stable concentration of radioactive substances in air (the recording is a horizontal line):

$$C_{air} = \frac{N\lambda_1}{K C_{rel}(\Theta)\, w\, B},$$

where K is the setup's counting efficiency, N is the recorded filter activity (counts per sec), and $\lambda_1 = 3.788 \cdot 10^{-3}\, sec^{-1}$ is the RaA disintegration constant

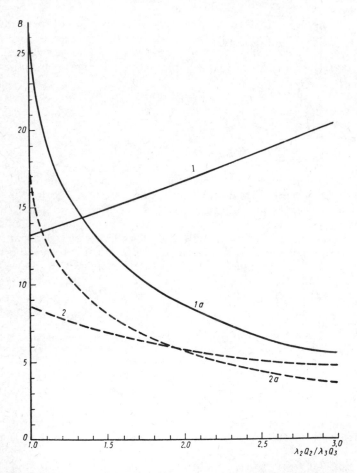

FIGURE 1. Ratio of maximum filter activity to air activity with:

1) $\dfrac{C_{\beta\,max}}{\omega C_{\beta\,air}}$, 1a) $\dfrac{C_{\beta\,max}}{\omega C_{Rn\,air}}$, 2) $\dfrac{C_{\alpha\,max}}{\omega C_{\alpha\,air}}$, 2a) $\dfrac{C_{\alpha\,max}}{\omega C_{Rn\,air}}$.

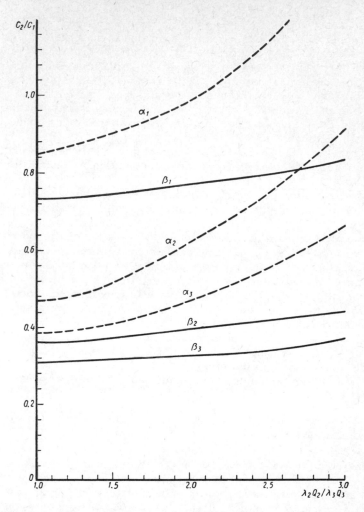

FIGURE 2. Ratio of filter activity for a recorder provided with two α- and β-radiation sensors. The curves for α_1 and β_1 correspond to $\Theta = 30$ min, $\tau = 1$ min; those for α_2 and β_2 correspond to $\Theta - 90$ min, $\tau - 1$ min; those for α_3 and β_3 correspond to $\Theta = 90$ min, $\tau = 15$ min.

No discrepancy in the limits of disintegration statistics was found by comparing theoretical and experimental curves of radioactive substance accumulation on mobile and fixed filters. It can be confirmed that the nonuniform distribution of radioactive substances over the window width of the recorder with mobile filter scarcely affects the counting geometry, at least for the investigated type of recorder ($b = 3$ cm, $\Theta = 1.5$ hrs, STS-6 counter).

An analysis reveals that the filter accumulation of α- and β- activity is practically identical. For $\Theta < 1$ hr, the activity of the mobile filter is about half that achieved by the fixed filter during the same activation time.

Nevertheless, the activation time for both types of recorder should never be taken longer than 1.5— 2 hrs, since a further increase of exposure time leads to practically no increase in the activity of the filter and the sensitivity of the entire setup, but produces a significant increase in the time constant of the instruments. If the radioactive substance concentration in the air suddenly varies, the recording of the new air activity starts only after the elapse of time Θ. In the case of air radioactivity fluctuations of short period $T < \Theta$, the recorded amplitude will be the more reduced, the shorter T as compared to Θ.

The diurnal air radioactivity variation obtained with the recorder can therefore differ considerably from the actual, due to radon and its disintegration products.

The correction for recording sections other than horizontal, i. e., the quantitative accounting for recorder inertia, is an object of independent investigation.

We have already said that the actual concentration of Rn and its disintegration products can only be calculated from the filter activity if it is known to what degree the equilibrium between them has been disturbed. Besides, only this can serve as a characteristic of the state of the ground layer of the atmosphere. The possibility was investigated of determining the relation between the radon disintegration products with a secondary counter positioned on a surface of similar activity and the same width b, and situated distance $l = v\tau$ from the activation window of the recorder filter, in the path of filter movement. Here τ is the time taken by the filter to move from one counter to the other.

Under stable conditions, the number of radioactive isotope atoms in the second window is

$$q_i' = q_i^{**}(\tau + 2\Theta) - q_i^{**}(\tau + \Theta).$$

Figure 2 presents the ratio of activities C_1 and C_2 recorded by the first and second counters vs. the ratio of radon disintegration products Θ and τ. It can be seen that the degree to which the equilibrium in the radon series has been disturbed can most promisingly be determined with an α-activity recorder, with a minimum distance l (l proportional to τ) between windows. For a β-recorder, such a determination is only possible at activities of more than 1,000 counts per minute.

BIBLIOGRAPHY

1. Bakulin, V. N. and B. G. Starikov. Razdel'noe opredelenie kontsentratsii v vozdukhe Rn, RaA, RaB i RaC po krivoi spada α-aktivnosti fil'tra (Separate Determination of Rn, RaA, RaB and RaC Concentrations in Air from the α-Activity Decay Curve of a Filter). — In this collection.
2. Golenetskii, S. P. Opredelenie i nepreryvnaya registratsiya soderzhaniya v vozdukhe aerozolei korotkozhivushshchikh radioaktivnykh izotopov metodom "nasyshcheniya" fil'tra (Determination and Continuous Recording of the Content of Short-Lived Radioactive Isotope Aerosols in Air by the Method of Filter "Saturation"). — Gigiena i Sanitariya, No. 7. 1962.
3. Kirichenko, L. V. Izmerenie korotkozhivushchikh radioaktivnykh aerozolei v svobodnoi atmosfere (Measurements of Short-Lived Radioactive Aerosols in the Free Atmosphere). — In sbornik: Voprosy yadernoi meteorologii (Problems of Nuclear Meteorology). Moskva, Gosatomizdat. 1962.

4. Matulyavichyus, V.P. Nekotorye rezul'taty izmereniya estestvennoi radioaktivnosti atmosfery s pomoshch'yu registratora s nepreryvno dvizhushchimsya fil'trom (Some Results of Natural Atmospheric Radioactivity Measurements Using a Recorder with a Continuously Moving Filter). — Trudy AN Litovskoi SSR, Series B, Vol. 1(52), 1968.

5. Serwant, I. Le rádon et ses dérivés. Thèse, Université de Paris, No. 4358. 1965.

UDC 551.510.71

COSMOGONIC SODIUM-22 AND BERYLLIUM-7 ISOTOPES IN INVESTIGATIONS OF ATMOSPHERIC DYNAMICS

V. Yu. Luyanas, R. Yu. Yasyulenis, and B. I. Styro

This paper deals with the possibility of using the ratio of concentrations of the cosmogonic radioisotopes Na^{22} and Be^7 for determining the penetration of stratospheric air to the earth's surface. The measurements were carried out at Elektrenai and Vilnius between 1965 and 1969. In some cases, the $\frac{Na^{22}}{Be^7}$ ratio reached values that were typical of stratospheric air. It is preferable to use a pair of isotopes of which one has a lifetime of several years, to study the air exchange between the stratosphere and troposphere.

The concentration of cosmogonic radioisotopes in air is clearly related to altitude. The stratospheric concentrations of many isotopes are tens or hundreds of times higher than their tropospheric ones. This provides favorable conditions for using cosmogonic radioisotopes to study air exchange between the stratosphere and troposphere.

As early as 1958, a group of Indian scientists /1/ tried to detect stratospheric-air penetration into the troposphere from changes in the concentration ratio of cosmogonic S^{35}/P^{32}. They carried out detailed analyses of samples from 21 rains but only once, in winter, did the ratio correspond to that of stratospheric air. Unfortunately, technical difficulties prevented corroboration of this unusual result by subsequent measurements. The results of the investigation are apparently in agreement with the well-substantiated opinion that the passage of stratospheric air into the lower atmosphere at the tropics is a very rare occurrence. Peters /1/ found it advisable to carry out similar investigations at moderate and high geomagnetic latitudes. The study of Aegerter, Bhandari, Rama and Tamhane into the ratios of Be^7 to P^{32} concentrations in ground level air in Switzerland /2/ was published in 1966. This experiment did not succeed in obtaining typical Be^7/P^{32} values for stratospheric air either. Aegerter et al. then assumed that more reliable results might be achieved using another pair of isotopes, Na^{22}/P^{32} or Na^{22}/Be^7, since longer-lived isotopes should display a clearer jump in concentration upon passing from the stratosphere to the troposphere.

The use of the Na^{22}/Be^7 ratio was thought possible by the present authors already in 1964; since spring 1965, they have carried out more than 50 measurements at Vilnius.

According to calculations and aircraft measurements, the equilibrium ratios of Na^{22}/Be^7 concentrations above 55°N or so should be of the order of $14 \cdot 10^{-3}$ for the stratosphere and $5 \cdot 10^{-3}$ for unpurified tropospheric air.

TABLE 1. Ratio of cosmogonic-isotope concentrations in ground level air

Sampling period	Na^{22}, atoms/g	Be^7, atoms/g	$Na^{22}/Be^7, 10^{-3}$
1965			
27 Apr. — 8 May	0.240	44	5.5
8 May — 18 May	0.020	28	0.7
18 May — 28 May	1.056	79	13.5
26 Aug. — 6 Sept.	0.055	19	2.9
6 Sept. — 15 Sept.	0.017	8	2.1
15 Sept. — 27 Sept.	0.101	11	9.1
27 Sept. — 4 Oct.	0.015	52	0.3
13 Oct. — 28 Oct.	0.051	17	3.0
28 Oct. — 4 Nov.	0.087	31	2.8
1966			
1 Apr. — 16 Apr.	0.104	16	6.5
22 Apr. — 11 May	0.171	25	6.8
11 May — 2 June	0.004	3	1.3
10 Sept. — 20 Sept.	0.571	43	13.3
30 Sept. — 10 Oct.	0.048	22	2.2
10 Oct. — 21 Oct.	0.014	16	0.9
21 Oct. — 1 Nov.	0.071	6	11.8
1 Nov. — 14 Nov.	0.063	26	2.4
1968			
5 Jan. — 9 Jan.	0.0032	3.20	1.0
30 Jan. — 1 Feb.	0.0016	3.52	0.45
9 Feb. — 12 Feb.	0.0016	7.84	0.20
26 Feb. — 1 Mar.	0.034	4.00	8.4
7 Mar. — 11 Mar.	0.133	8.32	16.0
29 Mar. — 1 Apr.	0.099	8.32	12.0
30 Apr. — 4 May	0.155	4.64	33.4
11 May — 13 May	0.064	5.92	10.8
24 May — 27 May	0.059	13.00	4.6
31 May — 3 June	0.082	7.20	11.3
14 June — 17 June	0.168	9.92	16.9
26 June — 1 July	0.067	3.20	21.0
19 July — 22 July	0.104	8.96	11.6
2 Aug. — 5 Aug.	0.042	8.32	5.0
16 Aug. — 19 Aug.	0.094	11.52	8.2
1969			
7 Feb. — 10 Feb.	0.068	4.8	14.2
17 Feb. — 19 Feb.	0.086	16.2	5.3
14 Feb. — 17 Feb.	0.260	16.4	15.8
24 Feb. — 26 Feb.	0.002	10.3	0.2
5 Mar. — 7 Mar.	0.027	16.8	1.6
10 Mar. — 12 Mar.	0.043	4.6	9.4
12 Mar. — 15 Mar.	0.035	6.6	5.3
15 Mar. — 17 Mar.	0.380	20.2	18.8
19 Mar. — 21 Mar.	0.140	12.3	11.4
21 Mar. — 24 Mar.	0.250	11.3	22.1
28 Mar. — 31 Mar.	0.042	16.4	2.6
15 Apr. — 18 Apr.	0.011	11.7	0.9
21 Apr. — 23 Apr.	0.035	5.2	6.7
28 Apr. — 30 Apr.	0.180	21.0	8.6
30 Apr. — 3 May	0.100	8.9	11.2
15 May — 17 May	0.120	13.2	9.1

Table 1 lists some measurements of the Na^{22}/Be^7 ratio in atmospheric aerosols at ground level. The samples were taken by filtration of large volumes of air (up to $4.5 \cdot 10^5$ m^3) through FPP-15—1.7 filters. In 1965—1966, the samples were taken in the Elektrenai area at 5 m above ground. The filter exposure time was about 10 days. In 1968—1969 the air was filtered in Vilnius 1 m above ground and the exposure time was about 2 — 3 days. It can be seen that the Na^{22}/Be^7 ratio for many a sample reaches values typical of stratospheric air. In some cases it attains 20 to $30 \cdot 10^{-3}$, which could be ascribed to the presence of a stratospheric air mass in the troposphere for 2—3 months without washout. This being improbable, one must consider the possibility of the presence in the stratosphere of a certain amount of Na^{22} of artificial origin, or some fractionation of Na^{22} and Be^7 isotopes during precipitation. In some cases, peak values of the Na^{22}/Be^7 ratio coincide with peak Na^{22} and Be^7 concentrations. This is apparently typical of "fresh" stratospheric air masses. If the Be^7 concentrations are not maxima, the stratospheric mass is "old." A comparatively high Be^7 concentration associated with low Na^{22} concentration may indicate that the air mass, before being released into the troposphere, resided in the stratosphere not long enough for equilibrium Na^{22} concentrations to be achieved.

As a rule, the Na^{22}/Be^7 ratio maxima are noticed in May every year, but increases were also often observed in fall and winter months.

We tried to find a connection between fluctuations of the Na^{22}/Be^7 ratio and meteorological factors, but a preliminary study of the criteria chosen by different authors for assessing the possibility of stratospheric air penetration into the troposphere revealed no unique connection with the variation of Na^{22}/Be^7 concentrations. More comprehensive experimental data are apparently necessary.

BIBLIOGRAPHY

1. M o n i n , A. S. (editor). Atmosfernaya diffuziya i zagryaznenie vozdukha (Atmospheric Diffusion and Air Pollution). — Moskva, Inostrannaya Literatura. 1962.
2. A e g e r t e r , S., N. B h a n d a r i , R a m a , and A. S. T a m h a n e. Be^7 and P^{32} in Ground Level Air. — Tellus, Vol. 18, Nos. 2 — 3. 1966.

UDC 551.510.7

ARGON SPALLATION YIELDS OF COSMOGONIC RADIOISOTOPES

R. Yu. Yasyulenis, V. Yu. Luyanas, and B. I. Styro

This paper deals with the evaluation of the rates at which cosmogonic isotopes are formed by argon spallation. The cross sections of isotope formation are calculated from a refined Rudstam formula. The yields are given for one star of F^{18}, Ne^{24}, Na^{22}, Na^{24}, Mg^{28}, Al^{28}, Al^{29}, Si^{31}, Si^{32}, P^{30}, P^{32}, P^{33}, S^{37}, Cl^{34}, Cl^{36} and Cl^{38} isotopes. The yield dependence on one star from the depth of the atmosphere is also given.

The interaction of high-energy cosmic-ray particles with atmospheric argon produces a whole series of radioactive isotopes. The rates of formation of the P^{32}, P^{33} and S^{35} isotopes were studied by exposing argon-filled balloons at a certain altitude /4/. Based on these measurements, Lal and Peters used Rudstam's formula to obtain the rates of formation of the radioactive Cl^{36}, Al^{26}, Si^{32} and Na^{22} isotopes /5/. No calculations are, however, available of the rates of formation of Mg^{28} /3/, Na^{24} /7/, Cl^{38} /6/, Cl^{34m}, Si^{31} /2/ and other isotopes recently discovered in rainwater. The rates of formation of 17 cosmogonic radioisotopes produced by argon spallation are calculated in this paper.

Spallation reactions ("stars") are the result of an interaction of cosmic-ray nuclides ($E > 40$ MeV) with nuclei of Ni^{14}, O^{16}, Ar^{40}, etc. The absolute rates of star formation and their relation to the depth of the atmosphere and the geomagnetic latitude have been adequately studied with the aid of nuclear emulsions /5/. The evaluation of a rate requires knowledge of the coefficient of formation in one star:

$$
k = \frac{\int_{40}^{\infty} \sigma_{Z,A} \cdot j_{(E,x)} \, dE}{\int_{40}^{\infty} \sigma_{inel} \, j_{(E,x)} \, dE}, \tag{1}
$$

where $\sigma_{Z,A}$ is the spallation cross section for the reaction product number Z of mass number A, σ_{inel} is the cross section of star formation, $j_{(E,x)}$ is the nuclide flow intensity, E is the energy of the bombarding particles, and x is the depth of the atmosphere. Rudstam's formula yields /8/

$$
\sigma_{Z,A} = F_{(A_t)} f_{(E)} \frac{Pe^{-P(A_t - A)}}{1 - (0.3/PA_t)} e^{-Q|Z - SA + TA^2|^{\frac{3}{2}}}, \tag{2}
$$

where Z is the number of the reaction product, A its mass number, A_t is the mass number of the target nucleus, S and T are coefficients (in our case $S = 0.486$, $T = 0.00038$), P is an energy-dependent parameter given by

$$P = 20\, E^{-0.77}, \qquad\qquad E < 2100 \text{ MeV},$$
$$P = 0.056, \qquad\qquad E > 2100 \text{ MeV};$$

Q is a parameter that depends on the mass number:

$$Q = 11.8\ A^{-0.45}\ ;$$

$F_{(A_t)}$ is the sum of parameters that depend on the atomic number of the target (for $A_t = 40$, $F_{(A_t)} = 590$ mb), and $f_{(E)}$ is the parameter of cross-section dependence on energy.

In the domain of high energies, the cross section of inelastic interaction of nuclides with the nuclei is well approximated by

$$\sigma_{\text{inel}} = \gamma_{(A,E)}\,\sigma_{\text{geom}}, \qquad\qquad (3)$$

where $\sigma_{\text{geom}} = \pi r_0^2\, A^{2/3}$ is the geometric cross section of the nucleus ($r_0 = 1.26 \cdot 10^{-13}$ cm), and $\gamma_{(A,E)}$ is a parameter describing the nucleus transmission. The transmission for N^{14}, O^{16} and Ar^{40} nuclei was calculated by interpolating corresponding data for C, Al and Cu nuclei. The differential intensity of proton and neutron flows is given by Rossi's formula /1/

$$j^n_{(E,x)} = \frac{D\,x}{(50 + E)^2}\, e^{-\frac{x}{L}}, \qquad\qquad (4)$$

$$j^P_{(E,x)} = \frac{D\,(E_m - E)}{u_{(E)}\,(50 + E)(50 + E_m)}\, e^{-\frac{x}{L}}, \qquad\qquad (5)$$

where x is the depth of the atmosphere, L is the free path length, $u_{(E)}$ are the energy losses for protons of energy E, and E_m is given by

$$R_{(E_m)} = R_{(E)} + x,$$

where $R_{(E)}$ is the effective free path of protons in air. At energies greater than 1,000 MeV it is assumed that the differential intensity of the nuclide flow is proportional to $E^{-2.5}$.

Ratios (1) were calculated on a computer with allowance for (2)—(5). The results are listed in Table 1.

The one-star yields of P^{32}, P^{33} and S^{35} isotopes, obtained in (5) bearing in mind that 0.9% of the stars form on argon, are $4.6 \cdot 10^{-4}$, $3.8 \cdot 10^{-4}$ and $8.5 \cdot 10^{-4}$, respectively. Table 1 shows that differing evaluations lie within the error of measurement.

TABLE 1. Argon spallation yield of isotopes in one star

Nuclide	Half-life	One-star yield	Nuclide	Half-life	One-star yield
Fe^{18}	1.87 hr	$2.34 \cdot 10^{-5}$	Si^{32}	710 years	$2.48 \cdot 10^{-5}$
Ne^{24}	3.4 min	$7.46 \cdot 10^{-6}$	P^{30}	2.55 min	$6.54 \cdot 10^{-5}$
Na^{22}	2.6 years	$3.15 \cdot 10^{-5}$	P^{32}	14.3 days	$4.84 \cdot 10^{-4}$
Na^{24}	15.0 hr	$4.68 \cdot 10^{-5}$	P^{33}	24.4 days	$2.26 \cdot 10^{-4}$
Mg^{28}	21.4 hr	$4.62 \cdot 10^{-5}$	S^{35}	87.1 days	$5.64 \cdot 10^{-4}$
Al^{28}	2.3 min	$1.49 \cdot 10^{-4}$	S^{37}	5.04 min	$5.76 \cdot 10^{-5}$
Al^{29}	6.56 min	$2.18 \cdot 10^{-4}$	Cl^{34}	38.4 min	$1.27 \cdot 10^{-4}$
Si^{31}	2.62 hr	$1.02 \cdot 10^{-4}$	Cl^{36}	$3.1 \cdot 10^{5}$ years	$2.25 \cdot 10^{-3}$
			Cl^{38}	37.3 min	$(3.09 \cdot 10^{-3})$

Isotope yields of one star, calculated as a function of the depth of the atmosphere, are listed in Table 2.

TABLE 2. Isotope yield of one star at different depths of the atmosphere

Depth of the atmosphere, g/cm^2	One-star yield						
	$Na^{22}\,10^{-5}$	$Na^{24}\,10^{-5}$	$Si^{32}\,10^{-5}$	$P^{32}\,10^{-4}$	$P^{33}\,10^{-4}$	$S^{35}\,10^{-4}$	$Cl^{36}\,10^{-3}$
50	3.23	4.80	2.50	5.08	2.35	5.82	2.28
150	3.38	4.98	2.50	5.06	2.34	5.78	2.27
250	3.36	4.89	2.41	5.02	2.32	5.73	2.27
350	3.29	7.87	2.39	4.94	2.30	5.70	2.26
450	3.23	4.76	2.38	4.92	2.28	5.67	2.24
550	3.17	4.68	2.36	4.86	2.26	5.66	2.24
650	3.13	4.63	2.35	4.85	2.25	5.64	2.24
750	3.11	4.60	2.35	4.84	2.25	5.64	2.24
850	3.08	4.57	2.35	4.83	2.24	5.64	2.24
950	3.06	4.52	2.34	4.81	2.23	5.63	2.23
1050	3.06	4.52	2.34	4.80	2.22	5.62	2.23

With increasing depth of the atmosphere, the energy spectrum of cosmic-ray nuclides shifts toward lower energies. Most of the stars forming at considerable depths have a limited number of rays. This accounts for the uneven distribution of the stars. The drop in yield with increasing depth of the atmosphere is, of course, most significant for Na^{22} and least significant for Cl^{36}.

BIBLIOGRAPHY

1. Rossi, B. Chastitsy bol'shikh energii (High-Energy Particles).— Gosudarstvennoe izdatel'stvo tekhniko-teoreticheskoi literatury, Moskva. [Russian translation, 1955.]
2. Bhandari, N. et al. Cosmic-Ray-Produced Mg^{28}, Si^{31}, S^{38}, Cl^{38} and Other Short-Lived Radioisotopes in Wet Precipitation.— Tellus, Vol. 18, No. 2—3, pp. 504—515. 1966.
3. Husain, L. and P. K. Kuroda. Magnesium-28 in Rain: Produced by Cosmic Rays.— Science, Vol. 154, No. 3653. 1966.

4. L a l , D., J. R. A r n o l d, and M. H o n d a. Cosmic-Ray-Produced Rates of Be^7 in Oxygen and P^{32}, P^{33}, S^{35} in Argon and Mountain Altitudes. — Phys. Rev., Vol. 118, p. 1626. 1960.

5. L a l , D. and B. P e t e r s. Cosmic-Ray-Produced Radioactivity on the Earth. — In: Handbuch der Physik, Vol. XLVI. Berlin — Heidelberg — New York, Springer-Verlag. 1967.

6. P e r k i n s , R. W. et al. Chlorine-38 and Sulphur-38 Produced by Cosmic Radiation. — Nature, Vol. 205, No. 4793, pp. 790 — 791. 1965.

7. R o d e l , W. Sodium-24 Produced by Cosmic Radiation. — Nature, Vol. 200, pp. 999 — 1000. 1963.

8. R u d s t a m , G. Systematics of Spallation Yields. — Z. Naturforschung, Vol. 21a, No. 7, pp. 1027 — 1041. 1966.

UDC 551.510.7

LONG-LIVED ALPHA-RADIOACTIVITY IN FALLOUT
AT VILNIUS AND AT VARIOUS ATLANTIC LATITUDES

B. I. Styro, N. K. Shpirkauskaite, V. N. Gasyunas, and
V. M. Kuptsov

The isotope composition of long-lived alpha-radiation in atmospheric precipitation at Vilnius and at different latitudes over the Atlantic is investigated. Relevant data were obtained for each 10° latitudinal strip between 60°N and 70°S over the Atlantic from 16 October 1966 till 1 March 1967 and from 21 October 1967 till 26 January 1968. The fallout density of long-lived alpha-radioactivity is described by the geographical distribution with maxima at $50-40°$ and $20-30°$N and S and with minima at $40-30°$N and S. The U^{238}, Th^{232} and Pu^{239} contents in atmospheric precipitation were measured using an alpha-spectrometer with ion chamber, and their ratios were calculated. For Vilnius, the U^{238} values are 0.41 to $7.33 \cdot 10^{-5}$ g/g, the Th^{232} values are 0.014 to $7.27 \cdot 10^{-5}$ g/g, and the Pu^{239} values are 0.04 to $3.10 \cdot 10^{-11}$ g/g; over the Atlantic the values are 0.18 to $9.5 \cdot 10^{-5}$, 0 to $(0.52-1.8) \cdot 10^{-5}$ and 0.06 to $7.37 \cdot 10^{-10}$ g per gram of ash residue, respectively.

Radioactive pollution has most seriously threatened the world ocean over the last two decades. One of the main sources of pollution is atmospheric fallout in the form of dry aerosols and atmospheric precipitation.

To date, a great amount of experimental data has been collected on the concentration of artificial radioactive substances at different points of the world ocean, but the distribution of α-radioactivity in atmospheric precipitation over the ocean has been studied so far comparatively little. Only data calculated by Revell et al. /3/ are available on the amount and concentration of long-lived α-radioactive substances over the water surface.

Our investigation was based on samples of atmospheric precipitation collected on board whalers sailing from the Baltic Sea to Antarctica between 16 October 1966 and 1 March 1967 and between 21 October 1967 and 26 January 1968. The voyage routes are shown in Figure 1, where the sample numbers are also indicated.

Atmospheric precipitation samples were taken with a waterproof poly-ethylene cone with a $0.3\text{-}m^2$ gauze stretched horizontally over it. A three-layer ash-free paper filter was placed on the bottom of the cone. Radio-active substances washed off the gauze during rain would fall into the cone to be retained by the filter. According to our observations at Vilnius, up to 10% of the α-active substances passed with the rainwater through the filter. As compared to the water vessel, the efficiency of collection was about 40%. The conditions of observation at Vilnius differed from those over the sea, where wind speed strongly affected the efficiency of collection. An analysis of ground synoptic maps of the hemisphere has revealed, however, that anticyclonic weather with reduced wind speed predominated during both voyages over almost 2/3 of the route (from 30°N to 40°S) across the Atlantic, the wind speed being 8 to 12 m/sec in only four cases. The sampler was removed at higher wind speeds.

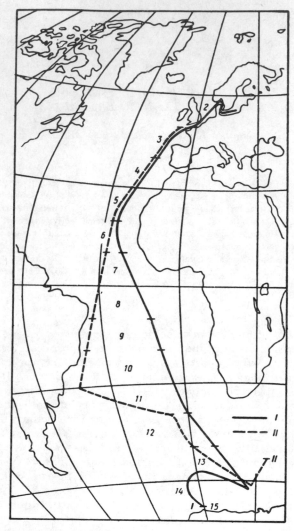

FIGURE 1. Voyage routes.

— first voyage (16 Oct. 1966 — 1 Mar. 1967); - - - second voyage (21 Oct. 1967—26 Jan. 1968).

The sampler was installed on the upper bridge. The gauze was replaced every 10° of latitude between 60°N and 70°S. The gauze exposure time is the time the ship remained in each 10° latitudinal strip. During the first voyage, one more gauze was exposed to investigate the changes in atmospheric precipitation with increasing distance from the continent.

Three samples were thus obtained: for under 200 km, for 200—800 km, and for over 800 km distance. The gauzes were processed in Vilnius after each voyage. The gauze would be calcinated in a porcelain dish at 350—400°C and the ash residue weighed. Eleven (of the 28) samples were radio-chemically analyzed to separate the long-lived α-active radioisotopes U, Th and Pu^{239}.

Uranium and thorium isotopes were separated from atmospheric samples by the method adopted at the absolute age laboratory of the Geological Institute of the USSR Academy of Sciences, Moscow /4/. Uranium isotopes were separated by quadruple extraction in diethyl ether. Thorium isotopes were also extracted, and separated on Dowex anion-exchange resin 2×10. The amount of uranium separated by chemical processing of the samples was determined with Pu^{238} as tracer. The uranium yield was usually 20 to 60%.

The main difficulty in the radiochemical separation of the isotopes and subsequent measurement was the low activity of the samples. Extensive radiometric measurements were therefore necessary to obtain the accuracy required; they took many days. The different isotopes in the samples, electrolytically precipitated on nickel disks, were measured using an alpha-spectrometer with ion chamber, built in the absolute age laboratory. The chamber background was about $5 \cdot 10^{-4}$ counts per minute per channel. The spectra were recorded on an AI-100 ("Raduga") 100-channel amplitude analyzer. The spectrometer resolution was about 1% for the alpha line of uranium. Preparations with 10^{-7} g of uranium per gram give a count rate comparable to the background; only the absolute content of uranium can be assessed, but not its isotope composition (Table 1).

The overall alpha activity of the samples was measured autoradiographically, using nuclear photoplates of A-2 type (with a 50-μ thick emulsion layer), at a 20-day exposure.

The latitudinal distribution of overall α-active fallout is represented in Figure 2, which shows noticeable differences between the northern and the southern hemisphere, but the asymmetry levels out as time passes from the last nuclear tests. A comparison of the results of the two voyages makes it clear. The noticeable difference in fallout between the two hemispheres confirms an earlier observation /1,6/, that the stratospheric reservoirs of fission products of the northern and southern hemisphere are separate.

En route from the Baltic Sea to the shores of North Africa, the ship during the first voyage passed through a zone of cyclonic activity, with warm and secondary cold fronts. Little precipitation was observed up to 40°N (less than 3 mm). Its radioactivity was higher, whereas between 30 and 40°N there was no precipitation and a minimum of radioactive fallout. A similar picture was observed during the second voyage: precipitation up to 40°N was 6—7 mm and caused a maximum of radioactive fallout. In the 40—30°N strip there was no precipitation and a minimum of fallout (Figure 2).

TABLE 1. Content of various alpha-radioisotopes at different latitudes over the Atlantic

Sample number	Latitude	U, g/g	Th, g/g	Th/U	Pu^{239}, g/g	Pu/U
	First voyage					
3	40—50° N	$(0.87 \pm 0.15)10^{-5}$	—	0.71	$(0.37 \pm 0.10)10^{-10}$	$(4.26 \pm 1.87)10^{-6}$
5	30—20° N	$(0.57 \pm 0.18)10^{-5}$	—	1.01	$(0.19 \pm 0.11)10^{-10}$	—
7	10—0° N	$(5.0 \pm 1.06)10^{-5}$	$(1.8 \pm 0.26)10^{-5}$	0.37 ± 0.11	—	—
13	50—60° N	$(1.75 \pm 0.58)10^{-5}$	$(0.98 \pm 0.24)10^{-5}$	0.56 ± 0.36	$(0.84 \pm 0.42)10^{-10}$	—
15	Antarctic shores.....	$(3.9 \pm 0.78)10^{-5}$	—	0.42	—	—
	Distance from shore, 0—200 km	$(9.5 \pm 2.38)10^{-5}$	—	0.15	$(7.37 \pm 1.83)10^{-10}$	$(7.76 \pm 3.86)10^{-6}$
	Distance from shore, 800 km	$(3.47 \pm 0.64)10^{-5}$	$(0.52 \pm 0.07)10^{-5}$	0.15 ± 0.02	$(1.49 \pm 0.50)10^{-10}$	$(4.28 \pm 2.23)10^{-6}$
	Second voyage					
3	40—50° N	$(0.46 \pm 0.14)10^{-5}$	—	—	$(0.07 \pm 0.04)10^{-10}$	—
6	20—10° N	$(0.67 \pm 0.16)10^{-5}$	—	—	$(0.20 \pm 0.06)10^{-10}$	—
11	30—40° S	$(0.43 \pm 0.07)10^{-5}$	—	—	$(0.15 \pm 0.04)10^{-10}$	$(3.50 \pm 1.56)10^{-6}$
14	60—70° S	$(0.18 \pm 0.04)10^{-5}$	—	—	$(0.06 \pm 0.02)10^{-10}$	$(3.67 \pm 1.63)10^{-6}$

Note: Here and below, a dash indicates no measurement.

204

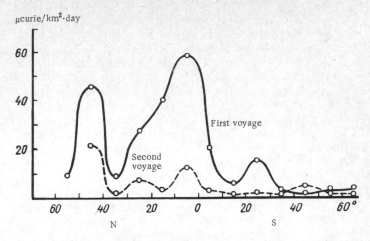

μcurie/km²·day

First voyage

Second voyage

60   40   20   0   20   40   60°
N   S

FIGURE 2. Density of long-lived alpha-active fallout over different latitudes of
the Atlantic.

At the same latitudes (40—50°) in the southern hemisphere, where a
cyclonic situation was observed during the first voyage but no precipitation,
there was no increase in radioactive fallout. Rains (20 mm) at 40—50°S
during the second voyage caused a noticeable increase in the fallout of
α-radionuclides. In the zone between 30°N (1st voyage), 10°N (2nd voyage)
and the equator there was a maximum of α-radioactive fallout. Precipitation there was little but continuous: 1 mm during the first voyage, 3 mm
during the second. This suggests that the fallout of α-radioisotopes in the
equatorial zone depends on the concentration of α-active isotopes in the
ocean water, which penetrate the atmosphere from the water surface; the
penetration of saline particles from the ocean surface into the atmosphere
is known /7, 8/.

By advection and mixing of ocean waters, the distribution of fission
radionuclides at the water surface differs considerably from the radioactivity distribution in the atmosphere over the ocean /2/. Fission radioactivity maxima have the same position in the ocean and atmosphere in the
middle latitudes, but the equatorial region, characterized by a concentration
minimum in the atmosphere, was in a zone of maximum because of peculiar
hydrophysical characteristics. The α-active atmospheric fallout in that
zone also pointed to a maximum, which apparently indicated the artificial
origin of the α-radioisotopes accumulating in equatorial waters and
penetrating the atmosphere along with saline particles.

An analysis of data on the contents of different α-radioisotopes of U, Th
and Pu^{239} confirms that the equatorial-zone maximum of α-radioactive
fallout is due to aerosols of marine origin (Table 1). Actually, a comparison
of the various isotope contents in different latitudinal strips shows that the
α-radioactivity of the equatorial zone is due mainly to U^{238} and Pu^{239}, while
Th contributes comparatively little (see the Th/U ratio). Th^{232} penetration
from seawater into the atmosphere is practically excluded because, in
contrast to uranium and plutonium, thorium in water is mainly in an insoluble
form and is deposited on the bottom after reaching the ocean. Increased
fallout at the Antarctic shores (1st voyage) can be ascribed to jet streams,

which at that time were flowing from South America toward the Antarctic shores and carrying continental aerosols.

We determined the contents of the various isotopes for some latitudinal strips only, which makes it hardly possible to judge the latitudinal distribution of their fallout from individual measurements (Table 1). One can nevertheless discern a tendency of the U^{238} content to decrease in fallout with increasing distance from the continent, which points to the continental origin of U^{238}. The measured Th^{232} amounts also correspond to its contents in rocks. The low values of the Th/U ratio indicate that a certain part of the U^{238} fallout is of artificial origin, since its values in natural objects, such as soil and rocks, are 3.7—4 (see data in Table 1), whereas the concentrations of natural U^{238} in seawater are of the order of 10^{-8} g/g /5/.

The Pu^{239} content in atmospheric fallout over the Atlantic varies between 0.06 and $7.37 \cdot 10^{-10}$ g per gram of the ash residue (Table 1). Pu^{239} fallout is higher in the southern hemisphere. Over the Atlantic, it was almost only a tenth during the second voyage, as compared to 1966.

To compare data on long-lived α-radioisotopes over the ocean and continents we investigated the isotope composition of long-lived α-radioactivity in atmospheric fallout collected at Vilnius. The 0.11-m^2 wide recipients with 10-cm high borders were installed on a TV tower at six levels up to a height of 200 m between 1966 and 1968. The exposure time was about 5 months in winter and about 7 months in summer.

Characteristic relationships exist in nature between the different natural isotopes for the earth's crust, seawater, igneous rocks, and cosmic dust. At present, these ratios are being determined experimentally /5/.

TABLE 2. Contents of different long-lived alpha-radioactive isotopes in samples of atmospheric fallout taken at Vilnius on a TV tower

Sampling height, m	$U \times 10^{-5}$, g/g	$\dfrac{U^{234}}{U^{238}}, (\gamma)$	Io/Th^{232}	$\dfrac{RdTh}{Th^{232}}$	Io/UX_1	$Th \times 10^{-5}$, g/g	Th/U	$Pu^{239} \times \times 10^{-12}$, g/g	$Pu/U \times \times 10^{-7}$
\multicolumn{10}{c}{Winter period 4 Nov. 1966 — 5 Apr. 1967}
30	1.69	1.13	0.88	1.01	—	7.27	—	3.50	2.10
90	1.22	1.08	0.97	1.42	0.18	0.81	0.66	5.50	4.50
130	6.50	1.14	—	—	—	0.35	0.54	0.39	0.60
\multicolumn{10}{c}{Summer period 7 Apr. 1967 — 5 Nov. 1967}
30	1.80	1.00	0.81	—	0.10	0.72	0.40	2.10	1.14
103	0.71	0.99	—	—	—	0.01	0.02	2.70	3.80
140	0.44	1.07	—	—	—	0.03	0.06	1.90	4.24
160	0.14	0.96	—	—	—	0.09	0.21	1.50	3.70
200	1.82	0.89	—	—	—	0.29	0.16	21.0	11.6
\multicolumn{10}{c}{Winter period 10 Nov. 1967 — 14 Apr. 1968}
30	2.41	1.14	—	—	—	0.24	0.10	1.90	0.79
90	5.13	1.13	—	—	—	4.82	0.94	3.50	0.69
140	3.07	1.15	—	—	—	0.58	0.19	5.60	1.80
160	7.33	1.14	1.58	1.10	0.29	3.74	0.51	5.90	0.81
200	5.43	1.18	—	—	—	3.31	0.61	5.10	0.94

We tried to determine the origin of atmospheric fallout over Vilnius from the proportions of the different isotopes; the results are listed in Table 2. In most samples, the uranium and thorium isotopes are not in radioactive equilibrium. The values obtained indicate a natural origin, with some artificial U^{238}; this can be seen from the Th/U ratios in samples taken both from Vilnius and from over the Atlantic (Tables 1, 2). A comparison of Pu^{239} fallout densities over the Atlantic and at Vilnius show the latter to be almost a hundredth of the former (Tables 1, 2). This indicates that Pu^{239} in the atmosphere is basically of technogenic origin.

In winter Vilnius samples, the U^{234}/U^{238} ratios are the same as those for seawater ($\gamma = 1.15 \pm 0.01$ /5/) (Table 2) which indicates that, in the cold season, the predominant fallout is due to strong circulation of marine air masses over the Baltic territory.

In summer, the U^{234}/U^{238} ratios are similar to those of earth-crust rocks, which points to a continental origin of long-lived α-active fallout. Establishing from what kind of soil the dusts stem is impossible owing to the long exposure of the samples (5 to 7 months). During such periods of time the Lithuanian territory is swept by varied air masses, and the fallout samples only reflect the total effect.

$Io(Th^{230})$ and $RdTh(Th^{228})$ were measured only in five samples, and any conclusion would therefore be premature (Table 2). It may be said, however, that the Io/Th^{232} ratios correspond to earth-crust values.

The Th/U ratios (in weight units) in Vilnius and ocean fallout samples are much lower than in natural formations. This may be due to the presence of artificial U^{238} and Th^{232} or to some fractionation features during the formation of the atmospheric dust.

BIBLIOGRAPHY

1. L a v r e n c h i k, V. N., G. N. S o f i e v, and V. M. S h u b k o. Sostav i kontsentratsiya radioaktivnykh zagryaznenii vozdukha v Indiiskom i Tikhom okeanakh v 1959—1960 gg. po materialam ekspeditsii e/s "Vityaz'"(Composition and Concentration of Radioactive Air Pollution over the Indian and Pacific Oceans in 1959—1960, from Data of the "Vityaz" Expedition).— In sbornik: Radioaktivnaya zagryaznennost' morei i okeanov (Radioactive Pollution of Seas and Oceans). Moskva, "Nauka." 1964.
2. N e l e p o, B. A. Issledovanie zakonomernostei rasprostraneniya radioaktivnogo zagryazneniya v moryakh i okeanakh (Investigation of Distribution Patterns of Radioactive Pollution in Seas and Oceans).— Author's summary of a Doctoral thesis (physical-mathematical sciences). Moskva. 1968.
3. R e v e l l, R. et al. Yadernaya fizika i okeanografiya (Nuclear Physics and Oceanography).— In: International Conference on the Peaceful Uses of Nuclear Energy, Geneva, 1955. Vol. 3. Problems of Public Health and Safety. Moskva, Medgiz. 1958.
4. C h e r d y n t s e v, V. V. et al.— Izv. AN SSSR, Seriya Geologicheskaya, Vol. 4, 1967.
5. C h e r d y n t s e v, V. V. Uran-234 v prirode (Uran-234 in Nature).— Moskva, Atomizdat. 1969.
6. J u n g e, C. Air Chemistry and Radioactivity.— New York, Academic Press. 1963.
7. B l a n c h a r d, D. C. and A. H. W o o d c o c k.— Tellus, Vol. 9, p. 145. 1957.
8. K i e n t z l e r, C. F., A. B. A r o n s, D. C. B l a n c h a r d, and A. H. W o o d c o c k.— Tellus, Vol. 6, pp. 1—7, 1954.

UDC 551.510.71

SEASONAL BERYLLIUM-7 VARIATIONS IN GROUND LEVEL AIR

L. I. Gedeonov, Z. G. Gritchenko, and V. M. Flegontov

The content of cosmogonic Be^7 in ground level air and atmospheric precipitation was determined in 1960 — 1968 in the environs of Leningrad from the γ-radiation with the aid of a scintillation and a Ge(Li) drift gamma-spectrometer.

In periods when the atmosphere was cleansed of short-lived radionuclides of artificial origin, Be^7 was determined in daily samples of atmospheric aerosols filtered from the air. It was found that Be^7 in ground level air sometimes varied tenfold from day to day.

A great amount of experimental material was collected in the seven years of observations and an average curve was plotted of the mean-monthly variation of Be^7 concentration in ground level air. It was thus possible to distinguish a constant and a variable component in the varation of Be^7 concentration. Be^7, continuously being formed in the troposphere, is apparently the constant component, with superimposed periodic components due to seasonal Be^7 penetration from the stratosphere, attaining great values in summer.

A statistical analysis of the variable component showed that it is well described by a Gauss function of type $P(t) \sim e^{-t^2/2\sigma^2}$, where t is the number of days elapsed from the peak Be^7 concentration in the ground level air, and $\sigma = 60 \pm 2$ days is the parameter of the Gaussian distribution.

Be^7 concentration in ground level air is highest every June, $(9 \pm 1) \cdot 10^{-14}$ curie/m^3, and lowest in December, $(3.5 \pm 1) \cdot 10^{-14}$ curie/m^3.

There is a 3-to-2 ratio of the overall number of Be^7 atoms in ground level air arriving from the stratosphere to those arriving from the troposphere.

A constant average of $(4.6 \pm 0.2) \cdot 10^{-5}$ atom of Be^7 is deposited annually per square centimeter of ground in the Leningrad area.

Nuclear reactions of types (p, n), (n, p), (p, α), $(n, 2n)$, $(p, xp\, yn)$, $(n, xp\, yn)$ etc., are always taking place in the atmosphere under the effect of cosmic rays. The latter two lead to the formation of cosmogonic radionuclides, which are of much interest in geophysical investigations.

Basing himself on experimental studies of neutron absorption in the atmosphere and taking into account neutron leakage into space, Fireman /11/ evaluated the rate of formation of neutrons that participate in the formation of cosmogonic radionuclides in the atmosphere at 4.3 $cm^{-2} \cdot sec^{-1}$. This agrees with Korff's evaluation /14/.

The cosmogonic radionuclide Be^7 most frequently forms by spallation of the nuclides $O^{16}(p(n), xp\, yn)$ Be^7, $N^{14}(p(n), xp\, yn)$ Be^7 and $C^{12}(p(n), xp\, yn)$ Be^7. Lal thought that neutrons of 30—50 MeV play the main role in the formation of cosmogonic radionuclides /16/. He assumes that the rate of their formation at a given point in the atmosphere is proportional to the frequency of the initiation of nuclear reactions of the "star" type, but this in turn depends on the distribution of the cosmic-ray flow density in the atmosphere, which depends on altitude, geomagnetic latitude, and time of observation.

Cosmogonic Be[7] in air was first discovered by V. A. Davydenko and V. K. Voitovetskii in the USSR in 1954, independently of Arnold and Al-Salih in the U.S.A. /9/. Benioff's /10/ and Lal's /5, 15/ theoretical calculations demonstrated that Be[7] concentration depends very much on the geomagnetic latitude of the place, which determines the energy spectrum of protons responsible for the formation of Be[7].

The first and most comprehensive data on Be[7] concentration in the stratosphere were obtained by the U.S. Ministry of Defence within the framework of a high-altitude sampling program /12/. An analysis of these data and of the vertical Be[7] concentration over Australia /13/ corroborates the results calculated from radioactive equilibrium conditions. The only exceptions are layers in the vicinity of the tropopause, where the exchange of air masses between stratosphere and troposphere plays a significant role /8/.

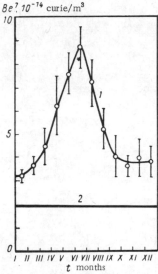

FIGURE 1. Mean-monthly Be[7] concentration in the ground layer of the atmosphere near Leningrad, from several years of observation:

1) observed concentration; 2) concentration due to Be[7] formation in the troposphere.

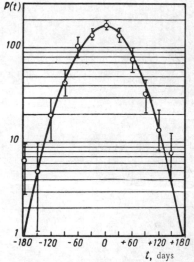

FIGURE 2. Gaussian distribution for $\sigma = 60$ days and the difference between observed and minimum Be[7] concentrations in the ground layer of the atmosphere near Leningrad.

In 1959—1965, V. N. Lavrenchik obtained data on Be[7] concentration in the atmospheric layer over water expanses for a wide range of latitudes, aboard expeditionary vessels of the USSR Academy of Sciences.

Data on continuous observations of Be[7] concentration variations in the ground layer of the atmosphere and atmospheric precipitation in the Leningrad area for 1960—1961 were first published in /7/. The present paper reviews the results of observations made up to the end of 1968.

In the presence of short-lived fission products Be[7] was usually determined radiochemically /5, 6/, and in their absence, by direct measurement in a gamma-radiation sample in the region of about 480 keV /7/.

In our case, the Be^7 concentrations were determined throughout the observation period with the aid of a scintillation gamma-spectrometer with sodium-iodide crystal. Such measurements are only possible when no gamma radiation of about 500 keV energy, such as $Ba^{140} + La^{140}$ and Ru^{103}, exists in the region of the 500 keV photopeak. Samples containing such radionuclides were measured with a precision gamma-spectrometer with Ge(Li)-drift detector /3/.

The diurnal Be^7 concentration in the ground layer of the atmosphere has been determined in the Leningrad area since 1966. There were sometimes tenfold variations under stationary meteorological conditions. Systematic measurements were also carried out every five days, to establish the mean-monthly Be^7 concentrations there.

Up to the end of 1968, the mean-monthly data covered seven years of observation, and an average curve of annual variation could be drawn for the Be^7 concentration in the ground layer of the atmosphere in the Leningrad area (Figure 1 and Table 1). The curve in Figure 1 has a constant component and a variable one.

TABLE 1. Mean-monthly Be^7 content in the ground layer of the atmosphere in the Leningrad area in 1960—1961 and 1964—1968 (concentration given in 10^{-15} curie/m^3 up to the end of the month)

Month	Year							Average for all years
	1960	1961	1964	1965	1966	1967	1968	
January	—	35	35	35	32	30	25	32 ± 3
February	34	42	39	40	33	40	30	37 ± 4
March	59	53	44	50	37	38	34	45 ± 8
April	58	67	82	85	50	60	40	63 ± 13
May	76	100	81	72	60	75	68	76 ± 9
June	100	100	89	90	80	70	80	87 ± 9
July	98	80	58	68	65	70	65	72 ± 10
August	85	45	30	50	52	53	52	52 ± 9
September........	58	—	26	32	49	41	37	40 ± 9
October	49	—	—	34	32	37	29	36 ± 5
November	50	—	—	48	35	32	33	40 ± 8
December	40	—	—	33	54	29	33	38 ± 7

A comparison of the seasonal variation in the concentration of artificial radionuclides and of Be^7 in the ground layer of the atmosphere reveals Be^7 components forming in the troposphere and stratosphere. The time of residence of radioactive aerosols in the lower troposphere is about 10 days /4/, and a great part of the constant component of the curve can apparently be ascribed to the Be^7 continuously forming in the troposphere under the effect of the penetrating cosmic rays. The periodic inflow of Be^7 from the stratospheric source, with a maximum in the summer months, is superimposed on the constant component. A similar variation was noticed by Lal and Suess /17/.

Observations conducted during the 20th voyage of the R/V "Mikhail Lomonosov" have shown that minimum, almost constant levels of Be^7 ($\approx 3 \cdot 10^{-14}$ curie/m^3) have been recorded at different times of the year in the equatorial parts of the Atlantic and Pacific. This Be^7 concentration is almost equal to the constant component in the Leningrad area. The inflow of radioactive aerosols from the stratosphere is known to be minimum in the equatorial zone; it can therefore be assumed that the minimum levels recorded in the ground layer of the atmosphere are mainly comprised of Be^7 formed in the troposphere.

A statistical analysis of the variation in Be^7 concentration has shown that the difference between the observed and the minimum concentration is well described by a Gauss function:

$$P(t) \sim e^{-\frac{t^2}{2\sigma^2}} ,$$

where t is the number of days elapsed since the Be^7 concentration attained a maximum in the ground layer of the atmosphere, and $\sigma = 60 \pm 2$ days is the parameter of the Gaussian distribution. Figure 2 shows the distribution of experimental data on the variable component in the Leningrad area.

A similar distribution can be found in the annual variation of long-lived artificial nuclide concentration in the ground layer /2/. Every year, the difference between observed and minimum concentrations is also described by a Gaussian distribution with $\sigma = 60$ days. The minimum concentration of long-lived radioactive admixtures from the stratosphere is 18% of the maximum; this value may be adopted for Be^7 from the stratosphere as well. The concentration of Be^7 formed in the troposphere should then be regarded as constant ($\approx 2 \cdot 10^{-14}$ curie/m^3). The Be^7 amount annually fed by the stratosphere is in the ratio of approximately 3 to 2 relative to the latter value.

According to the results of 7 years of observations, the average number of Be^7 atoms deposited annually per cm^2 of ground in the Leningrad area is $(4.6 \pm 0.2) \cdot 10^5$, which agrees with data of Arnold and Ali-Salih /9/. Its constancy may indicate that the large-scale processes of air-mass exchange between stratosphere and troposphere feeds a roughly constant annual amount of Be^7 to the troposphere. In spite of the wide discrepancies between the annual meteorological conditions, the number of Be^7 atoms deposited on the ground remains constant. This may indirectly point to a constant high-energy component of cosmic rays which forms Be^7 atoms in nuclear reactions with the components of the atmospheric air.

BIBLIOGRAPHY

1. Gedeonov, L. I., Z. G. Gritchenko, and L. V. Drapchinskii. Raspredelenie Be^7 v atmosfere nad okeanom (Be^7 Distribution in the Atmosphere over the Ocean). — In Sbornik: Gidrofizicheskie issledovaniya Tikhogo i Atlanticheskogo okeanov v krugosvetnom plavanii NIS "Mikhail Lomonosov" (Hydrophysical Investigations of the Pacific and Atlantic Oceans During the World Voyage of R/V "Mikhail Lomonosov"). Sevastopol', Izd. MGI AN USSR, 1967.
2. Gedeonov, L. I., Z. G. Gritchenko, and V. M. Flegontov. Postuplenie radioaktivnykh produktov deleniya v prizemnyi sloi vozdukha v raione Leningrada ot yadernykh ispytanii 1964 — 1967 gg. (Penetration of Radioactive Fission Products from 1964—1967 Nuclear Tests into the Ground Layer of the Atmosphere in the Leningrad Area). — In this collection.

3. Gritchenko,Z.G.,T.P.Makarova,Yu.Ts. Oganesyan, Yu.E.Penionzhkevich, and
   A.V.Stepanov. Gamma-izluchenie nekotorykh redkozemel'nykh elementov-produktov deleniya
   U tyazhelymi ionami (Gamma Radiation of Some Rare-Earth Elements Due to Uranium Fission by
   Heavy Ions).— Yadernaya fizika, Vol.10, No.5. 1969.

4. Karol',I.L. and V.D.Vilenskii. Otsenka parametrov vertikal'nogo obmena i srednei skorosti
   udaleniya aerozolei oblakami i osadkami v nizhnei chasti troposfery po dannym o estestvennoi
   radioaktivnosti prizemnogo vozdukha (Evaluation of Vertical Exchange Parameters and Mean Rate of
   Aerosol Removal by Clouds and Precipitation in the Lower Troposphere, from Data on the Natural
   Radioactivity of the Ground Layer of the Atmosphere).— In Sbornik: Radioaktivnye izotopy v
   atmosfere i ikh ispol'zovanie v meteorologii (Radioactive Isotopes in the Atmosphere and their
   Utilization in Meteorology). Moskva, Atomizdat. 1965.

5. Lal,D. and B.Peters. Report No.1626 Presented by India at the 2nd International Conference on the
   Peaceful Uses of Nuclear Energy. Geneva. 1958.

6. Rysev,O.A., S.P.Rosyanov, M.I.Zhilkina, and L.I.Gedeonov. Metodika radiokhimicheskogo
   vydeleniya berilliya-7, fosfora-32, fosfora-33, sery-35 iz odnoi proby pri izuchenii atmosfernykh
   osadkov i aerozolei (Radiochemical Separation of Be^7, P^{32}, P^{33}, S^{35} from One Sample When Studying
   Atmospheric Precipitation and Aerosols).— Radiokhimiya, Vol. VII, No. 2. 1966.

7. Shvedov,V.P., Z.G.Gritchenko, and L.I.Gedeonov. Kontsentratsiya Be^7 v prizemnom sloe
   vozdukha i atmosfernykh osadkakh (Be^7 Concentration in the Ground Layer of the Atmosphere and in
   Atmospheric Precipitation).— Atomnaya energiya, Vol. 12, No. 1. 1962.

8. Junge,C. Air Chemistry and Radioactivity.— New York, Academic Press. 1963.

9. Arnold,J.R. and H.A.Ali-Salih. Beryllium-7 Produced by Cosmic Rays.— Science, Vol. 121,
   p.451. 1955.

10. Benioff,P.A. Cosmic-Ray Production Rate and Mean Removal Time of Beryllium-7 from the
    Atmosphere.— Phys. Rev., Vol. 104, p. 1122, 1956.

11. Fireman,E.L. Measurement of the (n, H^3) Cross Section in Nitrogen and its Relationship to the
    Tritium Production in the Atmosphere.— Phys. Rev., Vol. 91, p. 922. 1953.

12. HASP. High Altitude Sampling Program.— Washington 25. D.S.DASA 5396. 1961.

13. Hiks,B.B. Concentration of Be^7 Over Australia.— Nature, Vol. 216, p. 250. 1967.

14. Korff,S.A. Cosmic Ray Neutron Studies.— Nuovo Cimento Suppl., Vol. 18, p. 796. 1958.

15. Lal,D., P.K.Malhorta, and B.Peters. On the Production of Radioisotopes in the Atmosphere by
    Cosmic Radiation and their Application to Meteorology.— J. Atmos. Terrest. Phys., Vol. 12, p. 306. 1958.

16. Lal,D. and B.Peters. Cosmic-Ray-Produced Isotopes and their Application to the Problems in
    Geophysics.— Progress in Elementary Particle and Cosmic Ray Physics, Vol. 6. 1962.

17. Lal,D. and H.E.Suess. The Radioactivity of the Atmosphere and Hydrosphere.— Annual Review of
    Nuclear Science, Vol. 18, p. 407. 1968.

UDC 551.510.71

CONCENTRATION OF SODIUM RADIOISOTOPES IN THE GROUND LAYER OF THE ATMOSPHERE AND IN PRECIPITATION

R. Yu. Yasyulenis, V. Yu. Luyanas, and B. I. Styro

The paper examines measurements of sodium isotope concentrations in rainwater. The sodium was extracted with KU-2 cationite. Na^{22} was measured from the positronic radiation, and Na^{24} from beta-gamma coincidences. The ratios of Na^{22} and Na^{24} concentrations in the same rainwater sample were found to be 70 and 120. The measured ratios are compared with theoretical evaluations of the concentration ratios in the air.

The following sodium isotopes are formed as a result of "stars" in the atmosphere produced by the breaking of argon nuclei by cosmic rays: Na^{22} ($T_{1/2}=2.6$ years) and Na^{24} ($T_{1/2}=15.0$ hrs). The former was first measured in rainwater by Marquez et al. /5/, the latter by Roedel /6/. An attempt is made here at measuring them both simultaneously in one rainwater sample.

About 200 liters of rainwater were passed through KU-2 cationite. The 5-cm-diameter columns were 50 cm high. A 1.5 N hydrochloric acid solution was used for washing, and the eluate portions, containing 90% sodium, were concentrated by evaporation. The yields were determined with the aid of a flame photometer. Na^{22} was measured with a twin-channel positron spectrometer /1/, and Na^{24} with a beta-gamma coincidence setup /3/. The setup background was 3 counts per hr and its efficiency 1.8%. The results are listed in Table 1.

TABLE 1. Sodium isotope concentration in rainwater

Date of sampling	Concentration			Na^{22}/Na^{24}
	Na^+, mg/liter	Na^{22}, 10^4 atoms/liter	Na^{24}, atoms/liter	
4 May 1967	0.23	2.1	—	—
21 Nov. 1967	0.49	2.64	—	—
24 June 1968	0.32	7.95	640	122
30 Oct. 1968	0.17	0.87	130	67
15 June 1969	0.80	12.4	430	288
29 Oct. 1969	0.80	11.4	690	165
13 Nov. 1969	0.2	1.6	450	46

The volume of air from which the sodium had been collected by rain was unknown and allows no conclusion as to the concentration of these isotopes in the air. To a first approximation, however, the ratios may be considered as similar. It is therefore interesting to compare the calculated ratios of sodium isotopes in the air with those measured in water.

Assuming that the air mass is investigated during the interval between two successive washings by rain and that there is no exchange with the surrounding air masses, the isotope concentration change due to cosmic rays in the atmosphere is

$$\frac{dC_i}{dt} = k_i S - \lambda_i C_i,$$ (1)

where C_i is the concentration of the ith isotope in the air, λ_i is its decay constant, S is the rate of star formation, and k_i is the yield of the ith isotope of one star.

If the troposphere is assumed to be fairly well stirred and the rate of star formation is equal to the mean value S_τ for the troposphere, the isotope concentration can be calculated if certain hypotheses are made:

1) for a perfectly cleansed air mass $C_{i(t=0)} = 0$,

$$C_{i(t)} = \frac{k_i S_\tau}{\lambda_i} (1 - e^{-\lambda_i t});$$ (2)

2) for an air mass in which the isotope concentration has reached equilibrium typical of the troposphere, $C_{i(t=0)} = \dfrac{k_i S_t}{\lambda_i + \lambda_\tau}$, where $\lambda_\tau = \dfrac{1}{\tau_\tau}$, and τ_τ is the average lifetime of the aerosol in the troposphere:

$$C_{i(t)} = \frac{k_i S_\tau}{\lambda_i} \left[1 - e^{-\lambda_i t} \left(\frac{\lambda_\tau}{\lambda_i + \lambda_\tau} \right) \right];$$ (3)

3) for a stratospheric air mass shifted into the troposphere and with a typical stratospheric equilibrium concentration, $C_{i(t=0)} = \dfrac{k_i S_{st}}{\lambda_i + \lambda_{st}}$; the rate of star formation in the stratosphere is assumed to be sixfold that in the troposphere: $S_{st} = 6S_\tau$; the stratospheric lifetime of Na^{22} is $\tau_{st} = 12.5$ months /7/:

$$C_{i(t)} = \frac{k_i S_\tau}{\lambda_i} \left[1 + \left(\frac{S_{st}}{S_\tau} \frac{\lambda_i}{\lambda_i + \lambda_{st}} - 1 \right) e^{-\lambda_i t} \right].$$ (4)

Under these assumptions, the concentration ratios $\dfrac{C_{i(t)}}{C_{j(t)}}$ calculated from formulas (2) to (4) do not depend on the absolute rate of star formation, and can be calculated if the isotope yield of one star is known. The Na^{22} yield of one star was evaluated by Lal /4/; the same results were obtained by another method /2/, where the Na^{24} yield is also evaluated. Figure 1 represents the variation in time of the Na^{22}/Na^{24} ratio of isotope concentration in the air.

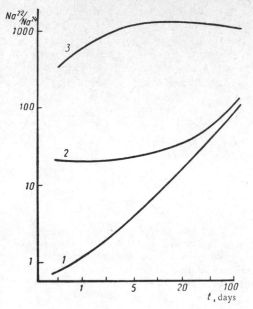

FIGURE 1. Ratio of sodium radioisotope concentration in a tropospheric air mass:

1) for a perfectly cleansed air mass; 2) for an air mass with equilibrium values typical of the troposphere; 3) for a stratospheric air mass shifted into the troposphere.

The ratios measured in rainwater (Table 1) are higher than those of tropospheric equilibrium concentrations (Figure 1, curves 1 and 2) and, in case 3, even higher than the values possible after prolonged irradiation in the troposphere. This would indicate the stratospheric origin of part of that air mass from which the sodium had been eluted. It must be stressed that the curves in Figure 1 have been plotted for mean values of the rate of star formation in the troposphere, which may not always be accurate for concentrations of the short-lived N^{24}. This would explain the divergence between experimental and theoretical data, although the explanation given above is not excluded.

BIBLIOGRAPHY

1. Luyanas, V. Yu. Tezisy 16 soveshchaniya po yadernoi spektroskopii i struktury atomnogo yadra (Reports of the 16th Conference on Nuclear Spectroscopy and Atomic Nucleus Structure). Moskva-Leningrad. 1966.
2. Yasyulenis, R.Yu., V. Yu. Luyanas, and B. I. Styro. K voprosu o skorostyakh vozniknoveniya kosmogennykh radioizotopov v reaktsiyakh "skalyvaniya" na argone (Argon Spallation Yields of Cosmogonic Radioisotopes). — In this collection.
3. Jasiulionis, R. Beta-gamma sutapimu schema mazsiems aktyvumams matuoti. — Mokslas ir technika, Vol. 8. 1969.
4. Lal, D. and B. Peters. Cosmic-Ray-Produced Radioactivity on the Earth. — Handbuch der Physik, Vol. XLVI/2 Berlin — Heidelberg — New York, Springer-Verlag. 1967.
5. Marquez, L., N. L. Costa, and I. G. Almeida. The Formation of Na-22 from Atmospheric Argon by Cosmic Rays. — Nuovo Cim. Sci., Vol. 6, p. 1292. 1957.
6. Roedel, W. Sodium-24 Produced by Cosmic Radiation. — Nature, Vol. 200, pp. 999 — 1000. 1963.
7. Roedel, W. Tracer Studies of Atmospheric Exchange Based on Measurements of Cosmic-Ray-Produced Na^{22}. — Naturforsch., Vol. 23a, pp. 51 — 55. 1968.

UDC 551.510.71

CONCENTRATION OF PHOSPHORUS RADIOISOTOPES IN THE GROUND LAYER OF THE ATMOSPHERE AND IN PRECIPITATION

D. A. Shopauskene and V. P. Shvedov

Results of systematic measurements of P^{32} and P^{33} concentrations are reported. The measurements were carried out in 1967—1969 in the areas of Vilnius, Lithuania and Cornesti (Moldavian SSR). The maximum values reached $13.8 \cdot 10^{-15}$ curie/m^3 for P^{32} and $3.6 \cdot 10^{-15}$ curie/m^3 for P^{33}; the minima did not exceed 0.4 and $0.15 \cdot 10^{-15}$ curie/m^3, respectively, in air samples taken from the ground layer of the atmosphere. The average P^{32} concentration in atmospheric precipitation was $0.47 \cdot 10^{-12}$ curie/liter at Vilnius; in samples taken from torrential rains at Cornesti the P^{32} concentration reached $10.9 \cdot 10^{-15}$ curie/liter.

A series of radioactive isotopes are created from the interaction of cosmic rays and argon atoms in the atmosphere. The rate of their formation is fairly dependent on altitude and geomagnetic latitude. The relationship was used for studying the vertical exchange of air masses. Most interesting cosmogonic radioisotopes are P^{32} and P^{33}, whose half-lives are commensurate with large-scale vertical motions in the atmosphere /5—7/.

Few publications have reported the results of phosphorus isotope measurements /4, 7, 8/, which are difficult owing to the low energies of β-radiation of P^{33} and its small half-life difference from the high-energy β-radiation of P^{32}.

Since 1967, we have been measuring the P^{32} and P^{33} concentrations in atmospheric samples taken at Vilnius. Large volumes of air (6 to $14 \cdot 10^4 m^3$) have been pumped through FPP-15—1.7 filters. Air filtration usually takes 3 days.

The samples were analyzed radiochemically by isotope dilution. The activated filter was burned and slightly calcinated in a muffle furnace at 450—500°C.

The calcinated sample was treated with a mixture of HCl and HNO_3 on a hot water bath. The insoluble residue filtered out was discarded, because special tests had shown it to contain no P^{32} or P^{33}. After preliminary dehydration with silicic acid, the phosphate ion was precipitated as ammonium phosphomolybdate in an acid solution of ammonium molybdate. After several chemical operations, it was precipitated as magnesium-ammonium phosphate ($MgNH_4PO_4$) and calcinated for an hour at 800—900°C. The magnesium pyrophosphate ($Mg_2P_2O_7$) obtained was weighed to determine the chemical yield, then subjected to the measurement of the β-radiation of P^{32} and P^{33}. Laboratory tests have shown /3/ that, during such a radiochemical analysis, radiophosphorus is purified of the other β-emitters present in the atmospheric samples.

Atmospheric precipitation samples (of 40 to 80 liter volume) were taken from surfaces covered with a polyethylene film. The phosphorus radio-isotopes were concentrated from the water by coprecipitation on iron hydroxide. The further steps in the chemical analysis were the same as above.

The chemical output of radiophosphorus fluctuated between 70 and 90% for air samples and between 65 and 80% for the samples of atmospheric precipitation. The radiochemical purity of the separated phosphorus was checked by the decay curves.

The β-radioactivity of the samples was measured on a low-background setup with an end-window SBG-13 counter with window thickness 3 mg/cm^2 (background 3 to 4 counts per min). The counter was calibrated against a C^{14}, Co^{60}, Tl^{204} and Sr^{90}+Y^{90} standard by plotting the counting efficiency vs. the energy of β-particles /1, 2/; the counting efficiency was taken as 21.7% for P^{32} and 10.0% for P^{33}.

The amount of P^{32} was determined from the decay curves after deduction of P^{33} activity; that of P^{33} was determined from the absorption of β-particle energy in aluminum filters and by decomposition of P^{32}+P^{33} decay curves. The P^{33} amounts obtained by these two methods were compared with each other and a mean value was taken as P^{33} activity. The relative error in P^{32} determination was under 10%; for P^{33}, it reached 30% for some samples.

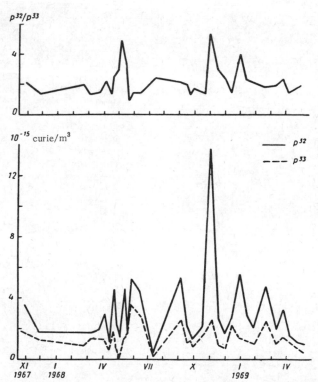

FIGURE 1. Concentrations of phosphorus radioisotopes, and their proportions in the ground layer of the atmosphere at Vilnius.

TABLE 1. P^{32} concentration in atmospheric precipitation (Vilnius)

Date	Time of sampling, hrs	P^{32} concentration, curie/liter
3 May 1967	1300 — 1400	1.31
	1450 — 1500	0.40
	1510 — 1600	0.32
5 October 1967	1742 — 1800	0.84
	1810 — 1820	0.44
	1835 — 1905	0.42
	1910 — 1920	0.42
	1950 — 2035	0.26
15 January 1968 (snow)	1000 — 1115	0.41
14 February 1968 (snow)	0815 — 0945	0.37
10 April 1968 (snow)	0035 — 0355	0.27
	0035 — 0355	0.21

TABLE 2. P^{32} concentration in atmospheric precipitation (Cornesti, Moldavian SSR)

Date	Time of sampling, hrs	P^{32} concentration, curie/liter
17 July 1967	1135 — 1140	10.9
	1330 — 1400	7.1
18 August 1967	1230 — 1250	2.3
	1250 — 1310	2.7
	1310 — 1330	2.0
	1330 — 1520	1.9
	1330 — 1520	2.0
20 June 1968	1605 — 1610	4.9
	1610 — 1625	2.7
	1630 — 1645	2.4
	1550 — 1705	2.0
	1710 — 1735	2.1
	1735 — 1800	2.0
	1800 — 1830	2.2
	1905 — 1937	1.6
	2010 — 2045	1.6
21 June 1968	1800 — 1810	1.8
	1812 — 1850	1.9
22 June 1968	0730 — 0853	1.1
	0853 — 0910	1.1
18 July 1968	0917 — 0930	0.5
	1300 — 1400	1.8
	1610 — 1634	1.5
	1907 — 1915	1.3
	2200 — 0350	0.6

The P^{32} and P^{33} concentrations observed in the ground layer of the atmosphere and their distribution in time are given in Figure 1. Peak P^{32} values attain $13.8 \cdot 10^{-15}$ curie$/m^3$ ($3.6 \cdot 10^{-15}$ curie$/m^3$ for P^{33}); the minimum values do not exceed 0.4 and $0.15 \cdot 10^{-15}$ curie$/m^3$, respectively; the mean concentrations are 2.68 and $1.4 \cdot 10^{-15}$ curie$/m^3$.

Figure 1 shows wide time fluctuations in the P^{32} and P^{33} concentrations. By and large, the P^{33} concentration repeats the variation in the P^{32} concentration. Against the background of these fluctuations one can notice a tendency of P^{32} and P^{33} concentrations to increase in April—June 1968, possibly due to a springtime increase in the intensity of vertical exchange. An increase in the P^{32}/P^{33} ratio indicates a "rejuvenation" of the samples, i.e., a release of air from the upper layers of the troposphere. An increase in the concentration of both P^{32} and P^{33} was noticed in some samples taken in September and November 1968 and in January—April 1969. Increases in both P^{32} and P^{33} are usually accompanied by an increase in their ratio as well.

The P^{32} concentration in atmospheric precipitation is given in Tables 1 and 2. The average is $0.47 \cdot 10^{-12}$ curie/liter for Vilnius, which corresponds to the coefficient of P^{32} concentration of atmospheric precipitation from the air ($0.2 \cdot 10^6$). In precipitation samples taken from torrential rain clouds at Cornesti the P^{32} concentration reached $10.9 \cdot 10^{-12}$ curie/liter.

Interestingly enough, the P^{32} concentration is always highest in the first samples of a precipitation, and then decreases. This may be partly due to droplet evaporation in an air not yet saturated with water vapor. A significant role is probably played here by the much longer duration of the activation of the first rain portions, formed in the clouds before the beginning of the precipitation. Samples taken later during the rainfall are formed mainly of drops which appeared during cloud regeneration, in a partly cleansed atmosphere, and have less extensive contact with the surrounding air.

BIBLIOGRAPHY

1. Vasil'ev, I. A., K. A. Petrzhak, and V. D. Sushchkovskii. Opredelenie absolyutnoi aktivnosti tortsovym schetchikom (Absolute Activity Determination with the End-Window Counter). — PTE, No. 4. 1961.
2. Vasil'ev, I. A. and K. A. Petrzhak. Effektivnost' tortsovogo schetchika v zavisimosti ot zhestkosti beta-spektrov (Efficiency of the End-Window Counter as a Function of the Hardness of Beta Radiation). — PTE, No. 1. 1959.
3. Shopauskene, D. A. and V. P. Shvedov. — Trudy AN LitSSR, Seriya B, Vol. 3(58). 1969.
4. Drevinsky, P. J., J. T. Wasson, F. C. Couble, and N. A. Dimon. Be^7, P^{32}, P^{33}, S^{35}. Stratosphere Concentrations and Artificial Production. — J. Geophys. Res., Vol. 69, No. 8, pp. 1457—1467. 1964.
5. Marquez, L. and N. L. Costa. The Formation of P^{32} from Atmospheric Argon by Cosmic Rays. — Nuovo Cimento, Vol. 2, p. 1038. 1955.
6. Marenco, A., D. Blanc, J. Fontan, J. Lacombe, and G. Grozat. — Chimie Analytique, No. 3, p. 50. 1968.
7. Lal, D., N. Narasappaya, and P. K. Zutshi. Phosphorus Isotopes P^{32} and P^{33} in Rain Water. — Nuclear Phys., Vol. 3, pp. 69—75. 1957.
8. Rama, and M. Honda. Natural Radioactivity in the Atmosphere. — J. Geophys. Res., Vol. 66, pp. 3227—3231. 1961.

UDC 551.510.7

RADIUM-226 IN ATMOSPHERIC PRECIPITATION, AND THE POSSIBILITIES FOR LEAD-210, BISMUTH-210 AND POLONIUM-210 TO PENETRATE THE ATMOSPHERE FROM THE EARTH'S SURFACE

V. D. Vilenskii

The author determined the intensity of atmospheric Ra^{226} and Pb^{210} fallout in the Moscow area in 1967—1969. It varied between 0.08 and 1.8 μcurie/$km^2 \cdot$day for Ra^{226} (mean-annual value 0.18 mcurie/$km^2 \cdot$yea and between 1 and 18.6 μcurie/$km^2 \cdot$day for Pb^{210} (mean-annual value 2.1 mcurie/$km^2 \cdot$year). The ratio of Ra^{226} to Pb^{210} concentrations in atmospheric precipitation varied between 0.024 and 0.222, the mean-annual value being 0.086. Assuming Ra^{226} penetrates the atmosphere from the earth's surface along with dust, the proportions of Pb^{210}, Bi^{210} and Po^{210} penetrating the atmosphere with the dust have been evaluated along with the overall concentration of these radioisotopes in atmospheric precipitation. The natural radioactivity of atmospheric dust is shown to possibly influence the proportion of isotopes used for evaluating the rate of atmospheric scavenging.

When dust from the earth's surface penetrates the atmosphere, it introduces natural radioactive isotopes contained in every object in nature. Of these isotopes we shall discuss Ra^{226}, parent isotope of Rn^{222}, as well as Pb^{210}, Bi^{210} and Po^{210}, i. e., those natural radioisotopes which form in the atmosphere upon decay of Rn^{222} and are widely used for studying atmospher scavenging. Obviously, the Ra^{226} content is an indication of Pb^{210}, Bi^{210} and Po^{210} penetration in the atmosphere with the dust.

It has been ascertained that Ra^{226} is present in noticeable concentrations (0.2 to $1 \cdot 10^{-12}$ curie/liter) in atmospheric precipitation /4, 6/. Nevertheless, the patterns of Ra^{226} behavior in the atmosphere and atmospheric precipitation are not very well known, and it would be interesting to determine the Ra^{226} content in atmospheric precipitation for a longer period of time and compare it with the Pb^{210} content. Such determinations were carried out in 1967—1969 in the Moscow area.

The precipitation was collected in a metal container. The samples were acidified to pH = 2 with nitric acid and evaporated to dryness. The dry residue was calcinated at 450— 500°C. The ashes (usually 1 g) were melted together with a mixture of alkali and soda after adding barium and lead salts as carriers. The radium was determined by the α-scintillation method from the α-radioactivity of Ra^{226} and its short-lived decay products after radiochemical purification and coprecipitation of the radium isotopes with barium sulfate. Pb^{210} was determined from the β-radiation of Bi^{210}, accumulated in preparations of lead sulfate, separated after lead purificatio on EDE-10P anionite. The rms error in the Ra^{226} determination did usuall not exceed 10% (5 to 10% for Pb^{210}). The results provide some idea as to the nature of Ra^{226} fallout in the Moscow area.

TABLE 1. Characteristics of Ra^{226} and Pb^{210} fallout in 1967—1969 in the Moscow area

Period	Fallout intensity, μ curie/km^2·day		Ra^{226} content in fallout, 10^{-12} curie/g (calculated for calcinated substance)	Ra^{226}/Pb^{210} concentration ratio (units of radio-activity)
	Ra^{226}	Pb^{210}		
July — November 1967	0.23	9.6	1.0	0.024
November 1967 — February 1968	1.8	12.0	3.0	0.150
1968				
February — March	0.45	10.7	1.3	0.042
April	0.50	18.6	2.0	0.027
April — May	0.45	11.7	2.8	0.038
May — July	0.23	3.7	1.3	0.062
July	0.31	2.0	1.6	0.155
August — September	0.24	9.0	0.3	0.027
September — October	0.08	< 1.4	0.3	—
October — November	0.50	6.7	1.5	0.075
November — December	0.45	4.7	1.6	0.096
December 1968 — January 1969	0.76	8.8	2.2	0.086
January — March 1969	1.2	5.4	1.7	0.222
March — April 1969	0.63	3.3	1.6	0.191
July 1967 — April 1969	0.64	7.8	1.8	0.082
April 1968 — April 1969	0.50	5.8	1.5	0.086

The rate of Ra^{226} fallout onto the earth's surface (Table 1) fluctuates between 0.08 and 1.8 μcurie/km^2·day, the mean-annual value* being 0.5 μcurie/km^2·day (0.18 mcurie/km^2·year). This corresponds to a mean-annual Ra^{226} concentration of approximately $0.3 \cdot 10^{-12}$ curie/liter in atmospheric precipitation, or almost the values obtained for atmospheric precipitation in other areas /4,6/. The Ra^{226} content in ashes falling with atmospheric precipitation (Table 1) fluctuates between 0.3 and $3 \cdot 10^{-12}$ curie/g, the mean-annual value being $1.5 \cdot 10^{-12}$ curie/g. The rate of Ra^{226} fallout depends both on its content in the fallout, and on the rate of the fallout. The fallout rate (in calculations for a calcinated substance) varied between 0.163 and 0.710 g/m^2·day during our period of investigation (mean-annual value 0.341 g/m^2·day). The observed fluctuations in the Ra^{226} rate of fallout and content in atmospheric precipitation obviously reflect certain local conditions, which determine the dustiness of the atmosphere and the radio-chemical composition of the atmospheric dust; in principle, these can be different in other areas. Besides, it should be remembered that Ra^{226} carried by atmospheric precipitation does not characterize its accumulation by the soil and plant cover, and only reflects the rate of exchange of Ra^{226} (or dust) between the earth's surface and the atmosphere.

---

* All mean-annual values refer to the period April 1968 — April 1969.

It was of interest to compare the Ra^{226} fallout characteristics found by us with those of Pb^{210} fallout in the same samples.

In 1967—1969, the rate of Pb^{210} fallout in the Moscow area (Table 1) varie between less than 1 and $18.6\,\mu$curie/km^2·day (mean-annual value $5.8\,\mu$ curie/km^2·day or 2.1 mcurie/km^2·year). This value is slightly lower than that found in 1961—1963 for the same area, which confirms the possibil of some changes in Pb^{210} fallout from year to year /1, 2/.

To assess the share of Pb^{210} from atmospheric dust in the total rate of Pb^{210} fallout observed, one can use the Ra^{226}/Pb^{210} ratio obtained for atmospheric precipitation (Table 1).

When Ra^{226} is used as an indicator of penetration into the atmosphere of natural isotopes connected with atmospheric dust, the proportions of Ra^{226}, Pb^{210}, Bi^{210} and Po^{210} concentrations are very important. Dust forming from any natural or artificial object older than a few years obviously contains Pb^{210}, Bi^{210} and Po^{210} in amounts corresponding to those expected on the basi of radioactive equilibrium. Objects older than, say, 100 years thus act as sources of a dust containing Ra^{226} and Pb^{210} in amounts approaching radio-active equilibrium. For most dust sources it may therefore be assumed that Ra^{226}, Pb^{210}, Bi^{210} and Po^{210} reach the atmosphere in near-equilibrium amounts. Excess Pb^{210} previously supplied by the atmosphere may accumulate in the upper soil horizons /3/. This may lead to "secondary" penetration into the atmosphere, along with the dust, of Pb^{210} that is in radioactive equilibrium with Bi^{210} and Po^{210}, but can exceed the Ra^{226} concentration. The Pb^{210}/Ra^{226} ratios in the upper horizons of some soils (Table 2) can be used for a very rough assessment of such an excess.

TABLE 2. Concentration ratio Pb^{210}/Ra^{226} in the upper horizons of some soils

Soil	Horizon, cm	Pb^{210}/Ra^{226}
Sandy.............	0 — 4	25.3
Sandy loam	0 — 5	3.8
Loamy	0 — 5	3.1

In upper soil horizons, the Pb^{210} concentration considerably exceeds that of Ra^{226}. If the radiochemical composition of dust lifted by wind from the surface of the soil cover is similar to that given in Table 2, the Pb^{210} (or Bi^{210} and Po^{210}) concentration in the atmospheric dust may considerably exceed the Ra^{226} concentration. Nevertheless, the data here are mere indications, and additional investigations are necessary.

Thus, the Pb^{210}, Bi^{210} and Po^{210} concentrations penetrating the atmosphere along with dust from the earth's surface correspond, and in some cases may exceed, the Ra^{226} concentration. The concentration ratios Ra^{226}/Pb^{210} in atmospheric precipitation listed in Table 1 are therefore to be seen as minimum values of the ratios of Pb^{210}, Bi^{210} and Po^{210} concentrations due to dust from the ground, to the overall Pb^{210} concentration in atmospheric precipitation. The minimum value of the ratio is over 0.02, the maximum over 0.2, and the mean over 0.09. In the atmospheric precipitation at Moscow the average Bi^{210}/Pb^{210} and Po^{210}/Pb^{210} ratios should be 0.08—0.09 at least on account of the dust from the ground, and not on account of the Bi^{210} and Po^{210} accumulating in the atmosphere from Pb^{210} that forms as a decay product of Rn^{222}; these ratios may vary within wide limits.

We compared our assessments with known ratios of these isotopes, used for characterizing the atmospheric scavenging rate for radioactive aerosols. For atmospheric precipitation, the Bi^{210}/Pb^{210} ratio of concentration varies between 0.25 and 0.78, the average being 0.46 /7/, and the Po^{210}/Pb^{210} ratio varies between 0.03 and 0.37, the average being 0.13 /5, 8, 9/.

Consequently, the radioisotope concentration ratios observed in practice are comparable with our assessments of the ratios of these isotopes due to atmospheric dust, mainly for Po^{210}/Pb^{210}. The effect of Pb^{210} in dust raised from the ground on the behavior in the atmosphere of Pb^{210} from Rn^{222} decay is apparently indeterminate, as a rule. Nevertheless, Pb^{210} in dust raised from the ground can probably be one of the reasons for a fairly high proportion of dry Pb^{210} fallout, observed when studying atmospheric fallout in some areas /2, 8/.

The relative share of Pb^{210}, Bi^{210} and Po^{210} carried by dust into the atmosphere apparently depends on local conditions, i. e., on atmosphere dustiness and the radiochemical composition of dust in the area. But the possible presence of such radioisotopes in the atmosphere of various areas must be taken into account when assessing the atmospheric scavenging rate for radioactive isotopes on the basis of data concerning the nonequilibrium of Rn^{222} decay products in the atmosphere.

BIBLIOGRAPHY

1. Baranov, V. I. and V. D. Vilenskii. Pb^{210} v atmosfere i atmosfernykh vypadeniyakh (Pb^{210} in the Atmosphere and Atmospheric Precipitation). — Atomnaya Energiya, Vol. 18, No. 5. 1965.
2. Baranov, V. I. and V. D. Vilenskii. Use of Pb^{210} in the Study of Atmospheric Scavenging Processes. — In: Atmospheric Scavenging of Radioisotopes. Israel Program for Scientific Translations, Jerusalem. 1970.
3. Vilenskii, V. D. Raspredelenie svintsa-210 i radiya-226 v nekotorykh pochvakh (Pb^{210} and Ra^{226} Distribution in Some Soils). — Geokhimiya, No. 12. 1969.
4. Benerji, P. and S. D. Chatterjee. Radium Content of Rainwater. — Nature, Vol. 211, No. 5048. 1966.
5. Burton, W. M. and N. G. Stewart. Use of Long-Lived Natural Radioactivity as an Atmospheric Tracer. — Nature, Vol. 186, No. 4725. 1960.
6. Damon, P. E. and P. K. Kuroda. On the Artificial Radioactivity of Rainfall. — Nucleonics, Vol. 11, No. 12. 1953.
7. Fry, L. M. and K. K. Menon. Determination of the Tropospheric Residence Time of Lead-210. — Science, Vol. 137, No. 3534. 1962.
8. Lambert, G. and M. Nezami. Importance des retombées sèches dans le bilan du plomb-210. — Annales de Géophysique, Vol. 21, No. 2. 1965.
9. Lehman, L. and A. Sittkus. Bestimmung von Aerosolverweilzeiten aus dem RaD and RaF-Gehalt der atmosphärischen Luft und des Niederschlags. — Naturwissenschaften, Vol. 46, No. 1. 1959.

UDC 551.510.71

POLONIUM-210 IN THE ATMOSPHERE AND ITS RATIO TO LEAD-210

S. S. Shalaveyus and B. I. Styro

The Pb^{210} and Po^{210} concentrations in atmospheric air and precipitation were measured in the environs of Vilnius. Po^{210} was determined from its α-activity after being separated from the other α-radiating elements by spontaneous precipitation on copper. The purity of Po^{210} separation was checked with the aid of A-2 nuclear emulsions. EDE-10P anionite was used to separate Pb^{210}. The chemical yield was determined from the carrier, and the purity from the Bi^{210} accumulation curve.

In 1966 — 1968, the Po^{210} concentration in atmospheric air was 3.5 to $71.4 \cdot 10^{-16}$ curie/m^3. The Po^{210}/Pb^{21} ratio in that period fluctuated between 0.07 and 0.22; the higher values indicate that air in which Pb^{210} and Po^{210} has accumulated for a long time was sometimes released into the ground layer.

In 1967 — 1968, the Po^{210} concentration in precipitation varied between 0.2 and $1.9 \cdot 10^{-12}$ curie/liter, and the Po^{210}/Pb^{210} ratio varied between 0.1 and 0.37. An inverse correlation was found between the Po^{210} concentration in precipitation and that in the atmosphere. The average residence time of Po^{210} and Pb^{210} in the atmosphere was about 32 days.

One aim of investigations of atmospheric scavenging of radioactive admixtures is the behavior and migration of various radioisotopes in the atmosphere. Radionuclides of special interest are the long-lived radon decay products Pb^{210} and Po^{210}, which are widespread but have hardly been studied at all under natural conditions.

The Po^{210} and Pb^{210} concentrations in atmospheric air and precipitation were measured in the environs of Vilnius. Large volumes of air were passed through porous FPP-15 filters, containers with a receiving surface of up to several square meters were exposed for long periods of time, and large amounts of precipitation were collected. The Pb^{210} and Po^{210} were concentrated from the large volumes of water by coprecipitation with aluminum hydroxide $Al(OH)_3$. The water was heated in order to speed up the coagulation and settling of the precipitates. The carrier used was lead nitrate (or acetate) free of Pb^{210}, as both Po^{210} and Pb^{210} were separated from the same sample /3/.

Po^{210} was determined from its α-activity after being separated from other α-radiating elements by spontaneous precipitation on copper /1/. Complete Po^{210} deposition on a copper disk was achieved from an acid solution of about 6% (2N) hydrochloric acid and at least 2% citric acid. Such a medium ensures the presence of Po^{210} in the ionic state and prevents its sorption on glass or on the impurities in the solution. Since the precipitation of Po^{210} on the copper disk is hampered by tetravalent iron ions, ascorbic acid was added to the solution to convert the tetravalent iron into bivalent.

The copper disk was cleaned and rinsed with alcohol for degreasing, then immersed in a beaker with the solution over a boiling water bath, and turned slowly around for 3 hrs. This ensured uniform deposition of Po^{210} on the disk, which was then washed with distilled water and dried with ethyl alcohol. Its α-activity was then measured on a DP-100 setup with an α-attachment. The counting efficiency was 22%. The radiochemical yield of Po^{210} against standard solutions varied between 80 and 90%. The purity of Po^{210} separation was checked experimentally. The copper disks were exposed to a nuclear emulsion and, after the development of the emulsion, the lengths of the α-particle tracks were measured and compared to histograms. Almost no other α-radiating element was deposited on the copper disk; its presence did not affect the calculation of Po^{210} concentration.

To determine Po^{210} in air, the exposed FPP-15 filters with the lead carrier were burnt at 450—500°C. The sample was then acidified with hydrochloric and nitric acids and evaporated to dryness. After drying at 100—110°C the residue was dissolved in 2N hydrochloric acid and Po^{210} was separated on a copper disk of 24-mm diameter.

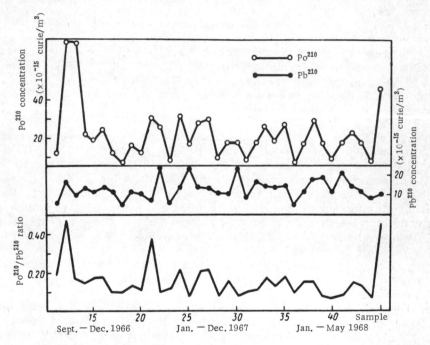

FIGURE 1. Time variation in Po^{210} and Pb^{210} concentrations and their ratio in the environs of Vilnius during 1967—1968.

Stoepples /8/ shows that filter burning at 450—500°C leaves practically all of the Po^{210} in the ash.

EDE-10P anionite was used to separate the Pb^{210}. The chemical yield of Pb^{210} was determined from the carrier, and the purity from the Bi^{210} accumulation curve. We evaluated the possible error in measurement due to Po^{218}, Pb^{214} and Bi^{214} deposited on the filter. The error did not exceed 3% at radioactive equilibrium. Pb^{210} was measured with a DP-100 setup containing a BFL-25 end-window counter. The counting efficiency was 18—20%.

The measurement of the Po^{210} concentration and the determination of its ratio to the parent isotope Pb^{210} are very interesting, as they make it possible to judge the age and place of formation of the air mass, and to determine the residence time of Po^{210}-carrying aerosols in the air. The variation of the Po^{210}/Pb^{210} radioactivity ratio is apparently due to a variation in the residence time of the Po^{210}- and Pb^{210}-carrying aerosols in the troposphere, and to the release of "older" air from the stratosphere and upper troposphere into the ground layer of the atmosphere. Each factor is individually assessed only by comparing the variation of the Po^{210}/Pb^{210} ratio to the variation in the concentration of Po^{210} and Pb^{210}.

In 1966—1968, the Po^{210} concentration in atmospheric air varied between 3.5 and $71.4 \cdot 10^{-16}$ curie/m^3; the mean values were $20.2 \cdot 10^{-16}$ curie/m^3 in 1966, $20.0 \cdot 10^{-16}$ curie/m^3 in 1967, and $17.2 \cdot 10^{-16}$ curie/m^3 in January——May 1968. The Po^{210}/Pb^{210} ratio in that period varied between 0.07 and 0.22. In view of the fact that ratios between 0.07 and 0.14 are typical of tropospheric air, because the half-life of Po^{210}- and Pb^{210}-carrying aerosols is 10 to 40 days, ratios of 0.14 to 0.22 apparently characterize "older" air; in other words, during the period of investigation, air was released from the stratosphere or the upper troposphere into the ground layer of the atmosphere.

Burton and Stewart /4/ measured the Po^{210} concentration at various altitudes and found that the Po^{210}/Pb^{210} ratio grows from 0.13 at ground level to 0.65 at 14 km in the lower stratosphere. This would indicate that Po^{210} accumulates in the stratosphere for lack of washout. This can be seen in Figure 1, which shows that, in certain periods of time, not only the Po^{210} concentration increases, but also the Po^{210}/Pb^{210} ratio. Higher values of this ratio indicate that air in which Pb^{210} and Po^{210} had long accumulated were doubtlessly released during the investigated period. The washout of radioactive aerosols is more or less intense in the troposphere and the conditions are hardly suitable for an increase in the Po^{210}/Pb^{210} ratio. Such an increase is apparently linked with stratospheric air penetration into the ground layer of the atmosphere.

It should be remembered that stratospheric air release is accompanied by isotope dilution. Besides, air mass advection greatly affects the variation of Po^{210} and Pb^{210} concentrations in the air. Only a comparison of variation in Po^{210} and Pb^{210} concentrations and their ratios offers the possibility of determining the "age" of air masses. An increase in the Po^{210}/Pb^{210} ratio was noticed from 10 to 20 September 1966 (sample 12), 28 December 1966 to 4 January 1967 (sample 21), 23 January to 2 February 1967 (sample 24) and from 20 to 24 May 1968 (sample 45). During these periods the Po^{210} concentrations were above the mean-annual values. These data seem to be one more proof that stratospheric air penetrated the ground layer of the atmosphere during the period of investigation.

In 1967—1968, the Po^{210} concentration in precipitation varied between 0.2 and $1.9 \cdot 10^{-12}$ curie/liter, and the Po^{210}/Pb^{210} ratio between 0.1 and 0.37. The ratios were higher in January—February, May, and October—November 1967 (0.30—0.37, Figure 2). Figure 2 shows a fair inverse correlation between Po^{210} and Pb^{210} concentrations in the precipitation and those in the atmosphere.

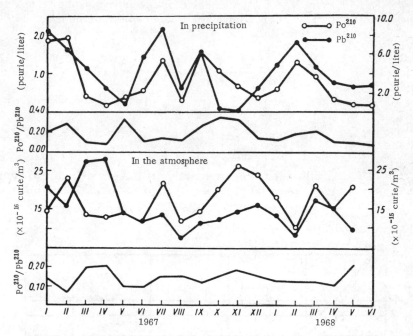

FIGURE 2. Comparative variations of Po^{210} and Pb^{210} concentrations in the atmosphere and in precipitation at Vilnius during 1967—1968.

The average residence time of Po^{210} and Pb^{210} in the atmosphere is usually calculated from

$$N_1 \lambda_1 = \ldots = N_2 \lambda_2 = N_3 (\lambda_3 + \Delta),$$

$$\frac{N_4 \lambda_4}{N_2 \lambda_2} = \frac{\lambda_3 \lambda_4}{(\lambda_3 + \Delta)(\lambda_4 + \Delta)} . \tag{1}$$

Here and below, N is the number of atoms, λ is the radioactive decay constant, Δ is a washout constant, and the subscripts correspond to the links in the radon decay chain (e. g., N_1, N_2, N_3 and N_4 are the numbers of atoms of Rn^{222}, Pb^{210}, Bi^{210} and Po^{210}, respectively).

Much of the Pb^{210} doubtlessly forms in the troposphere. According to numerous measurements /4—6/, the average residence time of radioactive aerosols in the troposphere is about 30 days. Thus, there is apparently radioactive equilibrium between Pb^{210} and Bi^{210}, at least in the middle and upper troposphere, but not between Pb^{210} and Po^{210}. Like Lambert and Nezami /5/ we shall denote by f_τ that proportion of Pb^{210} atoms forming in the troposphere on account of Bi^{214} decay. The Bi^{210} and Po^{210} concentrations depend on the average residence time τ of the radioactive aerosol in the troposphere, because the atoms of these isotopes are washed out of the troposphere by precipitation, in proportion to $\Delta = \dfrac{1}{\tau}$. Part of the Pb^{210} $(1-f_\tau)$ enters the stratosphere or upper troposphere, and decay produces equilibrium or near-equilibrium between the amounts of Bi^{210} and Po^{210}. These assumptions lead to

$$p = \frac{\lambda_3 \lambda_4}{(\lambda_3 + \Delta)(\lambda_4 + \Delta)} \left[1 - \frac{f_\tau}{e} \left(1 - \frac{\lambda_4}{\Delta} \right) \right], \qquad (2)$$

where

$$p = \frac{N_4 \lambda_4}{N_2 \lambda_2}.$$

The value of p is established experimentally; it is very difficult to evaluate f_τ, which depends very much on altitude. At ground level f_τ is doubtlessly unity, and practically zero in the stratosphere.

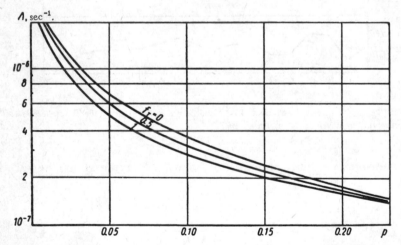

FIGURE 3. Variation in washout constant Δ vs. the concentration ratio Po^{210}/Pb^{210} in the air.

An analysis of equation (2) (Figure 3) proves that coefficient f_τ hardly depends on variations in Δ or its inverse quantity τ, i.e., the same values of f_τ are obtained for different values within the error limits of measurement ($\pm 20\%$). This method of determining the rate of radioactive aerosol removal from the atmosphere has other shortcomings too. The Po^{210} and Pb^{210} concentrations are taken as averages for the entire troposphere, but they are usually measured in the ground layer of the atmosphere, although they are known to vary with altitude /4, 7/. The vertical turbulent diffusion and the washout of radioactive aerosols are not considered separately in this scheme.

Karol' /2/ discussed the scheme of radioactive aerosol removal from the atmosphere. In this scheme, it was assumed that: 1) the atmosphere consists of two layers: a lower one where diffusion takes place along with washout, and an upper one where washout is missing; 2) the turbulent diffusion coefficient K_z is constant for the entire troposphere; 3) radioactive aerosols in the lower layer are being washed out according to the first-order law of kinetics; 4) to a first approximation, the horizontal and vertical nonuniformity of the process of radioactive-aerosol washout may be neglected. The vertical distribution of the volumetric concentration of any isotope in the Rn decay chain in the first layer $0 < z < h$, under these assumptions, is

$$q(z) = \frac{E}{K_z} \prod_{m=2}^{i-1} \eta_{im} \left[\frac{\exp(-\alpha_1 z)}{\alpha_1 \prod\limits_{l=2}^{i} (\eta_{il} + \xi - 1)} + \right.$$

$$\left. + \sum_{s=2}^{i} \frac{L_s \, \mathrm{ch}\, \alpha_s z - \exp(\alpha_s z)}{(1 - \xi - \eta_{is}) \prod\limits_{\substack{l=2 \\ l \neq s}}^{i} (\eta_{il} - \eta_{is})} \right], \tag{3}$$

where

$$\alpha_1 = \sqrt{\lambda_1 / K_z} \; ; \qquad \eta_{li} = \frac{\lambda_i}{\lambda_1} \; ; \qquad \xi = \frac{\sigma}{\lambda_1} \; ; \qquad \varkappa = h \sqrt{\lambda_1 / K_z} \; ;$$

$$L_s = \frac{\exp(\varkappa \sqrt{\eta_{is} + \xi})[1 + \sqrt{\eta_{is}(\eta_{is} + \xi)^{-1}}] - e^{-\varkappa} \xi (1 + \sqrt{\eta_{is}})^{-1}}{\mathrm{sh}(\varkappa \sqrt{\eta_{is} + \xi}) + \sqrt{\eta_{is}(\eta_{is} + \xi)^{-1}} \, \mathrm{ch}(\varkappa \sqrt{\eta_{is} + \xi})} \; ;$$

$$i = 1, 2, 3, 4 \quad (Rn^{222}, \, Pb^{210}, \, Bi^{210}, \, Po^{210}) \, ;$$

$\xi = \dfrac{\sigma}{\lambda_1}$ is a dimensionless coefficient of nonradioactive removal of the isotope, λ_1 is a constant of radioactive decay of an Rn-chain isotope, and σ is the washout coefficient.

For $h = 2$ to 4 km and $K_z = 10$ to 50 m^2/sec, $\varkappa$ varies between 0.4 and 1.8. The ratio of specific activities of Po^{210} to Pb^{210} in the ground layer, P, is obtained from equation (3) for $i = 2$, $i = 4$. The similar dimensionless coefficient ζ of nonradioactive removal of Po^{210} and Pb^{210} from the atmosphere according to the "nonradioactive equilibrium" scheme is calculated with the aid of equation (1):

$$\zeta = \frac{\Delta}{\lambda_1} \; .$$

From Table 1 it can be seen that ζ and ξ differ, on the average, by almost one order of magnitude for $\varkappa = 1.0$ to 0.7. This is only natural, since ζ in Karol's scheme signifies the total rate of aerosol removal from the entire troposphere under the effect of turbulent diffusion and washout, while ξ is the washout rate from the lower troposphere.

TABLE 1. Parameters of atmospheric scavenging

Date of sampling	P	ζ	ξ		
			$\varkappa = 0.7$	$\varkappa = 1.0$	$\varkappa = 1.6$
1967					
4 — 16 January	0.10	0.22(24)*	3.5 (1.5)*	1.8 (3.1)	0.75(7.4)
16 — 23 January	0.12	0.16(34)	2.7 (2.0)	1.5 (3.7)	0.66(8.4)
23 January — 2 February	0.22	0.0 (105)	0.8 (7.9)	0.60(9.3)	0.3 (18.5)
2 — 15 February	0.07	0.26(21)	6.4 (0.9)	2.7 (2.1)	1.1 (4.9)
14 — 20 March	0.20	0.09(57)	1.1 (4.9)	0.68(8.1)	0.35(15.8)
27 March — 7 April	0.21	0.07(95)	0.9 (6.2)	0.60(9.2)	0.32(17.3)
3 — 12 May	0.08	0.23(23)	4.8 (1.2)	2.2 (2.5)	0.95(5.8)
12 — 22 May	0.16	0.12(48)	1.15(4.8)	0.9 (6.21)	0.50(11.1)
22 — 29 May	0.07	0.26(21)	6.4 (0.9)	2.7 (2.1)	1.1 (41.9)
29 May — 13 June	0.10	0.22(24)	3.5 (1.5)	1.8 (3.1)	0.75(7.4)
13 — 26 June	0.11	0.20(28)	2.6 (2.1)	1.6 (3.4)	0.65(8.5)
7 — 17 July	0.17	0.11(50)	112 (4.6)	0.85(6.5)	0.45(12.3)
17 — 31 July	0.13	0.15(36)	2.8 (1.9)	1.4 (3.9)	0.60(9.3)
15 — 24 November	0.18	0.10(52)	1.3 (4.2)	0.8 (7.9)	0.40(13.9)
1968					
9 — 19 February	0.10	0.22(24)	3.5 (1.5)	1.8 (3.1)	0.75(7.4)
22 February — 4 March	0.14	0.14(40)	2.0 (2.8)	1.1 (4.9)	0.53(10.5)
7 — 21 March	0.24	0.14(40)	2.0 (2.8)	1.1 (4.9)	0.53(10.5)
25 March — 5 April	0.08	0.23(23)	4.8 (1.2)	2.2 (2.5)	0.95(5.8)
8 — 12 April	0.07	0.26(21)	6.4 (0.9)	2.7 (2.1)	1.1 (4.9)
15 — 19 April	0.08	0.23(23)	4.8 (1.2)	2.2 (2.5)	0.95(5.8)
22 — 26 April	0.14	0.14(40)	2.0 (2.8)	2.0 (4.9)	0.53(10.5)
29 April — 3 May	0.13	0.15(36)	2.8 (1.9)	1.4 (3.9)	0.60(9.3)
6 — 10 May	0.07	0.26(21)	6.4 (0.9)	2.7 (2.1)	1.1 (4.9)
Average	0.12	0.17(32)	3.2 (1.7)	1.4 (3.9)	0.6 (9.2)

* Figures in parentheses denote the mean residence times of Po^{210} or Pb^{210} in days.

In the environs of Vilnius, for $\varkappa = 0.7$ to 1.6, we obtained $\xi = 0.6$ to 3.2, $\sigma = 1.3$ to $6.7 \cdot 10^{-6}$ sec^{-1}, $\tau_1 = 1.7$ to 9.2 days, $\zeta = 0.77$, $\Delta = \zeta$, $\lambda_1 = 3.6 \cdot 10^{-7}$ sec^{-1}, $\tau_2 = 32$ days. A comparison of our data with similar figures published earlier proves that the Karol' quantitative scheme describing radioactive aerosol removal from the atmosphere by clouds and precipitation reflects more faithfully the main features of the phenomenon.

BIBLIOGRAPHY

1. Bagnall, K. W. Chemistry of Rare Radioelements. Polonium-Actinium. — New York, Academic Press. 1957.
2. Karol', I. L. Otsenka srednei skorosti udaleniya estestvennykh radioaktivnykh aerozolei iz atmosfery oblakami i osadkami (Evaluation of the Mean Removal Rate of Natural Radioactive Aerosols from the Atmosphere by Clouds and Precipitation). — Izv. AN SSSR, Seriya Geofizicheskaya, No. 11. 1963.
3. Shalaveyus, S. S. O metodike izmereniya RaD v atmosfernykh osazhdeniyakh i v vozdukhe (Methods of RaD Measurement in Air and Atmospheric Precipitation). — In: Sbornik dokladov po voprosam issledovaniya klimatoobrazuyushchikh protsessov (Collected Reports on Problems of Investigating Climatogenic Processes). Vilnius, "Mintis." 1969.
4. Burton, W. M. and N. G. Stewart. Use of Long-Lived Natural Radioactivity as an Atmospheric Tracer. — Nature, Vol. 186, No. 4725. 1960.
5. Lambert, G. and M. Nezami. Importance des retombées sèches dans le bilan du plomb-210. — Annales de Géophysique, Vol. 21, p. 2. 1965.
6. Lehmann, L. and A. Sittkus. Bestimmung von Aerosolverweilzeiten aus dem RaD und RaF Gehalt der atmosphärischen Luft und des Niederschlages. — Naturwissenschaften, Vol. 46, p. 1. 1959.
7. Peirson, D. H., R. S. Cambray, and G. S. Spicer. Lead-210 and Polonium-210 in the Atmosphere. — Tellus, Vol. 18, p. 2. 1966.
8. Stoepples, M. Trennverfahren für die natürlich vorkommenden radioaktiven Nuclide Polonium-210, Schwefel-35, Blei-210 und-Beryllium-7 im Rahmen eines allgemeinen Trennungsganges. — Nukleonik, Vol. 6, No. 7. 1964.

UDC 551.510.71

TIME FLUCTUATIONS OF LEAD-210 CONCENTRATION
IN THE GROUND LAYER OF THE ATMOSPHERE

S. G. Malakhov, V. A. Trufakin, and Z. S. Shulepko

Data on the mean-annual Pb^{210} concentration in the ground layer of the atmosphere are given for various points in the world. This concentration varies between 10^{-14} and 10^{-15} curie/m^3 deep inland, 1 and $2 \cdot 10^{-15}$ curie/m^3 over the oceans in the northern hemisphere, and equals 10^{-16} curie/m^3 in the polar areas of both hemispheres. Measurements in the Antarctic have revealed seasonal variations with a maximum in summer. Short-term (2 — 3 day) fluctuations are studied and assessed from measurements around Kirov. It is shown that cold-air advection from the Arctic usually reduces considerably the Pb^{210} concentration.

Very little is known of the distribution and variation in time of lead-210 concentration in the ground layer of the atmosphere. Relevant measurements have been carried out in about twenty places, mainly in the northern hemisphere, and on aerosol samples collected over periods of one month. No data are available for shorter periods of time. This makes it impossible to assess the range of fluctuation for each month and hinders the search for a link between such fluctuations and meteorological factors.

The data in this paper cover two areas in the USSR: Kirov (Kirov Region) and Obninsk (Kaluga Region), and one in Antarctica: Mirny. At Obninsk and Mirny the measurements were conducted on monthly samples, while the samples at Kirov were taken every 2 or 3 days. Both seasonal and short-term fluctuations in the lead-210 concentrations were investigated. At Kirov, the relation to meteorological factors was also studied.

The method used for aerosol sampling at Obninsk was described in /2, 4/ At Kirov, the aerosol samples were taken with a filtering setup of 1200—1500 m^3/hr output. FPP-15 filters were used. The time of setup operation was established by synchronous electric clocks. The exposed filters were calcinated in a muffle furnace at 330—250°C. The temperature was controlled by an RT-2 thermostat.

RaD was separated radiochemically on EDE-10P ion-exchange resin in Cl$^-$ form. A Pb(NO$_3$)$_2$ amount of 50 g (reduced to the metal) was therefore added to the ash. The sample was then twice processed in aqua regia, and twice evaporated with 6N HCl to dryness in order to remove the No$^-_3$ ions. The dry residue was dissolved in 25 ml of 2N HCl and filtered. The filtrate was diluted twofold in distilled water to obtain a 1N solution of HCl, which led to the formation of a complex lead compound, easily absorbed on EDE-10P anionite in Cl$^-$ form.

The 1N solution obtained was passed through an ion-exchange column filled with EDE-10P anionite in Cl$^-$ form. The lead separated from the interfering elements and from its daughter isotope Bi^{210}. The complex lead compound was retained by the anionite, which was then washed with

25 ml of 1N HCl. Subsequent rinsing of the anionite with 250 ml of distilled water completely removed the lead from the resin. The carrier yield was determined by weighing, after precipitating $PbSO_4$ from solution. The precipitate was dried, weighed, and positioned for the measurement of its β-activity.

The activity of the lead was determined from the daughter Bi^{210} after equilibrium had been attained. The chemical purity was checked from the curve of Bi^{210} accumulation. The radioactivity of Bi^{210} was measured on a low-background UMF-1500M setup, energized from a stabilized source and provided with an SBT-13 end-window counter. The soft β-radiation of the lead and the α-radiation of Po^{210} were intercepted by an aluminum screen of 50 mg/cm^2 thickness. The counting efficiency was 35—36%. K^{40} preparations were used for calibration.

1. SEASONAL FLUCTUATIONS IN LEAD—210 CONCENTRATION

Mean-annual Pb^{210} concentrations found in the ground layer of the atmosphere are listed in Table 1, which includes similar data taken from the literature. There are wide variations from one place to another. Continental values are 10^{-14} to 10^{-15} curie/m^3; in the British Isles and some littoral areas of the continent the value is 10^{-15} curie/m^3. The average concentration over midocean in the northern hemisphere is 1 to $2 \cdot 10^{-15}$ curie/m^3 /1, 3/. The lowest values were measured in the polar areas ($\sim 10^{-16}$ curie/m^3).

Table 2 shows the seasonal variations in the mean-monthly concentration. The seasonal variation was nearly always the same over the continents in the northern hemisphere, with a maximum in winter and a minimum in summer or late spring. Other authors have obtained similar data for the northern hemisphere. A similar seasonal variation was found in India /6/ and at several points in Finland /6, 8/, as well as at stations along the 80°W meridian /9, 11/.

No clearcut phase shift can be noticed in the seasonal variation of radon and lead-210 in the ground layer of the atmosphere. Pb^{210} at Obninsk had a maximum in December and a minimum in May and June. This conclusion is corroborated by the fairly constant ratio of mean-monthly lead-210 to radon concentrations throughout the year /2/ and by the very simple calculations in /4/.

The seasonal variations in Pb^{210} may be due to seasonal variations in the intensity of the vertical turbulent motions in the troposphere. Partial inversion of winter temperatures in the lower troposphere and a general reduction in the intensity of vertical turbulent motion lead to Pb^{210} accumulation there. On the other hand, in summer, intense vertical turbulence facilitates the loss of Pb^{210} to the upper troposphere and a drop in the concentration of the said isotopes in the ground layer of the atmosphere.

Other authors reach similar conclusions /5, 6, 10/. An additional winter source of Pb^{210} can be the discharge into the atmosphere of smoke and soot from the burning of certain fuels /8/.

TABLE 1. Mean-annual lead-210 concentration (in 10^{-15} curie/m^3) in the ground layer of the atmosphere at different points on the globe

Point of observation	Year	Concentration	Source
Obninsk	1956 — 1965	7.2	Our data
Kirov	1966 — 1968	8.5	The same
Vilnius	1965 — 1966	7.3	/ 5/
England	1957, 1961 — 1964	4.9	/10/
Winchester, Massachusetts	1964 — 1965	20.0	/12/
India:	1962 — 1965		
Srinagar	1962 — 1965	30	/ 6/
Delhi	1962 — 1965	26.0	/ 6/
Ostakamund	1962 — 1965	22.0	/ 6/
Helsinki	1968	6.8	/ 8/
Hays Is., Franz Josef Land	1960 — 1963	0.36	/ 2/
Thule, Greenland	1961	7.6	/11/
Moosonee, Canada	1961	12.5	/11/
Wellington, U. S. A.	1961	16.0	/11/
Lima, Peru	1961	3.7	/11/
Santiago, Chile	1961	6.9	/11/
Puerto-Mont, Chile	1961	1.6	/11/
Punta-Arenas, Chile	1961	0.6	/11/
South Pole	1959 — 1963	0.40	/ 7/
Little America, Antarctica	1956 — 1957	0.38	/ 7/
Mirny, Antarctica	1966	0.15	Our data
In mid-ocean over the Pacific and Indian			
Ocean in the northern hemisphere . . .	1960	1.5	/ 1/
Off the coasts of the Pacific and Indian			
Ocean in the northern hemisphere . . .	1960	8.0	/ 1/

In Antarctica, the Pb^{210} concentrations are highest in summer and lowest in winter. A similar but less clearcut result was obtained by some Americans /7/. The reason for this peculiar seasonal variation is still unknown and more measurements are necessary. The summer high may be due to the fact that part of the land in the littoral area is freed of snow and ice. On the other hand, according to our measurements and other data /7/, the mean-monthly concentrations of long-lived fission products in the ground layer of the Antarctic atmosphere have about the same seasonal variation as the mean-monthly Pb^{210} concentrations. In this case the cause of the seasonal fluctuations can be the seasonal variation in the inflow of Pb^{210} and fission products from the stratosphere over the Antarctic continent, as well as seasonal variations in the interlatitudinal exchange in the troposphere.

TABLE 2. Seasonal variation in lead-210 concentration (in 10^{-15} curie/m^3) in the ground layer of the atmosphere over the continent

Point of observation	Period of observation	Mean-monthly concentration												Source
		I	II	III	IV	V	VI	VII	VIII	IX	X	XI	XII	
Kirov	1966—1968	14.0	13.3	7.9	10.6	4.0	3.1	4.4	5.7	6.3	7.2	17.0	10.0	Our data
Obninsk	1956—1968	9.6	3.5	6.6	4.7	4.2	4.5	6.7	7.6	8.2	7.5	14.4	9.4	The same
Chilton, England . . .	1961—1965	4.6	6.2	6.5	4.4	3.7	3.6	3.2	2.9	5.0	5.1	6.0	5.8	/10/
Washington, U.S.A.	1961	24.5	24.5	15.6	15.6	14.4	14.4	9.8	9.8	24.3	24.3	8.1	8.1	/11/
Moosonee, Canada.	1961	19.4	18.4	21.9	21.9	3.6	3.6	6.7	6.7	7.0	7.0	15.9	15.9	/11/
Helsinki	1958	13	5	2	6	2.5	2.0	3	6	10	5	7.5	15.5	/ 8/
Mirny, Antarctica	1936	0.30	0.30	0.30	0.30	0.02	0.02	0.04	0.04	0.04	0.04	0.17	0.17	Our data

The Pb^{210} data for the Mirny area are provisional, to be checked by measurements in coming years. A possible source of errors is the method used for taking aerosol samples at Mirny, with no systematic control of the air filtration rate. The results can be most seriously affected in winter.

2. SEVERAL-DAY FLUCTUATIONS OF Pb^{210} CONCENTRATION IN THE GROUND LAYER OF THE ATMOSPHERE

Systematic measurements of Pb^{210} concentrations, made at Kirov for comparatively short periods of time (2 to 3 days), made it possible to study their variations in time within each month and to establish a tentative relation to meteorological conditions. Table 3 lists maximum and minimum Pb^{210} concentrations for 2—3 days during every month of the year. The concentrations are expressed in relative units, the mean-monthly concentration in each of the investigated years (1966—1968) being taken as unit. The second and third columns contain the mean maximum and minimum Pb^{210} concentrations for every year of measurement. The fourth column contains the highest maxima and lowest minima observed in the given month during all those years. The Pb^{210} concentrations undergo comparatively wide fluctuations within the limits of every month.

The meteorological conditions associated with extreme concentrations were examined. In most cases, minimum Pb^{210} concentrations corresponded to a mean-daily air temperature that was lower than the mean-monthly temperature, or occurred during a drop in air temperature. In the synoptic plane this corresponded to cold air advection from Arctic areas. Maximum concentrations, on the other hand, were usually found when the air temperatures were higher than their mean-monthly values. This corresponded either to lack of cold-air advection from the northern regions of the country, or sometimes, mainly in winter, it was accompanied by an inflow of warm air from the southern regions of the country. Table 4 is a statistical record of extreme Pb^{210} concentrations in relation to variations in the temperature of the ground air. It confirms the above statement. Thus, even for a continental area such as Kirov, the advection of cold air, poor in Pb^{210}, from the polar regions can play a significant role in the fluctuations of Pb^{210} concentration near the ground.

TABLE 3. Mean-monthly fluctuations in Pb^{210} concentration in the ground layer of the atmosphere in the Kirov area (in relative units)

Month	Mean maximum concentration	Mean minimum concentration	Highest maxima and lowest minima
January	1.9	0.5	2.1 — 0.4
February	2.4	0.1	2.8 — 0.1
March	2.7	0.4	3.9 — 0.3
April	2.0	0.3	2.5 — 0.1
May	2.4	0.4	2.8 — 0.3
June	1.9	0.4	2.4 — 0.3
July	2.6	0.5	4.2 — 0.4
August	2.2	0.2	2.7 — 0.1
September	2.8	0.2	3.4 — 0.2
October	2.3	0.4	3.2 — 0.2
November	2.4	0.2	2.8 — 0.1
December	2.0	0.3	2.2 — 0.2

The correlation of Pb^{210} concentration in the ground layer and air temperature fluctuations was therefore examined closer. An attempt to find a linear correlation was discarded due to the wide scatter of experimental values of Pb^{210} concentration, which depends not only on advection, but also on many other factors of synoptic or local importance.

The measured Pb^{210} concentrations were divided into two large groups. One corresponded to mean-daily air temperatures that were lower, by 0.5 deg or more, than the mean-monthly temperature t_0. The other group included Pb^{210} concentrations for days when the mean-daily air temperature exceeded, by 0.5 deg or more the mean-monthly temperature. The concentrations were expressed as the ratios

$$\frac{\Delta q}{q_0},$$

where q_0 is the mean-monthly concentration and $\Delta q = q_i - q_0$. Here, q_i is the concentration measured for 2—3 days. Table 5 compares the two groups. It appears that most values for lower temperatures lie below the mean-monthly level of concentration. No such conclusion can be reached as to days with air temperatures higher than the mean-monthly values. Thus,

Table 5 also points to a significant influence of Pb^{210}-poor air advection from arctic regions on the variation in the concentration of this isotope in the ground layer of the Kirov atmosphere.

TABLE 4. Statistics of extreme mean-monthly Pb^{210} concentration recordings in relation to ground-air temperature fluctuations (Kirov, 1966 – 1968)

Concentration	Extreme concentrations observed at			Total number of cases
	low temperatures	high temperatures	moderate temperatures	
Maxima	6	27	3	36
Minima	29	4	3	36

The effect that the passage of air masses of different origins over the measurement area has on the Pb^{210} concentration in the ground layer of the atmosphere was established by other workers. According to Shlein and Friend /12/, the Pb^{210} concentration in the USA was low in continental-arctic air and in air of marine origin. The drop in concentration in the Vilnius area during the passage of cold fronts has been described elsewhere /5/.

TABLE 5. Statistics of Pb^{210} concentration variation at air temperatures higher or lower than the mean-monthly value t_0

Temperature deviation from the mean-monthly value	Concentration deviation from the mean-monthly value			
	$\frac{\Delta q}{q_0} > 1.2$	$\frac{\Delta q}{q_0} < 0.8$	$\frac{\Delta q_i}{q_0} \sim 1.0 \pm 0.2$	$\frac{q_i}{q_0}$
$t > t° + 0.5°C$	34 cases	34 cases	22 cases	1.0 ± 0.2
$t < t° - 0.5°C$	12 cases	45 cases	12 cases	0.44 ± 0.15

Note. The last column averages the cases of the second and third columns.

We tried to find a connection between Pb^{210} concentration fluctuation and some meteorological elements: wind speed and amount of precipitation. The attempts were made separately for the cold snowy season and the summer season. No correlation could be found. There is just some general tendency of Pb^{210} concentrations to decrease with increasing amount of precipitation and wind speed, but the experimental points are very scattered. It would probably be better to look for such correlations separately for each type of synoptic situation and air mass advection. This will be the object of our further investigations.

Thus, preliminary investigations of the connection between relatively short-time fluctuations of Pb^{210} concentrations (over a few days) and meteorological factors, carried out in the Kirov area on the Eurasian continent, have shown that the advection of arctic air, usually poor in Pb^{210}, may have the strongest effect on these fluctuations.

BIBLIOGRAPHY

1. Baranov,V.I. and V.D.Vilenskii. Pb^{210} v atmosfere i v atmosfernykh vypadeniyakh (Pb^{210} in the Atmosphere and in Atmospheric Precipitation). — Atomnaya Energiya, Vol. 18, No. 5. 1965.
2. Vilenskii,V.D., E.N.Davydov, and S.G.Malakhov. K voprosu o sezonnykh i geograficheskikh izmeneniyakh soderzhaniya svintsa-210 v atmosfere (Seasonal and Geographical Variations of Pb^{210} Content in the Atmosphere). — In sbornik: Radioaktivnye izotopy v atmosfere i ikh ispol'zovanie v meteorologii (Radioactive Isotopes in the Atmosphere and their Utilization in Meteorology). Moskva, Atomizdat. 1965.
3. Vilenskii,V.D., G.V.Dmitrieva, and Yu.V.Krasnopevtsev. Estestvennaya i isskustvennaya radioaktivnost' atmosfery nad okeanami i ee svyaz' s meteorologicheskimi faktorami (Natural and Artificial Radioactivity of the Atmosphere over Oceans and its Relation to Meteorological Factors). — Ibid.
4. Malakhov,S.G. and P.G.Chernysheva. O sezonnykh izmeneniyakh kontsentratsii radona i torona v prizemnom sloe atmosfery (Seasonal Variations in Radon and Thoron Concentrations in the Ground Layer of the Atmosphere). — Ibid.
5. Shalaveyus,S.S. O nekotorykh zakonomernostyakh osedaniya i vymyvaniya RaD iz atmosfery (Some Patterns of RaD Deposition and Washout from the Atmosphere). Author's summary of dissertation for the degree of Candidate of Physical and Mathematical Sciences. Vilnius. 1968.
6. Joshi,L.U. and C.Rangarajan. SMT Sarada Gopalakrishkan Measurement of Lead-210 in Surface Air and Precipitation. — Tellus, Vol. 21, No. 1. 1969.
7. Lockhart,L.B., R.L.Patterson, and A.W.Saunders. Atmospheric Radioactivity in Antarctica 1956 — 1963. — Naval Research Laboratory, USA Report 6341. 1965; Geophys. Res., Vol. 71, No. 8. 1966.
8. Mattson,R. Seasonal Variation of Short-Lived Rn Progeny, Pb-210 and Po-210 in Ground Level Air in Finland. — Abstracts CACR. Symposium on Atmospheric Trace Constitutes and Atmospheric Circulation. Heidelberg, W. Germany. 8 — 13 September 1969.
9. Patterson,R.L. and L.B.Lockhart. Geophysical Distribution of Lead-210 (RaD) in the Ground-Level Air. The Natural Radiation Environment 1964, Chicago, pp. 383 — 393.
10. Peirson,D.H.,R.S.Cambrey, and G.S.Spicer. Lead-210 and Polonium-210 in the Atmosphere. — Tellus, Vol. 18, No. 2 — 3. 1966.
11. Radiological Health Data, Vol. IV, No. 2. 1963.
12. Shlein,B. and A.G.Friend. Local Ground-Level Air Concentrations of Lead-210 at Winchester, Massachusetts. — Nature, Vol. 210, No. 5036, pp. 579 — 580. 1966.

UDC 551.510.71

ASSESSMENT OF RADON EMANATION FROM THE SURFACE OF EXTENSIVE TERRITORIES

T. I. Sisigina

The paper discusses a method of assessing radon emanation from a surface covered by one type of soil, under uniform and stable conditions (dry weather, constant barometric pressure, weak wind below 3 m/sec).

The results of comprehensive observations are examined, including measurements of the flux density of radon from the soil surface into the atmosphere, of radon concentration in the soil profile to a depth of 2 m, emanation factors and radium content in the soil, and the determination of soil porosity and water content. Based on experimental data obtained at about 40 different locations in European USSR, the author establishes a correlation between radium content in the surface soil layer and radon emanation into the ground layer of the atmosphere.

For convenience, the author introduces a specific emanation factor β, i. e., the radon flux density due to unit radium concentration in the soil. Factor β is calculated from measurements at different points, but on soils of similar mechanical composition, and diverges 8 to 10% from its average value for the given soil type; typical values are $1.8 \cdot 10^{-5}$ (for sandy soil) and $3.7 \cdot 10^{-5}$ curie/km^2·sec·g Ra·g^{-1}(for highly-textured gray forest and light chestnut loams). In addition to her own measurements, the author used literature data on radium content in the soils of European USSR to calculate radon emanation from extensive territories.

For the territory bounded by the latitude of Leningrad to the north and the Northern Caucasus foothills to the south, the weighted-mean radon flux density into the atmosphere is $E_{w.m} = 24 \cdot 10^{-8}$ curie/km^2·sec. For the northern part of this territory, half of which is covered by sands and sandy loam, $E_{w.m} = 19 \cdot 10^{-8}$ curie/km^2·sec. In the southern part, with widespread, highly textured and strongly emanating chernozems and chestnut soils, $E_{w.m} = 30 \cdot 10^{-8}$ curie/km^2·sec.

In nuclear meteorology, which employs radon (Rn^{222}) and its decay products as tracers, the flux density (emanation) of radon from the ground surface into the atmosphere is an important parameter /3, 8/. This paper discusses the variation of Rn^{222} emanation as a function of the radium content in the soils, their emanating power and texture under uniform and stable conditions (dry weather, constant barometric pressure, weak wind below 3 m/sec). The influence of meteorological elements on the emanation variation is not discussed here, although its role in this process may sometimes be extremely important /9, 10/.

To assess radon emanation from the surface of extensive territories we conducted comprehensive observations, including measurements of the flux density of radon from the surface of various soils and radon concentrations in the soil layer to a depth of 1—2 m. In addition, soil samples were taken from every observation point to determine the radium concentration, the soil type in terms of mechanical composition, and, in some cases, to determine the porosity and moisture content. The emanation factor was determined by a standard method /1/ for every investigated soil.

The radon flux density was measured with the aid of storage chambers and an RAL-1 α-radiometer. The relative error of the field observations was 15 to 25%; statistical errors did not exceed 3 to 10%. The method of measuring Rn emanation is described elsewhere in more detail /5/. The data obtained by storing radon in a chamber placed on the ground were supplemented by radon flux density calculations using the "balance" method (i.e., from the profile of the Rn concentration in the soil air). The measurements were conducted simultaneously by the two methods. The correlation graph (Figure 1) shows satisfactory agreement between the results.

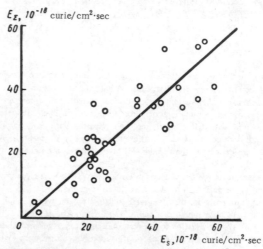

FIGURE 1. Comparative values of radon flux density obtained by different methods:

E_s) measured by the storage method (x), E_{Σ}) calculated by the "balance" method (y). Correlation coefficient $r = 0.91$; regression equation $y = 0.86\,x + 0.08$.

The radium content in the investigated soils varied between $2\cdot10^{-13}$ (sands) and $1.5\cdot10^{-12}$ g/g (heavy loams and clays). It was thus possible to follow the dependence of the emanation on the radium content in the soil.

The emanation factor η was determined from 40 samples. Table 1 lists emanation factors obtained for various soils.

Table 1 shows that, of the investigated soils, clay and floodplain alluvium have the highest emanation factors. By and large, this agrees with Vinogradov's statement /2/, that the emanation process is the stronger, the higher the proportion of highly-dispersed and colloidal fractions in the soil composition.

Effective radon diffusion coefficients were calculated to describe the soil's permeability to gas. Profiles of radon concentration in the soil were measured for this purpose. The calculation was made using homogeneous diffusion equations (see, e. g., /7/). Table 2 lists the results obtained.

TABLE 1. Emanation factor η of soils in relation to their mechanical composition

Mechanical composition of soil	Value of η, %			Number of samples measured
	mean	maximum	minimum	
Sands	14	18.5	6	7
Sandy loams	21	36	10	7
Poor silty loams	24	40	18	7
Heavy loams	20	23	17	12
Clays	28	40	18	5
Floodplain alluvium	29	—	—	1

Note: Each sample was measured four times; the scatter of η values about the arithmetic mean for the given sample was ±10%.

Table 2 shows that the diffusion coefficient D varies tenfold for soils of different mechanical composition. It is highest for highly-textured soils with the largest volume of open, water-free "translation" pores.

Analysis of data obtained from about 40 locations all over European USSR revealed certain emanation patterns depending on the radium content in the soil cover.

TABLE 2. Radon diffusion coefficients D in some soils and pedogenic rocks

Type of soil or pedogenic rock	D, 10^{-2} cm²/sec	Overall porosity P, %	Moisture content, %	Number of observations
Medium podzolic sandy	2.53	39 — 48	12 — 15	35
Medium podzolic heavy loams...	0.27	37 — 46	20	20
Chestnut dusty loams	3.2	38 — 53	3 — 8	26
Chestnut calcareous heavy loams .	0.48	30 — 48	5	10

Figure 2 represents the correlation between radon flux density (measured during a period of stable dry weather) and radium content in the soil. There is an almost functional correlation between comparable values (overall correlation coefficient $r=0.84$, $n=29$ points). For convenience, we introduced the concept of "specific emanation" β, i.e., the radon flux density corresponding to unit concentration of radium in the soil (dimensions, curie/$cm^2 \cdot sec \cdot g_{Ra} \cdot g^{-1}$).

Figure 2 presents the three main types of linear relationship between radon emanation and radium content in soil.

a. Highest values of radon emanation into the atmosphere ($\beta=(3.7\pm0.28) \cdot 10^{-5}$) correspond to the given content of radium in the soil. All these points refer to stretches composed of loose sediments, rich in clayey elements (chestnut dusty and gray forest loams). The increase in "specific emanation" here may be due not only to a high emanation factor (up to 40%), but also to maximum soil porosity (up to 60%).

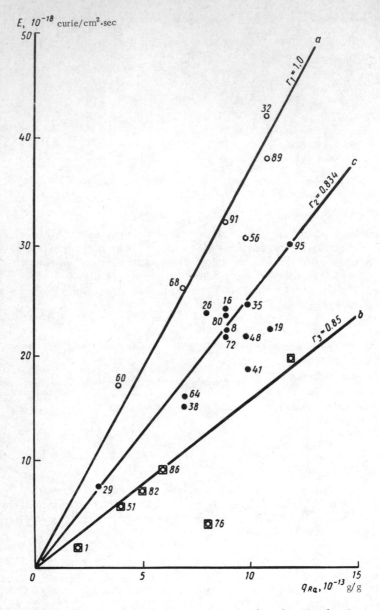

FIGURE 2. Correlation between radon emanation flux from the soil surface into the atmosphere and radium content at the given point of observation.

b. Minimum specific emanation $\beta = (1.8 \pm 0.16) \cdot 10^{-5}$ is measured on sandy soils (points enclosed in little squares). Notable among them are the rewashed sands in the littoral zone of the Sea of Azov (No. 76) which have the lowest emanation factor (6%).

c. Points corresponding to clays and heavy loams occupy an intermediate position. These soils have a comparatively high emanation factor (sometimes 35 to 40%), but a denser texture and a lower volume of free pores, $\beta = (2.8 \pm 0.1) \cdot 10^{-5}$. Factors β calculated from measurements made at different points but on soils of similar mechanical composition vary within 9 and 10% from average for the given soil type.

All these assessments prove that, within the limits of measurement accuracy, the empirical factors β are constant for a given soil type. They can be used for assessing the radon emanation from extensive areas covered by one kind of soil or another, if the radium content is known. The patterns are obviously disturbed after the fall of precipitation and significant moistening of the earth's surface.

Radon emanation from that part of European USSR bounded by the latitude of Leningrad to the north and the Northern Caucasus foothills to the south was calculated with the aid of experimental values obtained for the specific emanation β. The data on radium content resulted from an analysis of soil samples taken from our observation points along the route from Moscow to the shores of the Sea of Azov (100 samples). Morozova's data /5/ were also used. The areas covered by the different soil types were evaluated from a 1:5,000,000 soil map /6/, on the assumption that $E = 0$ for water expanses and bogs.

TABLE 3. Total radon flux ε from the surface of several soil types covering European USSR (in curie/sec)

Soil type	$s, 10^5$ km^2	$q_{Ra}, 10^{-12}$ g/g	$\beta, 10^5$ curie/km$^2 \cdot$sec	ε
Podzolic, sandy, and sandy loam ..	590	0.5	1.8	5.31
Podzolic, clays and loams	635	1.0	2.8	17.75
Gray forest	202	1.0	3.7	7.48
Podzolized chernozems	272	0.9	2.8	6.85
Chernozems of the steppe zone ..	720	1.0	2.8	20.16
Chestnut	205	0.8	3.7	6.07

The total flux from the surface of the different soils covering the territory under study was calculated from the relationship

$$\varepsilon = S \, q_{Ra} \, \beta, \tag{1}$$

where S is the area covered by a given soil type, β is the specific emanation, and q_{Ra} is the mean radium content. Table 3 lists the results.

The weighted-mean values of the flux density were calculated from data listed in Table 3. It was found that, on the whole, $E_{w.m} = 24.2 \cdot 10^{-18}$ curie/cm$^2 \cdot$sec for the territory considered. For the northern part, covered half by podzolized soils and half by sands and sandy loams, $E_{w.m} = 19 \cdot 10^{-18}$ curie/cm^2·sec. In the southern part, covered by gray forest soils, chernozems and chestnut soils, $E_{w.\overline{m}}$ $30 \cdot 10^{-18}$ curie/cm^2·sec.

According to Kirichenko /4/, who calculated the radon emanation from soils using the profile of daughter products of radon decay in the free atmosphere, the average is $E = 20 \cdot 10^{-18}$ curie/cm^2·sec for the middle strip of European USSR (Leningrad, Moscow and Kaluga regions).

BIBLIOGRAPHY

1. Baranov, V.I., A.S. Serdyukova, L.V. Gorbushina, I.M. Nazarov, and Z.N. Efimkina. Laboratornye raboty i zadachi po radiometrii (Laboratory Work in Radiometry).— Moskva, Atomizdat. 1966.
2. Vinogradov, A.P. Geokhimiya redkikh i rasseyannykh khimicheskikh elementov v pochvakh (Geochemistry of Rare and Scattered Elements in Soils).— Moskva, Izd. AN SSSR. 1957.
3. Karol', I.L. and S.G. Malakhov. Primenenie estestvennykh radioaktivnykh izotopov v atmosfere dlya meteorologicheskikh issledovanii (Use of Natural Radioactive Isotopes in the Atmosphere for Meteorological Investigations).— In sbornik: Voprosy yadernoi meteorologii (Problems of Nuclear Meteorology). Moskva, Atomizdat. 1962.
4. Kirichenko, L.V. Otsenka emanatsionnosti bol'shikh territorii po raspredeleniyu produktov raspada radona v svobodnoi atmosfere (Evaluation of the Emanating Capacity of Extensive Territories from the Distribution of Radon Decay Products in the Free Atmosphere).— Trudy IEM, No. 5. 1970.
5. Morozova, N.G. Estestvennaya radioaktivnost' pochv Evropeiskoi chasti SSSR i opyt sostavleniya kart rasprostraneniya radioaktivnykh elementov (Natural Radioactivity of Soils in European USSR and a Tentative Distribution Map of Radioactive Elements).— Thesis, Institute of Geochemistry of the USSR Academy of Sciences. 1967.
6. Pochvennaya karta SSSR, Masshtab 1:55,000,000 (1:55,000,000 USSR Soil Map).— Moskva, Izd. Glavnogo upravleniya geodezii i kartografii. 1959.
7. Serdyukova, A.S. and Yu. T. Kapitanov. Izotopy radona i korotkozhivushchie produkty ikh raspada v prirode (Radon Isotopes and Short-Lived Products of its Decay in Nature).— Moskva, Atomizdat. 1969.
8. Sisigina, T.I. Ekskhalyatsiya radona s poverkhnosti neskol'kikh tipov pochv Evropeiskoi chasti SSSR i Kazakhstana (Radon Emanation from the Surface of Several Soil Types in European USSR and Kazakhstan).— In sbornik: Radioaktivnye izotopy v atmosfere i ikh ispol'zovanie v meteorologii (Radioactive Isotopes in the Atmosphere and their Utilization in Meteorology). Moskva, Atomizdat. 1965.
9. Sisigina, T.I. Kolebaniya ekskhalyatsii radona iz pochvy v atmosferu v svyazi s izmeneniem meteorologicheskikh uslovii (Fluctuations in Radon Emanation from Soils into the Atmosphere in Relation to Variations in Meteorological Conditions).— Trudy IEM, No. 5. 1970.
10. Pearson, J.E. and G.E. Jones. Soil Concentrations of "Emanating Radium-226" and the Emanation of Radon-222 from Soils and Plants.— Tellus, Vol. 18, p. 2. 1966.

VI. EQUIPMENT AND METHODS FOR THE STUDY OF RADIOACTIVE CONTAMINATION IN THE ENVIRONMENT

UDC 621.039.55

FILTERING AEROSOLS WITH NATURAL ATMOSPHERIC RADIOACTIVITY THROUGH FIBROUS MATERIALS

B. I. Ogorodnikov, V. I. Skitovich, and E. A. Sitalo

It has been proved experimentally that, at a filtration rate of about 150 cm/sec, FPP-15 and FPA-15 materials have approximately the same efficiency, but the former is more effective at a rate of about 1 to 10 cm/sec owing to the presence of electrostatic charges on its fibers. FP material is suitable for use in the upper atmosphere, as its efficiency in trapping aerosols of all sizes increases. For instance, the efficiency of FPA-15 material in trapping aerosols of about 0.035μ particle radius at filtration rates of 1 to 65 cm/sec is approximately 10 to 12 times as high at 27 km as at ground level. A study of radioactivity distribution over the layers of the filtering material has shown that particles of that size account for 40 to 60% of the radioactivity of radon daughter products in the ground layer of the atmosphere. EP filtering was studied experimentally with air containing coarse aerosols (1 to 15μ) and with practically pure air containing a large amount of free atomic Ra daughter products. The "free" products filter with very high efficiency with a high diffusion coefficient, even at rates of 300 cm/sec.

The study of the properties and atmospheric distribution of naturally occurring radioactive aerosols usually requires their prior accumulation on filters. Fibrous FP materials are the most widely used for such purposes in the USSR /9/. As with other fibrous filters, their efficiency depends on fiber diameter, the presence of electrostatic charges, filter porosity, the disperse composition of the aerosols, pressure, temperature, and airflow filtration rate. This paper examines the influence of some of these factors on the efficiency of trapping aerosols whose radioactivity is due to short-lived daughter products of radon decay. The relationships derived may apply to aerosols of other noble radioactive gases, and to radioactive aerosols formed by the action of cosmic rays on atmospheric nitrogen, oxygen and argon.

Aerosols of natural atmospheric radioactivity form by the addition of atomic radioactive products to aerosol particles contained in the atmosphere. The radon daughter products are atomic isotopes of polonium, bismuth, and lead, which owing to their physicochemical properties are readily sorbed onto any surface. Their diffusion coefficient is very high and, according to some measurements /4/, reaches 0.068 cm^2/sec for Po^{218}. The time of their existence in the "free" atomic state depends on the computed concentration and particle size of the aerosols in the surrounding medium. The higher the aerosol concentration, the shorter the lifetime of the atoms in the free state. According to observations by Billard et al. /10/, the proportion of "free" atoms in the ground layer of the atmosphere can be as high as 10%. In stagnant air, for instance in unventilated mine galleries where the aerosol concentration is low, the proportion of free atoms can reach 80—90% /3/. A similar picture should be found in the upper atmosphere too, where the forming Be^7, Be^{10}, Si^{32}, P^{32}, P^{33} and S^{35} atoms can exist for a long time in the free atomic state owing to the low aerosol concentration.

Consider trapping by aerosols of the short-lived daughter products of radon decay using fibrous filtering materials, FPP-15 and FPA-15, most often used in practice. The filters investigated were specially manufactured and their standard aerodynamic resistance $[\Delta p]$ was approximately only one-twentieth that of industrially-produced materials. A stack of seven to ten superposed disks was positioned in the filter holder; short-lived radon daughter-tagged atmospheric air was then blown through them during a period of 30 min. Then the stack was dismantled and the alpha-activity of each filter measured. The experimental method is described in more detail in /8/.

The coefficient K of passage through the first one, two, etc., filters was calculated from the activity on each filter and plotted on a graph (Figure 1) as a function of standard resistance. It can be seen that, at low filtration rates, FPP-15 works much better than FPA-15. At a rate of 2 cm/sec, an FPP-15 layer with a standard resistance of only 0.3 mm H_2O traps 99% of the total radioactivity, as compared to 60% for FPA-15. At high filtration rates, the two materials have about the same efficiency, which is lower than that for low rates. The efficiency of an FPP-15 layer of 1 mm H_2O standard resistance is about 82% at a rate of 150 cm/sec, comparable with 75% for FPA-15 at 130 cm/sec.

The great differences in efficiency at low filtration rates and the practically equal efficiencies at high rates are easily explained by the presence of electrostatic charges on the fibers of the FPP-15 material: as the rate increases, the aerosols no longer polarize in the electric field of the fibers, and the efficiency drops. This pattern is easily observed in Figure 1. At high rates and insignificant polarization, FPP-15 and FPA-15 materials of almost equal fiber diameter and packing have about the same efficiency.

The FPP-15 and FPA-15 materials are produced industrially with a standard resistance of 1.5 to 2 mm H_2O. Their efficiency in trapping aerosols of natural atmospheric radioactivity can easily be calculated by extrapolating the results in Figure 1, for the corresponding $[\Delta p]$ indicated in the instructions for the given material. Good results are obtained by such extrapolation for the FPP-15—1.7 material investigated in /1/ and for the AFA-RMP filters manufactured from this material and investigated in /5/.

The curves in Figure 1 are particularly interesting when assessing the size of aerosols on which the short-lived radon daughter products settle in the atmospheric air. These curves are almost linear. Only the beginning of each curve has some curvature. This indicates that, in the ground layer of the atmosphere, the short-lived daughter products settle on aerosols of narrow size range. The straight ends of the curves indicate that the filtration of the monodisperse aerosol runs out already after two or three filters, while about 40 to 60% of the radioactivity of the entire sample is concentrated on that monodisperse fraction. The straight parts of the curves are flatter than the initial parts, because the first filters retain the coarser and finer particles. This is why Labushkin and Ruzer /5/ found a higher throughflow of radon daughter-product aerosols for AFA—RMP and NEL filters positioned second rather than first in the direction of flow.

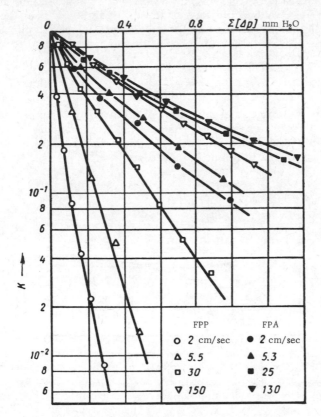

FIGURE 1. Coefficient of passage for aerosols of natural atmospheric radioactivity vs. standard resistance of FPP-15 and FPA-15 materials at various rates of filtration.

Many workers have tried to evaluate the size of aerosols on which radon daughter products concentrate. In our opinion, the best results were obtained in /6, 11, 12, 14, 15, 16/: the radon daughter products are practically totally linked to aerosols of 10^{-5} to 10^{-6} cm radius, with a maximum for particles of 2 to $5 \cdot 10^{-6}$ cm radius.

From the filtration curves in Figure 1, one can also evaluate the size of particles corresponding to the curve section for monodisperse-aerosol filtration. LFS-2 material was therefore calibrated for filtration rates of 5 to 200 cm/sec* with the aid of monodisperse selenium aerosols of

---

* This operation was carried out by E. A. Druzhinin.

0.046μ particle radius, obtained in a La Mer generator. Radon daughter-tagged atmospheric air was filtered through this material at the same rates. The filter pack was composed of three disks, each of standard resistance 1.3 to 1.4 mm Hg. It may again be assumed that only the monodisperse aerosols we are interested in reached the second and third filters. This was confirmed by calculations of the coefficients of passage, which were practically equal for the second and third filters. Coefficients of filtering effect α (Figure 2) were calculated from the results obtained for the second filter with the formula

$$\alpha = \frac{-\log K}{[\Delta p]}.$$

The filtration curve for radon daughter-product aerosols possesses the same shape and similar absolute values as that for monodisperse aerosol. Calculations show that radon daughter products concentrate mainly on monodisperse particles of about 0.035μ diameter.

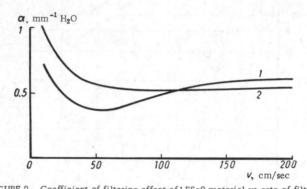

FIGURE 2. Coefficient of filtering effect of LFS-2 material vs. rate of filtration:

1) monodisperse selenium aerosol of 0.046μ particle diameter; 2) monodisperse fraction of the aerosols of natural atmospheric radioactivity.

When studying aerosols in the upper atmosphere, low-density air has to be passed through filtering material. Studies of FP materials have shown their resistance to decrease in rarefied air, and their aerosol trapping efficiency to increase. Figure 3 shows the trapping of aerosols with short-lived radon daughter products by the FPA-15 material at rates of 1 to 65 cm/sec and a pressure of 13 mm Hg, corresponding to 27 km above sea level.

The samples were taken from a 200-liter tank filled with unfiltered atmospheric air, and brought to the required underpressure with the aid of a vacuum pump. For convenience, the data in Figures 1 and 3 were plotted in Figure 4 as coefficient of filtering effect vs. rate. It can be seen that aerosol filtration is much more effective in rarefied air: at 40 cm/sec and a pressure of 13 mm Hg an FPA-15 material of 1 mm H_2O standard resistance has an efficiency of at least 99.999%, as against only 70% at normal pressure. The reason is the increased diffusion coefficient of the particles, and the gliding of the airflow over the fiber surface. According to /2, 7, 13/, the increase in filter efficiency in rarefied air can be evaluated by calculating the coefficients of capture of aerosols of 0.035μ radius by the fibers of an FPA-15 filter with a packing density of 0.02. The calculations covered aerosol capture due to diffusion, meshing, and the combined effect of both mechanisms. Table 1 lists the results and the relationship between total capture coefficients and the coefficients of filtering effect for pressures of 13 and 760 mm Hg. The experimental and theoretical data are in agreement.

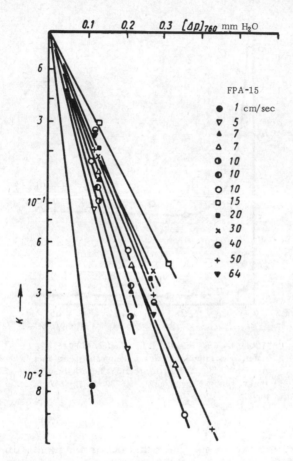

FIGURE 3. Coefficient of passage of aerosols with natural atmospheric radioactivity vs. standard capture of FPA-15 material for various air filtration rates and a pressure of 13 mm Hg.

The filtration of coarser monodisperse aerosols, with a particle radius of about 0.42μ, is presented in Figure 5. The aerosols were obtained in a La Mer generator from stearic acid. Before reaching the pack of FPA-18 filters, only slightly different from FPA-15, it was blown over a radium preparation for radon daughter-product labeling. The relationship between the coefficients of filtering effect and rate shows that the inertial mechanism of aerosol retention plays an important role for aerosols of suc sizes at rates above 20 cm/sec. Efficiency increases with rate. As in the case of fine aerosols, a drop in pressure leads to increased efficiency, but the differences are not very significant between 760 and 300 mm Hg.

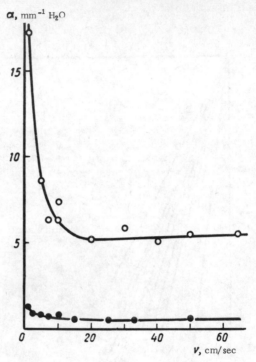

FIGURE 4. Coefficient of filtering effect of FPA-15 materials vs. rate of filtration of the monodisperse fraction of aerosols with natural atmospheric radioactivity at pressures of 13 mm Hg (top curve) and 760 mm Hg (bottom curve).

We shall discuss two more cases that occur frequently in laboratory practice: the filtration of aerosols with natural atmospheric radioactivity at high concentrations of coarse, inert particles, and the opposite case: filtration of comparatively pure air with a low content of condensation nucle

The first case can occur in the ground layer of the atmosphere during strong winds, tornadoes and dust storms. Similar conditions in mine galleries with an atmosphere rich in radon are produced by rock blasting, d drilling, scraping and loading.

TABLE 1. Total values of capture coefficients ε and experimental values of the coefficients of filtering effect α for FPA-15 material

Filtration rate, cm/sec	Total coefficients of capture		$\dfrac{\varepsilon_{13}}{\varepsilon_{760}}$	Experimental coefficients of filtering effect		$\dfrac{\alpha_{13}}{\alpha_{760}}$
	13 mm Hg	760 mm Hg		13 mm Hg	760 mm Hg	
1	4.40	0.616	7.15	17.2	1.22	14.1
5	1.89	0.222	8.52	8.6	0.82	10.5
10	1.33	0.143	9.3	6.3	0.65	9.7
25	0.86	0.083	10.4	5.2	0.52	10
50	0.633	0.055	11.4	5.4	0.52	10.4

At high concentrations of coarse particles, some of the atoms that form by radon decay will settle on the coarse particles and, as a result, the efficiency of radioactivity trapping will differ from that for common atmospheric air. Figure 6 /8/ shows that the presence of coarse dust particles of 1 to 1.5μ diameter increases the efficiency of radioactivity filtration through FPA-15 material, particularly at filtration rates above 20 cm/sec, when the inertial mechanism of aerosol trapping starts manifesting itself clearly. Radioactivity concentrated on coarse particles is retained by frontal filters, and radioactivity bound to fine particles reaches a deeper layer. The curve sections corresponding to the filtration of these fine particles are linear in Figure 6. If they are transposed to the origin of coordinates (dashed straight lines) and compared with the results in Figure 1, the agreement is perfect. This very interesting result shows that, even in different geographic regions, the natural radioactivity is distributed over the same fine aerosol particles of about 0.035μ radius.

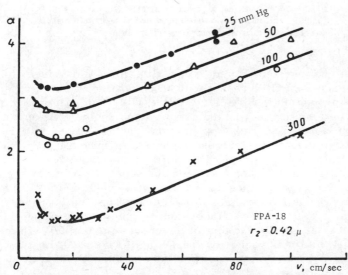

FIGURE 5. Coefficient of filtering effect of FPA-18 material that is not fluffy vs. the rate of filtration of monodisperse stearic-acid aerosol of 0.42μ particle radius tagged with radon daughter products; air pressures (mm Hg) are marked on the curves.

251

In comparatively clean, dust-removed air, the radon daughter products can subsist for a fairly long time in the form of free atoms. In this case, the efficiency of radioactivity trapping depends on the efficiency of trapping the atomic "aerosols" themselves. Owing to the high diffusion coefficient /4/ the free-atom trapping efficiency will depend entirely on the diffusion mechanism of filtration, even at rates of about 300 cm/sec. Calculations show that, at this rate, the diffusion coefficient of trapping is 3.5, and so the efficiency of free-atom trapping is about the same as for aerosols of 0.035μ diameter at a pressure of 13 mm Hg and a rate of 30 cm/sec (Figure 4). At filtration rates below 300 cm/sec the free atoms are trapped even better.

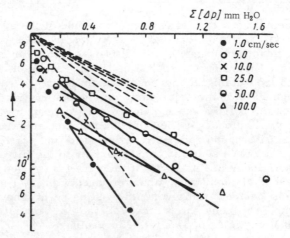

FIGURE 6. Coefficient of passage of aerosols with natural atmospheric radioactivity vs. standard resistance of the FPA-15 material at high concentrations of coarse industrial dust in air.

Special tests were conducted to check the filtration of free atoms. Air passed through a 20-liter vessel with an emanating radium preparation was blown through a high-efficiency filter with a microaperture in the middle. The forming radon daughter products could settle on the vessel walls, on the aerosol particles passing through the microaperture, while part of them remained in the free atomic state. The air from the vessel was filtered through a pack of FPP-20 filters. Figure 7 shows the experimental results. Each filtration curve has two distinct sections: the first for the filtration of free atoms, and the second for the filtration of radioactivity deposited on aerosol particles. The first section is very steep, indicating a high efficiency of free-atom trapping. The slope of the second section is milder, similar to that of the curves for the FPP-15 material in Figure 1. As in the presence of coarse dust (Figure 6), the second section refers to the filtration of aerosol particles of about 0.035μ diameter.

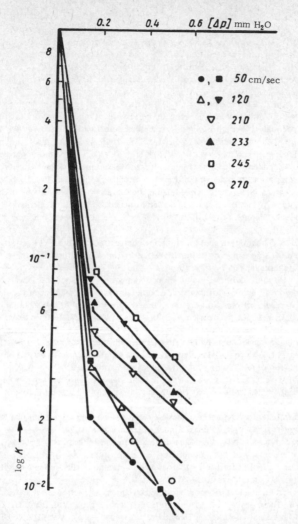

FIGURE 7. Coefficient of passage of aerosols with natural atmospheric radioactivity vs. standard resistance of FPA-15 material for a deficit of condensation nuclei and an excess of "free" atomic daughter products of radon.

In the experiments conducted with free atoms, the concentration of aerosol particles passing through the filter was not checked; it is, however, clear that the proportion of free atoms depends on the number of inert aerosol particles. This is also demonstrated by the vertical shift of the kink of the curves in Figure 7. A method for determining the amount of free atoms in atmospheric air and in industrial premises was devised on the basis of the filtration patterns of atomic radon daughter products /3/.

The authors are grateful to V. N. Kirichenko, Candidate of Chemical Sciences, for organizing the work and for his active participation.

BIBLIOGRAPHY

1. Zykova, A. S., V. A. Schastnyi, and G. P. Efremova. K voprosu ob opredelenii estestvennykh radioaktivnykh aerozoloei v atmosfernom vozdukhe (Determination of Natural Radioactive Aerosols in Atmospheric Air). — Gigiena i Sanitariya, Vol. 10, p. 62. 1958.

2. Kirsh, A. A. Issledovaniya v oblasti voloknistykh aerozol'nykh fil'trov (Research on Fibrous Aerosol Filters). Dissertation. 1968.

3. Kirichenko, V. N., B. I. Ogorodnikov, V. D. Ivanov, A. A. Kirsh, and V. I. Kachikin. Soderzhanie submikroskopicheskikh aerozolei korotkozhivushchikh dochernikh produktov radona v rudnichnom vozdukhe (Content of Submicroscopic Aerosols with Short-Lived Radon Daughter Products in Mine Air). — Gigiena i Sanitariya, Vol. 11, p. 115. 1965.

4. Korpusov, V. I., B. I. Ogorodnikov, and V. N. Kirichenko. Izmerenie koeffitsienta diffuzii atomov RaA metodom osazhdeniya iz laminarnogo potoka (Measurement of the Diffusion Coefficient of RaA Atoms by Precipitation from a Laminar Flow). — Atomnaya Energiya, Vol. 17, p. 221. 1964.

5. Labushkin, V. G. and L. S. Ruzer. Opredelenie koeffitsientov proskoka dochernikh produktov radona cherez fil'try tipa AFA — RMP, NEL i LFS (Determination of the Coefficients of Passage of Radon Daughter Products Through Filters of AFA — RMP, NEL and LFS Types). — Trudy VNIIFTRI, No. 89, p. 149. 1967.

6. Makhon'ko, K. P. O kharaktere spektra razmerov chastits radioaktivnoi pyli estestvennogo proiskhozhdeniya (Size Range of Radioactive Dust Particles of Natural Origin). — Izv. AN SSSR, Seriya Geofizicheskaya, Vol. 1, p. 183. 1963.

7. Natanson, G. L. Vliyanie skol'zheniya na effekt kasaniya pri zakhvate amikroskopicheskikh aerozol'nykh chastits tsilindrom iz potoka (Influence of Gliding on the Contact Effect in the Retention of Non-microscopic Aerosol Particles by a Cylinder During Flow). — Kolloidnyi Zhurnal, Vol. 24, p. 52. 1962.

8. Ogorodnikov, B. I., V. N. Kirichenko, P. I. Basmanov, and I. V. Petryanov. Ulavlivanie korotkozhivushchikh dochernikh produktov raspada radona fil'trami FP (Trapping of Short-Lived Radon Decay Daughter Products by FP Filters). — Atomnaya Energiya, Vol. 15, p. 230. 1963.

9. Petryanov, I. V., V. I. Kozlov, P. I. Basmanov, and B. I. Ogorodnikov. Voloknistye fil'truyushchie materialy FP (Fibrous FP Filtering Materials). — Moskva, "Znanie." 1968.

10. Billard, F., J. Miribel, and G. Medeleine. Methodes de mesure du radon et de dosage dans les mines d'uranium. — In: Radiological Health and Safety in Mining and Milling of Nuclear Materials, Vol. 1. Vienna. 1964.

11. Jacobi, W. Die Anlagerung von natürlichen Radionukliden an Aerosolpartikel und Niederschlagselemente in der Atmosphäre. — Geophys. Pura e Appl., Vol. 50, p. 260. 1961.

12. Kawano, M. and S. Nakatani. Size Distribution of Naturally Occurring Radioactive Dust Measured by a Cascade Impactor and Autoradiography. — Geofis. Pure e Appl., Vol. 50, p. 243. 1961.

13. Pich, J. Theory of Aerosol Filtration by Fibrous and Membrane Filters. — In: Aerosol Science, p. 223, edited by C. N. Davies, Academic Press. 1967.

14. Renoux, A. Noyaux de condensation radioactifs electroquement neutres et repartition granulometrique de la radioactivité fixeé par les aerosols naturels. — J. Rech. Atmos., Vol. 1, p. 197. 1963.

15. Schumann, G. Investigation of Radon Daughters. — J. Geophys. Res., Vol. 68, p. 3867. 1963.

16. Twomey, S. and G. T. Severynse. Measurements of Size Distributions of Natural Aerosols. — J. Atmos. Sci., Vol. 20, p. 392. 1963.

UDC 621.039.55

DEVELOPMENT OF A METHOD FOR DETERMINING THE SIZE DISTRIBUTION OF RADIOACTIVE AEROSOLS WITH THE AID OF FILTERING MATERIALS

B. I. Ogorodnikov, E. A. Sitalo, V. I. Skitovich, and I. E. Konstantinov

The efficiency of aerosol trapping by fibrous FP filtering materials depends on the rate of filtration, the diameters of the aerosol particles and of the filter fibers, and the thickness of the filtering layer. Through the right choice of parameters, one can achieve a selective retention of aerosols of a certain size range in the successive layers of filtering material.

The filtering characteristics of FPP-3, FPP-70 and FPA-100 materials were determined in the laboratory with aerosols of 0.035 to 0.5 μ particle radius. Linear filtration rates of about 1.5 — 2.0 m/sec were found to be adequate for investigating the size distribution of artificial radioactive aerosols, when the aerosols are mainly trapped by inertial effect. In this case, if FPP-70 — 0.3 material is used in the front layer and FPP-3 — 1.2 in the rear, the first filter retains over 95% of the aerosol particles of 0.5μ radius and less than 20% of the particles of about 0.035μ radius. The latter are practically all trapped by the rear filter.

Various combinations of layers of FPP-70 and FPP-3 filtering materials were tested while taking radioactive aerosol samples at filtration rates of 1.0 to 1.6 m/sec. Much of the Zr^{95}, Cs^{137} and Be^7 is bound to particles of 0.2 to 0.25μ average radius. For all isotopes, at least 10% of the overall activity is carried by particles below 0.1μ.

Methods based on the use of cascade impactors, thermal and electric precipitators, centrifuges, and diffusion batteries are used for determining the sizes of aerosol particles contained in the atmosphere. If the concentration of the investigated radioactive atmospheric aerosols is, however, very low, this equipment is of limited use owing to the low speed of sampling.

Air filtration through a series of successive filters, followed by an analysis of the activity accumulated on each, was suggested /4/ for determining the size distribution of radioactive aerosols. We think the use of multilayer filters of fibrous FP materials for such purposes can give very good results. Their high efficiency in aerosol trapping and low hydrodynamic resistance facilitate the taking of high-concentration samples of radioactive aerosols in a comparative short time from tens and hundreds of thousands of cubic meters of air.

The filtering properties of the FP materials depend on the diameter of the aerosol particles, that of the filter fibers, the rate of filtration, and the thickness of the filtering layer. By adequate choice of these parameters one can achieve a selective retention of aerosols of a certain size range in successive layers of filtering material. The trapping of aerosol particles by the filter fibers is based on various mechanisms: diffusion, inertia, contact, and electrostatic attraction /2/.

The diffusion effect occurs at low rates of air flow and accounts for most of the highly-disperse aerosol retained. Diffusional retention has been used /5/ for determining the sizes of fine particles in relation to their depth of penetration into a homogeneous layer of filtering material. Maximum particle separation by size can be achieved using high rates of filtration. In that case, aerosols are trapped mainly on account of the inertial effect, the capture efficiency being proportional to the square of the particle radius. The present filtration theory does not permit an accurate calculation of the efficiency of aerosol capture by actual fibrous filters, which makes an experimental verification all the more necessary.

The filtration characteristics of the FPP-3, FPP-70 and FPA-100 materials with microscopically-determined fiber diameters of 0.3, 5.7 and 9.6μ, respectively, were determined in the laboratory. The tests were carried out with aerosols of 0.035 to 0.5μ particle radius.

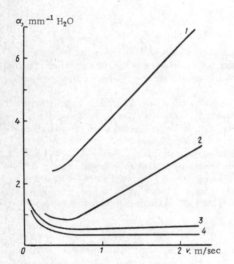

FIGURE 1. Coefficient of filtering effect of the FPP-70 material vs. rate of filtration for particles of various sizes:

1) $r = 0.5$; 2) $r = 0.32$; 3) $r = 0.15$; 4) $r = 0.035\mu$.

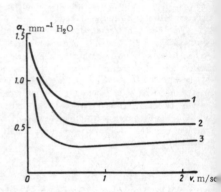

FIGURE 2. Coefficient of filtering effect of various materials vs. rate of filtration for particles of 0.15μ radius:

1) FPP-3; 2) FPP-70; 3) FPA-100.

The atmospheric aerosol fractions to which atomic radon decay products usually unite were used for the finest particles. Their mean radius, determined in /1/, was 0.035μ. Coarser particles were obtained with a generator of monodisperse aerosols, from stearic acid.

A filter pack was chosen for the determination of the trapping efficiency. Air containing the investigated particles tagged with radon daughter products was pumped through it. The amount of aerosols passed through each filter was calculated from the content of α-activity on the filters. Figure 1 represents the coefficient of filtering effect α, indicating the degree of action per unit of standard filter resistance in relation to the rate of filtration for the FPP-70 material.

At high linear rates over the range of predominantly inertial retention, one can notice a clear dependence of the trapping efficiency on particle size. For example, at a rate of 1.5 m/sec in a layer of FPP-70 material with a standard resistance of 0.3 mm H_2O, 97% of the particles over 0.5μ can be retained, as against only 20% of the aerosols of about 0.035μ.

To improve the precision of aerosol size distribution analysis with multilayer filters, one must use filters of distinctive filtering characteristics, the trapping efficiency of which increases along the air flow. Figure 2 represents the coefficient of filtering effect of various materials in relation to the linear air velocity for particles of 0.15μ radius. The most effective is the FPP-3 material: at high filtration rates it traps practically all the particles in the size range examined.

Various combinations of layers of filtering FPP-70 and FPP-3 materials of 0.5 m^2 area were tested during the sampling of artificial radioactive aerosols. The samples were taken from ground level, away from industrial enterprises, with the aid of a filtering setup of up to 3000 m^3/hr output. The overall volume of air pumped through reached 30,000 m^3 at a filtration rate of 1.0 to 1.6 m/sec. After sampling, each layer of material was calcinated separately and the isotopic radioactivity of the mixture was analyzed by γ-spectrometry.

The detector of the γ-spectrometer was made of an 80×80-mm NaI(TI) crystal. The count analysis of each sample was carried out for 10 hrs with a multichannel AI-100 amplitude analyzer. The measurement resolution of the setup was not worse than 13%. For resolving the photo-peaks relating to elements of similar γ-radiation energy, the samples were measured twice: immediately after being taken, and again two months later.

The artificial radioactive isotopes $Zr^{95}+Nb^{95}$, Cs^{137}, Ce^{141}, Ce^{144} and the radioisotope Be^7 which forms by interaction of cosmic rays with nuclei at atmospheric nitrogen and oxygen were found in the samples.

TABLE 1. Concentration of some radioactive isotopes in the atmosphere

Date of sampling	Sampling duration, hrs	Air volume pumped through, m^3	Isotope	Sample activity on day of sampling, curie	Concentration, curie/liter
21 Feb. 1969	17.2	30,000	Cs^{137}	$21.7\cdot10^{-10}$	$7.2\cdot10^{-17}$
			Ce^{141}	$7.4\cdot10^{-10}$	$2.5\cdot10^{-17}$
			Ce^{144}	$1.2\cdot10^{-10}$	$0.4\cdot10^{-17}$
			Be^7	$55.6\cdot10^{-10}$	$18.5\cdot10^{-17}$
22 Feb. 1969	13.4	30,000	Cs^{137}	$19.7\cdot10^{-10}$	$6.6\cdot10^{-17}$
			Ce^{141}	$8.6\cdot10^{-10}$	$2.9\cdot10^{-17}$
			Be^7	$65.5\cdot10^{-10}$	$21.8\cdot10^{-17}$

Table 1 gives data on the concentration of the various isotopes for two samples obtained by air filtration through multilayer filters. Table 2 shows the distribution of some isotopes and inert dust over the filter layers for one of the samples. An analysis of activity distribution over the filter layers of known filtering characteristics made it possible to evaluate the sizes of radioactive aerosol particles. Much of the Zr^{95} and Be^7 was found bound to particles of about 0.25μ radius; the mean radius of the Cs^{137} particles was slightly smaller, nearly 0.2μ. For all the isotopes, about 10% of the overall activity is carried by particles of less than 0.1μ radius. A layer-by-layer measurement of the total β-activity showed that, in general, the β-active elements have a similar size distribution of the particles. In the calculations, the particle density was taken as $2.0\ g/cm^3$.

TABLE 2. Distribution of radioactive isotopes and inert dust over filter layers

Layer No.	1	2	3	4
Material	FPP-70	FPP-70	FPP-70	FPP-3
Standard resistance, mm H_2O	0.4	0.4	0.4	1.2
Cs^{137}, curie	$15.9 \cdot 10^{-10}$	$2.4 \cdot 10^{-10}$	$1.3 \cdot 10^{-10}$	$2.1 \cdot 10^{-10}$
$Zr^{95}+Nb^{95}$, curie	$18.0 \cdot 10^{-10}$	$3.6 \cdot 10^{-10}$	$1.1 \cdot 10^{-10}$	$>10^{-10}$
Ce^{141}, curie	$4.0 \cdot 10^{-10}$	$>10^{-10}$	$>10^{-10}$	$>10^{-10}$
Be^7, curie	$32.0 \cdot 10^{-10}$	$3.0 \cdot 10^{-10}$	$1.8 \cdot 10^{-10}$	$2.0 \cdot 10^{-10}$
Inert dust, mg	1150	180	—	—

In some studies /3/, it has been established that fission products in the stratosphere occur as particles of about 0.02 to 0.05μ radius. The higher values we found are due to the fact that these particles, when passing to lower layers of the atmosphere, unite with more numerous, inert particles, the weighted-mean radius of which is $0.3-0.4\mu$. This value was determined by the same method as the size of radioactive aerosols. The accumulation of at least 0.3 mg inert dust per cm^2 of front layer area led to no increase in the resistance of the fibrous material and did not alter its initial filtering characteristics.

These investigations and their results determine the direction of further studies on the establishing of multilayer filtering combinations, in order to improve the accuracy and resolution of this method.

BIBLIOGRAPHY

1. Ogorodnikov,B.I.,V.I.Skitovich, and E.A.Sitalo. Fil'tratsiya voloknistymi materialami FP aerozolei estestvennoi atmosfernoi radioaktivnosti (Filtering Aerosols with Natural Atmospheric Radioactivity through Fibrous Materials). — In this collection.
2. Chen,Ch. Fil'tratsiya aerozolei voloknistymi materialami (Aerosol Filtration through Fibrous Materials). — Uspekhi Khimii, Vol. 25, p. 368. 1956.
3. Junge,C.E. Air Chemistry and Radioactivity. — New York, Academic Press. 1963.
4. Lockhart,L.B., R.L.Patterson, and A.W.Saunders. The Size Distribution of Radioactive Atmospheric Aerosols. — J. Geophys. Res., Vol. 70, p. 6033. 1965.
5. Silverman,M.D. and W.T.Browning. Fibrous Filters as Particle Size Analyzers. — Science, Vol. 143, p. 572. 1964.

UDC 621.039.55

PRELIMINARY DATA ON THE MEASUREMENT OF THE
ATMOSPHERIC AEROSOL CHARACTERISTICS WITH A
CENTRIFUGAL SPECTROMETER

Yu. N. Redkin

The paper examines an aerosol spectrometer which makes it possible to obtain continuous spectra of particles for Stokes radii R_S between 0.4 and 10μ. A relationship $\varphi = \varphi(R_S)$ whose log-log plot for particles of $R_S \geqslant 10^{-4}$ cm is almost a straight line is derived from the equation of particle motion in a viscous space for a rotating system of coordinates. Here φ is the angle of particle deviation from a radius passing through the point from which the particle started moving.

The spectrometer model was built as a hollow, rotating steel disk, through the axis of which aerosol is pumped. Owing to centrifugal sedimentation, part of the dust penetrates special slots to form a pencil of rays splitting more and more as the particles move away from the axis of rotation. The coarser the particle, the larger the angle of its deviation.

A theoretical evaluation of the efficiency of this device showed it to depend very little on particle size at $R_S > 10^{-4}$ cm (being 65 to 70%), as confirmed by the results of a calibration using puffball and lycopodium spores.

The distribution of α-activity of particles of $R_S = 0.4 \cdot 10^{-4}$ cm varies little and is almost only a hundredth of the specific overall α-activity measured on an FPP filter.

Several types of aerosol spectrometers are known which sediment the aerosol particles in a field of centrifugal forces. They include the aerosol centrifuge and conifuge described in /9/. Goetz and his co-workers /2, 11—13/ have lately developed a spectrometer whose channel is shaped as a three-dimensional spiral. Picca and Dumoulin /14/ obtained particle spectra on the inner surface of a tube spinning around its geometric axis, through which the aerosol is passed. Despite their structural differences, all these spectrometers sediment the aerosol particles from a flow, so the length of the spectra on the backings can reach dozens of centimeters (Goetz) and even 1.5 m (Picca). This causes difficulties in the microscopic investigation of the spectra and in their α-radiography.

The present paper discusses the construction of a spectrometer that differs from the others in that, in order to obtain a compact, continuous spectrum, it creates a pencil of particles in a gaseous medium that is immobile in relation to the device, in the direction of centrifugal forces.

CALCULATION OF THE ANGLES OF PARTICLE DEVIATION

If viscosity is taken into account, the equation of the particle's steady motion in an inertialess system of coordinates is /6/

$$m\frac{d\vec{v}}{dt} = 2m[\vec{v}\,\vec{\omega}] + m[\vec{\omega}\,[\vec{r}\,\vec{\omega}]] - \gamma\vec{v}. \tag{1}$$

259

Here m is the particle mass, $\vec{v}$ is the particle relative velocity vector, $\vec{\omega}$ is the vector of angular velocity of coordinate system rotation, $\vec{r}$ is the radius vector of the particle with origin on the axis of rotation, and γ is the resistance coefficient of the medium.

If the particle moves in a plane perpendicular to the axis of rotation of the system, the component of (1) along the axis of the natural trihedron yields the two scalar equations

$$
\begin{cases}
\omega^2 r\, \vec{r}_0 \vec{\tau} - \dfrac{dv}{dt} - \dfrac{\gamma}{m} v = 0, \\[2mm]
\omega^2 r\, \vec{r}_0 \vec{n} - v\dfrac{d\vec{\tau}}{dt}\vec{n} - 2v[\vec{\omega}\,\vec{\tau}]\,\vec{n} = 0,
\end{cases}
\tag{2}
$$

where $\vec{\tau}$ is the unit tangent vector, $\vec{n}$ is the unit normal vector, and $\vec{r}_0$ is the unit radius vector. Consider the second equation of system (2) which, in view of the formulas of differential geometry, can be expressed as

$$
\frac{\omega^2 r^2}{\sqrt{r^2+p^2}} + \frac{v^2\left[r^2+2p^2-rp\dfrac{dp}{dr}\right]}{(r^2+p^2)^{3/2}} - 2\omega v = 0,
\tag{3}
$$

where $p = \dfrac{dr}{d\varphi}$. After the substitution of $z = \sqrt{r^2+p^2}/r$, equation (3) becomes two equations, one of which has imaginary solutions and does not concern us; the other is the Bernoulli equation

$$
\frac{dz}{dr} + \frac{2z^2}{k} - \frac{r^2+k^2}{k^2 r}\,z = 0,
\tag{4}
$$

where $k = v/\omega$.

To integrate equation (4) one requires the relationship between the speed of particle motion and the distance to the system's axis of rotation, i. e., function $v = v(r)$. At low Reynolds numbers, the particle velocity is proportional to the acceleration applied to the particle, and can be determined using the Stokes formula with Cunningham's correction:

$$
v = \frac{2}{9}\,\frac{R_s^2\,(\rho-\rho')}{\eta}\left(1+A\frac{l}{R_s}\right)w,
\tag{5}
$$

where R_s is the Stokes radius of the particle, ρ is the density of particle substance, ρ' is the gas density, η is the dynamic viscosity, l is the free path length of gas molecules, A is Cunningham's constant, and w is the acceleration applied to the particle. The values of ρ' and l depend on gas pressure, and so on r. The pressure exerted by the elementary cylindrical gas volume $h\theta r\,dr$ in the centrifugal force field upon the cylindrical surface of area $hr\theta$, if infinitesimal second-order terms are neglected, can be calculated from

$$
dP = \rho'\,\omega^2 r\,dr.
\tag{6}
$$

Here θ is the sector angle of the elementary cylindrical volume and h is the height of the elementary volume. In view of the Mendeleev-Clapeyron equation, integration of (6) produces formulas for the pressure, density, and gas-molecule free path length in the centrifugal force field:

$$P = P_0 \exp\left(\frac{\mu \omega^2 r^2}{2RT}\right), \tag{7}$$

$$\rho' = \rho_0' \exp\left(\frac{\mu \omega^2 r^2}{2RT}\right), \tag{8}$$

$$l = l_0 \exp\left(-\frac{\mu \omega^2 r^2}{2RT}\right), \tag{9}$$

where P_0, ρ_0' and l_0 are the pressure, density, and gas-molecule free path length on the axis of rotation of the system, respectively; μ is the molecular weight of the gas, R is the gas constant, and T is the gas temperature in °K.

With expressions (5), (8) and (9), equation (4) becomes very complicated. It is therefore advisable to specify the conditions of the problem and, after evaluating the terms, to simplify the equation. Assuming the speed of rotation of the system to be 12,000 rpm and the maximum distance of the particles from the axis of rotation not to exceed 6 cm, expression (8) yields the value of the maximum gas density in the system. When $R = 8.316 \cdot 10^3$ joule/kmole·deg, $\mu = 28.0$ kg/kmole, $r = 6 \cdot 10^{-2}$ m, $\omega = 1256$ sec^{-1}, $T = 293$°K, $\rho' = 1.04$, and $\rho_0' \simeq 0.00134$ g/cm^3. Thus, for particles of density $\rho \geqslant 1$ g/cm^3, the value of the term ρ' is only thousandths of ρ; it may therefore be neglected in (5).

For angular velocities of system rotation $\omega < 2000$ sec^{-1} it makes sense to speak only of particles of at least 0.05μ radius, because for finer particles the agitating forces of the vibration waves and convection currents of the gaseous medium are comparable with the centrifugal forces. In this case, discarding of the Cunningham binomial in equation (5) produces a drop of about 7% in the speed of particles of $R_S = 10^{-4}$ cm as compared to the value obtained from (5); when $R_S = 10^{-5}$ cm the drop is already 45%, while the maximum variation in the gas-molecule free path length under such conditions is only 4%. It is therefore advisable to include the binomial and substitute $l = l_c -$ const.

Acceleration w in equation (5) is determined by the component of the centrifugal force acting upon the particle along the tangent to the trajectory. The cosine of the angle made by the radius vector and the unit vector of the tangent is given by the scalar product

$$\vec{r_0}\vec{\tau} = \frac{p}{\sqrt{r^2 + p^2}}, \tag{10}$$

whose value differs from unity by a factor of $4 \cdot 10^{-2}$ for a deviation angle $\varphi \leqslant 0.5$. Thus, for particles deviating from the radius by an angle $0 \leqslant \varphi \leqslant 0.5$ one can assume with practically sufficient accuracy that $w = w^2 r$. Replacement of expression (5) by the approximate formula

$$v = \frac{2}{9} \frac{R_S^2 \rho}{\eta} \left(1 + A \frac{l_c}{R_S}\right) \omega^2 r \tag{11}$$

increases the speed of particle motion throughout the radius range $5\cdot10^{-5} \leqslant R_s \leqslant 5\cdot10^{-4}$ by 10% at most.

Integration of equation (4) with consideration of (11) yields a second integral

$$\varphi = \int_a^r \frac{dr}{\sqrt{a\dfrac{r^b}{(r^d - C_1)^2} - r^2}} + C_2, \tag{12}$$

where

$$a = \left(\frac{q^2+1}{2q}\right)^2, \qquad b = 2\,\frac{2q^2+1}{q^2},$$

$$d = \frac{q^2+1}{q^2}, \qquad q = \frac{2}{9}\,\frac{R_s^2\,\rho\,\omega}{\eta}\left(1 + A\,\frac{l_c}{R_s}\right).$$

The constant C_1 of the first integration is found from the condition

$$\frac{dr}{d\varphi}\bigg|_{r=r_1} = \infty, \tag{13}$$

whence $C_1 = r_1^d$. Condition (13) presupposes that the direction of particle movement at distance r_1 from the system's axis of rotation is strictly radial. Reducing the expression under the radical sign in (12) to a common denominator and dividing polynomial by polynomial, substitution of the variable $f = \left(\dfrac{r}{r_1}\right)^d$ gives the sum of two tabulated integrals /3/

$$\varphi = \frac{1}{d\sqrt{a-1}}\ln\left|2\sqrt{(a-1)[(a-1)f^2+2f-1]} + \right.$$
$$\left. + 2(a-1)f+2\right| - \frac{1}{d}\,\arcsin\frac{f-1}{f\sqrt{a}} + C_2. \tag{14}$$

Constant C_2 is determined from the condition

$$\varphi\,|_{r=r_1} = 0. \tag{15}$$

With q increasing up to 0.63, the value of φ increases monotonically. Thus, the angle of particle deviation increases with increasing particle size and density, angular velocity of system rotation, and decreasing viscosity of the medium. The angle of deviation of an aerosol particle of given size can only increase due to increasing angular velocity of system rotation.

Figure 1 is a log-log plot of $\varphi=\varphi(R_s)$, calculated from formula (14) for aerosol particles of density $\rho = 1, 2, 3, 4$, and 5 g/cm^3 at $\dfrac{r}{r_1}=2$, $\omega = 1000$ sec^{-1}, $\eta = 181\cdot10^{-6}$ g/cm·sec, and $l_c = 0.924\cdot10^{-5}$ cm.

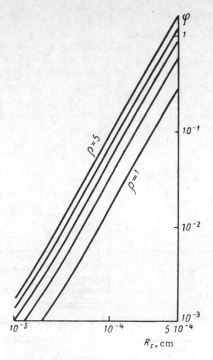

FIGURE 1. Plot of $\varphi = \varphi(R_S)$.

Figure 1 shows that, in the case of a chemically homogeneous polydisperse aerosol, particle sedimentation spectra with continuous variation in absolute radius should appear on the cylindrical surface. If the aerosol is of heterogeneous chemical composition, particles with a ratio of radii

$$\frac{R_{S\,max}}{R_{S\,min}} = \sqrt{\frac{\rho_{max}}{\rho_{min}} + \left(\frac{\rho_{max}}{\rho_{min}} - 1\right)\frac{A\,l_c}{R_{S\,min}}} \qquad (16)$$

can sediment at the same point of the spectrum. When $R_S \geqslant 10^{-4}$ cm, the particle size scatter is expressed by the simpler ratio

$$\frac{R_{S\,max}}{R_{S\,min}} \approx \sqrt{\frac{\rho_{max}}{\rho_{min}}}. \qquad (17)$$

In the presence of aerosols with densities ρ from 1 to 5 g/cm^3, particles with a ratio of radii equal to 2.2 can occur at every point of the spectrum. In Figure 1, this corresponds to a difference in logarithms of particle radius for the points of intersection of the horizontal line by the curves $\rho = 1$ and $\rho = 5$, which varies little for particles of $R_S \geqslant 10^{-4}$ cm; this is evident from the graph.

CONSTRUCTION AND CHARACTERISTICS OF THE DEVICE

The newly developed aerosol spectrometer is a hollow disk of 135 mm diameter (Figure 2), consisting of base (6) with hub (9), by which it is attached to the shaft of an electric motor, and cover (5) tightly screwed onto the base and integral with nut (2). A mandrel with radial channels (3) is screwed onto the disk center. The disperse air mixture is fed through the axial pipe (1) and spreads through channels (3), the configuration of which is shown in Figure 3. The geometry of the channel axes was calculated on the basis of the following considerations.

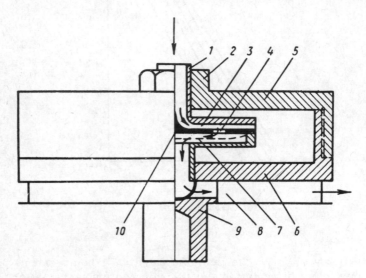

FIGURE 2. Diagrammatic cross section of the spectrometer in an axial plane:

1) inflow pipe; 2) nut; 3) radial channels; 4) orifices; 5) cover; 6) base; 7) filter; 8) blade wheel; 9) hub; 10) projection.

Assuming that the mean rate of gas flow in the channel is constant, we obtain the equation of a curve from equation (4) for $v = \text{const}$:

$$\varphi = \int \frac{y\,dr}{r\sqrt{1-y^2}} - C_2, \tag{18}$$

where

$$y = \frac{1}{r} \exp\left(-\frac{r^2}{2k^2}\right) \left[C_1 + \frac{1}{k} \ln \frac{r^2}{2k^2} + \right.$$

$$\left. + \sum_{n=1}^{+\infty} \frac{(-1)^n}{nn!} \frac{r^{2n}}{2^n k^{2n+1}} \right] \tag{19}$$

264

and $k=v/\omega$. Constant C_1 is determined from the condition that the point begins moving from the ring. There is just one possibility: the point (flow particle) starts moving on a circle of radius r_c with speed $v=\omega r_c$ in the opposite direction to the rotation of the device. Hence $k=r_c$ and

$$C_1 = r_c \sqrt{e} + \frac{\ln 2}{r_c} - \frac{1}{r_c} \sum_{n=1}^{+\infty} \frac{(-1)^n}{n\,n!} \frac{1}{2^n}. \tag{20}$$

When $r \geqslant 2r_c$, curve (18) differs little from a straight line. For uniform motion of the particles along the channel axis at the calculated speed, they should not undergo any acceleration perpendicular to the channel axis. However, since the particles precede the flow and the flow velocity near the channel axis is slightly higher than the average, particles of over 1μ deviate considerably from the axis to form a compact aerosol layer along wall A (Figure 3). The inertial sedimentation of particles on wall A is hampered by the fact that the flow velocity near it is very low. By passing through orifices (4 in Figure 2) the air can be additionally filtered through filter (7), which is tightly squeezed between the mandrel halves. When the airflow bends toward the orifices, all the aerosol particles over 0.5μ in size are thrust into the space of the slot (Figure 3). Part of the dust passes through the slot to form a narrow, flat radial beam, expanding as the particles move away from the axis of rotation; thus the coarser the particle, the larger the angle of its deviation. All the surfaces that come into contact with the airflow are chrome plated.

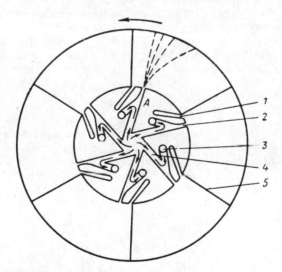

FIGURE 3. Diagrammatic cross section of the spectrometer in the plane of rotation:

1) control gaps; 2) slots; 3) orifices; 4) channels; 5) radial partitions; arrows indicate the airflow direction.

The volumetric rate of airflow through the device is determined by the mandrel's resistance to flow and the pressure drop between the space above pipe (1) (Figure 2) and the space on the axis of blade wheel (8). In view of formula (9), this pressure drop can be expressed as follows:

$$\Delta P = P_1 \left[1 - \exp \left(-\frac{\mu \, \omega^2 r_p^2}{2RT} \right) \right].$$ (21)

Here r_p is the outer radius of the blade wheel and P_1 is the atmospheric pressure (if the experiment is not being conducted in a pressure chamber).

EVALUATING THE EFFICIENCY OF THE DEVICE

Distortions in the spectrum of aerosol particles sedimented on the base are due to centrifugal and diffuse sedimentation of particles on the inner surface of the pipe, to inertial sedimentation of particles in the mandrel center as a result of the impactor effect, to diffuse sedimentation of particles on the walls of the radial channels, to the effectiveness of particle removal from the flow at its bending into the orifice, and to diffuse sedimentation of particles on the walls of the slots.

To calculate the centrifugal deposition of the aerosol inside the inflow pipe one must know the distribution there of the speeds at which the particles are whirled by the gas stream. An exact solution of the Navier-Stokes equation /5/ for the case considered is fairly difficult and not really justified, because the process takes place at near-critical Reynolds numbers. We shall therefore proceed from simplified considerations.

Let us single out a narrow ring of thickness dr from the gas volume in the pipe and, considering it as a solid body, let us write the equation of its motion in relation to the axis of rotation:

$$J \frac{d\omega}{dt} = (F_{v_1} - F_{v_2}) \, r.$$ (22)

Here J is the moment of inertia of the ring, ω is the angular velocity of its rotation, F_{v_1} is the viscous force acting from the outside of the ring and accelerating its motion, and F_{v_2} is the viscous force acting from the inside of the ring and retarding its motion. By differentiating the right-hand part of equation (22) and substituting the expression for the moment of inertia in the left-hand part, we obtain

$$\frac{d v_\varphi}{dt} = \nu \, \frac{\partial^2 v_\varphi}{\partial r^2},$$ (23)

where v_φ is the linear speed of rotation of the annular element of the gas and ν is the kinetic viscosity.

Applying the Laplace transform to the boundary conditions

$$v_\varphi (t, \, r)|_{t-0} = 0, \quad v_\varphi (t, \, r)|_{r-0} = 0, \quad v_\varphi (t, \, r)|_{r-R_0} = \Omega R_0,$$ (24)

where R_0 is the pipe radius and Ω is the angular velocity of rotation of the device, we obtain a solution for the transform in the form

$$U(r, p) = \frac{\Omega R_0}{P} \cdot \frac{\operatorname{sh} r \sqrt{\dfrac{p}{\nu}}}{\operatorname{sh} R_0 \sqrt{\dfrac{p}{\nu}}}. \tag{25}$$

The inverse transform is /4/

$$v_\varphi(t, r) = -\Omega \sqrt{\nu} \int_0^{\frac{r}{\sqrt{\nu}}} \Theta_0\left(\frac{\nu u}{2R_0}; \frac{\nu t}{R_0^2}\right) du, \tag{26}$$

where Θ_0 is a theta function. Integration yields

$$v_\varphi(t, r) = \Omega R_0\left[\frac{r}{R_0} + \frac{2}{\pi}\sum_{n=1}^{+\infty} \frac{(-1)^n}{n} \exp\left(-\frac{n^2\pi^2 t\nu}{R_0^2}\right)\sin\frac{n\pi r}{R_0}\right]. \tag{27}$$

From the conditions of the parabolic flow profile we have

$$v_z = \frac{2\overline{v}_z}{R_0^2}(R_0^2 - r^2), \tag{28}$$

where v_z is the velocity of an air particle along the axis and $\overline{v}_z$ is the mean speed of flow. Under the condition of gas incompressibility, we can find the time of twisting of the gas ring in a pipe of length z:

$$t = \frac{z}{v_z} = \frac{z R_0^2}{2\overline{v}_z(R_0^2 - r^2)}. \tag{29}$$

After substituting (29) in (27), we obtain the distribution of gas twisting speeds inside the rotating cylindrical pipe:

$$v_\varphi(z, r) = \Omega R_0\left[\frac{r}{R_0} + \right.$$

$$\left. + \frac{2}{\pi}\sum_{n=1}^{+\infty}\frac{(-1)^n}{n}\exp\left(-\frac{n^2\pi\nu}{2\overline{v}_z}\frac{z}{R_0^2 - r^2}\right)\sin\frac{n\pi r}{R_0}\right]. \tag{30}$$

Figure 4 shows the distribution of velocities for $\overline{v}_z = 150$ cm/sec. At $r = 0.8R_0$ the layer no longer has time to twist completely, and at $r = 0.65R_0$ the speed of rotation it obtains is 3% at most of the highest possible for this layer. With increasing flow speed, all the curves are extended to the right.

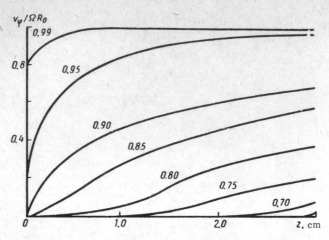

FIGURE 4. Distribution of linear speeds of rotation in the inflow pipe.
The value of the ratio $\dfrac{r}{R_0}$ for $\omega = 1000$ sec^{-1}, $R_0 = 0.4$ cm and $z = 3$ cm is indicated next to each curve.

To evaluate the centrifugal deposition of particles on the pipe walls we shall decompose the whole space inside into a series of coaxial cylinders of equal wall thickness Δr. The linear speed of rotation will be assumed constant throughout the layer thickness and to depend only on z. Settling on the cylinder wall, the particle will pass from one layer into another, which in turn moves along the axis at different speeds. The distance covered by the particle along the z axis when settling across the wall Δr of one layer is

$$\Delta z_i = \bar{v}_{zi}\,\frac{\Delta r}{\bar{v}_{si}} = \frac{9\,\Delta r\,\eta\,r_i\,\bar{v}_{zi}}{2\,\rho\,R_S^2\left(1 + A\,\dfrac{l_c}{R_S}\right)v_{\varphi i}^2}. \tag{31}$$

Here r_i is the radius of the ith layer, $\bar{v}_{\varphi i}$ is the speed of rotation averaged over the thickness of the ith layer, $\bar{v}_{zi}$ is the mean velocity of the axial motion of the layer, and $\bar{v}_{si}$ is the mean speed of particle sedimentation in the layer. Taking $\bar{v}_{\varphi i}$ from tables and summing Δz_i up to z, we find n (the layers are numbered from the inner surface of the cylinder to the axis of rotation):

$$z = \frac{9\,\eta\,(\Delta r)^2\,\bar{v}_z}{\rho\,R_S^2\left(1 + A\,\dfrac{l_c}{R_S}\right)} \sum_{i=1}^{n}\frac{i\,(2 - 3\,i\,k + i^2\,k^2)}{\bar{v}_{\varphi i}^2}. \tag{32}$$

Figure 5 represents the curves of deposition, in %, of aerosol particles on the pipe walls due to rotation (I) and diffusion (II), calculated for different mean flow velocities and $\frac{\Delta r}{R_0} = 0.01$. The diffuse deposition was calculated from the formula of Gormley and Kennedy (e.g., /8/) when

$$\mu = \frac{Dz}{R_0^2 \bar{v}_z} < 0.01, \qquad (33)$$

where D is the diffusion coefficient.

The centrifugal sedimentation is overestimated, because it was calculated on the assumption of a laminar flow of the layers and full capability of the aerosol particles to be entrained by the gas.

The diffusion deposition in the radial channels was evaluated from the formula of Gormley and Kennedy for plane parallel channels /8/. To reduce inertial deposition a hyperbolic projection (10) (Figure 2) was provided on the mandrel axis. Owing to the low rate of sedimentation of particles below 1μ within the slot, many of them settle on the walls.

The efficiency of one support in relation to the amount of air fed to it is represented in Figure 6. The summation took successively into account the assessed depositions and the efficiency of aerosol particle separation from the flow, which amounts to several percent for particles below 10^{-5} cm.

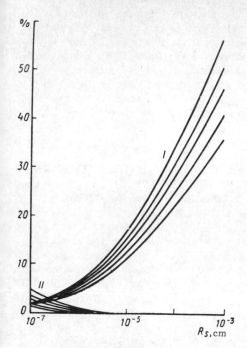

FIGURE 5. Proportion of particles settling in the inflow pipe (%):

I) due to rotation; II) due to diffusion. The curves correspond to the following values of $\bar{v}_z$ (from top to bottom): 150, 250, 350, 450, 550 cm/sec, when $\rho = 1$ g/cm^3.

The construction of the device facilitates microscopic examination of all channel and slot surfaces. A foil was therefore positioned inside the pipe.

A comparison of the theoretical evaluations of sedimentation in the pipe with the results obtained at the intake of the aerosol comprising L y c o p e r d o n P e r s and Lycopodiaceae spores revealed that no more than 30% of the particles settle on the surface of the pipe. The actual efficiency is higher than the theoretical: 65 to 70% for particles in the size range $0.5 \cdot 10^{-4} \leqslant R_S \leqslant 10^{-3}$ cm for $\bar{v}_z = 350$ cm/sec and a slot width of 0.65 mm.

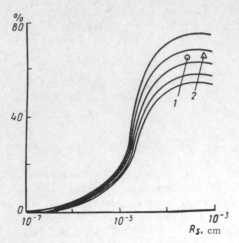

FIGURE 6. Theoretical efficiency of the device (in %) for $\overline{v}_z$ equal to 550, 450, 350, 250 and 150 cm/sec (from top to bottom):

1) efficiency for an aerosol comprising Lycoperdon Pers spores; 2) efficiency for an aerosol comprising Lycopodiaceae spores ($\overline{v}_z = 350$ cm/sec).

If all slots have the same width, the rms deviation in the particle concentrations of the spectra of one sample does not exceed 7% and varies little in the said range of radii. This makes it possible to determine the error due to using the size distribution of particles in all the spectra of one intake from the results measured on one spectrum.

MEASURING THE DISTRIBUTION OF THE α-ACTIVITY OF COARSELY-DISPERSE URBAN AEROSOL BY PARTICLE SIZE

The study was carried out with a six-section spectrometer with 0.65 × 2-mm slots. Photoplates with a nuclear emulsion type A-2-50μ of size 54 × 18 mm were placed in four sections, and clean glass plates of the same dimensions were placed in the other two. To prevent smashing of the glass plates, resin-impregnated laminated cloth was inserted between them and the cylindrical surface of the disk. The year, month, sample number and section number were marked on each plate. Before starting the intake of samples, a special metal ruler was used to mark the control plate in quick-drying paint or silicate glue with points corresponding to the central projection of the slot center on the plate. The points were marked by notches on the photoplates.

The method has been described elsewhere /1, 7/. Before use, the plates were kept for 15 min in a 0.15% solution of potassium ferricyanide, then rinsed for 1 hour under running water. After drying for 24 hrs at room temperature, the plates were positioned in the device.

The device rotated at about 9500 rpm, the time of intake was 4 hrs plus 4 hrs of retention in the device, after which the plates were processed. At the same time dust was collected on a filter for 15 min. The rate of air pumping through the device was 10.5 liter/min, and 230 cm/sec through the filter. The tracks counted on the photoplates were brought into agreement with the particle concentrations on the control glasses. The background was 12 to 15 tracks per cm^2, and was exceeded by a factor of 2 to 3.

Figure 7 is a histogram drawn from 729 tracks for particles of 0.8 to 10μ. The results are given on the basis of data measured in May 1969. The proportion of active particles is about 0.01% of the total number and does not vary much.

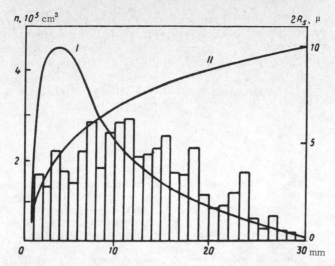

FIGURE 7. Distribution of α-tracks by particle size. The abscissa is the distance on the support, from the central projection of the slot:

I) counted particle concentration n; II) particle diameter $2R_S$.

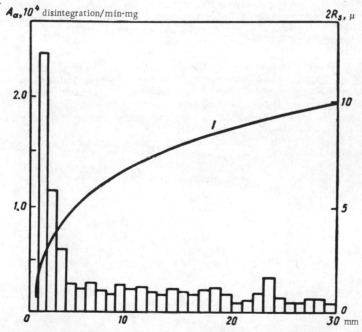

FIGURE 8. Distribution of specific α-activity by particle size. The abscissa is the distance, on the support, from the central projection of the slot:

1) particle diameter $2R_S$.

Figure 8 gives the distribution of specific activity in α-disintegrations per mg of aerosol substance. A comparison with the activity on the filter suggests that the total specific α-activity of the aerosol, trapped by the FPP filter, is hundreds of times as high as the activity of the coarsely-disperse aerosol of $R_S \geqslant 0.4\mu$.

The author expresses his gratitude to V. N. Bakulin for his assistance and to V. P. Matulyavichus for critical observations.

BIBLIOGRAPHY

1. Vebra, E. Yu. O nekotorykh protsessakh v oblakakh i tumanakh, privodyashchikh k samoochishcheniyu atmosfery ot radioaktivnykh zagryaznenii (Processes in Clouds and Fogs Leading to Atmospheric Scavenging of Radioactive Contamination). — Author's Summary of dissertation. Vilnius. 1967.

2. Goetz, A., O. Preining, and T. Kelly. Metastability of Natural and Urban Aerosols [Russian translation]. — In sbornik: Atmosfernye aerozoly i radioaktivnoe zagryaznenie vozdukha (Atmospheric Aerosols and Radioactive Air Pollutants). Leningrad, Gidrometeoizdat. 1964.

3. Dwight, H. B. Tables of Integrals and other Mathematical Data. — Macmillan. 1961.

4. Ditkin, V. A. and A. P. Prudnikov. Spravochnik po operatsionnomu ischisleniyu (Textbook of Operational Calculus). — Moskva, "Vysshaya shkola. " 1965.

5. Kochin, N. E., I. A. Kibel', and N. V. Roze. Teoreticheskaya gidromekhanika (Theoretical Hydro-mechanics). Part 2. — Moskva, "Fizmatgiz. " 1963.

6. Landau, L. D. and E. M. Lifshits. Mekhanika (Mechanics). — Moskva, "Nauka. " 1965.

7. Potsyus, V. Yu. Metodika issledovaniya radioaktivnosti oblachnykh elementov radiograficheskim metodom (Technique of Investigating the Radioactivity of Cloud Elements by Radiographic Methods). — Nauchnye soobshcheniya AN Litovskoi SSR, Geofizika i Klimatologiya, Vol. 10, No. 1. 1959.

8. Ruzer, L. S. Radioaktivnye aerozoly (Radioactive Aerosols). — Moskva, Izdatel'stvo standartov. 1968.

9. Fuchs, N. A. The Mechanics of Aerosols. — Oxford, Pergamon Press. 1964.

10. Jahnke, E. and F. Emde (with the assistance of F. Lösch). Tables of Higher Functions. — McGraw-Hill. 1960.

11. Goetz, A. An Instrument for the Quantitative Separation and Size Classification of Air-Borne Particulate Matter Down to 0.2 Micron. — Geofisica pura e applicata, Vol. 36, No. 1. 1957.

12. Goetz, A. and O. Preining. The Aerosol Spectrometer and its Application to Nuclear Condensation Studies. — Geophysical Monograph, No. 5. 1959.

13. Goetz, A., H. J. R. Stevenson, and O. Preining. The Design and Performance of the Aerosol Spectrometer. — J. APCA, Vol. 10, No. 5. 1960.

14. Picca, R. and C. Dumoulin. Captation par centrifugation de particules atmospheriques. — J. Rech. Atmos., Vol. 3, No. 1. 1967.

UDC 539.107

MEASURING THE CONCENTRATION OF HIGHLY-DISPERSE RADIOACTIVE AEROSOLS BY THE DIFFUSION METHOD

S. V. Kolerskii, Yu. V. Kuznetsov, S. O. Lekhtmakher,
N. M. Polev, L. S. Ruzer, and S. A. Stoyanova

The paper describes the application of the diffusion method to the determination of the proportion of free atoms and of all the ultrahighly dispérse aerosols (molecular complexes) formed through interaction of free atoms with the molecules of the various gases in the air, in the overall concentration of radioactive aerosols of emanation daughter products in the air. The coefficient of deposition of ultrahighly disperse particles in a cylindrical channel, calculated from formulas of Gormley and Kennedy, is shown to be affected by an error of 3 to 5% at most, due to the fact that the variable distribution of flow velocities in the inflow section of the channel is disregarded in the formulas. The errors of the method are discussed, and the method is shown to facilitate reliable measurements of the proportion of ultrahighly disperse radioactive aerosols of emanation daughter products, if this proportion is at least 10 to 20%.

A knowledge of the activity distribution over the different particle sizes is a prerequisite when studying the properties of radioactive aerosols and their effect on the human body. Relevant measurements of fine particles are very difficult, especially for radii below 10^{-6} cm. The usual methods comprise that of deposition in an electrostatic field, and that of diffusion. The former provides incomplete information, as only part of the electrically-charged aerosols are measurable.

The present paper discusses the possibility of using the diffusion method for determining the proportion of particles below 10^{-6} cm in the overall concentration of radioactive aerosols of radon daughter products.

Until recently, this application of the method was somewhat limited by the fact that the theory of Gormley and Kennedy /8/ concerning the calculation of diffusion deposition of aerosols in cylindrical tubes is based on a hypothetical parabolic distribution of flow in pipes. Such a flow distribution exists, however, only at some distance from the inflow, and this must be taken into account when measuring particles below 10^{-6} cm /4/; being very mobile, significant amounts of these particles settle in the inflow section of the pipe.

The numerical solution to the problem of the deposition of ultrahighly disperse particles in a cylindrical tube with allowance for the changing flow distribution in its inflow section was published elsewhere /2/. The results make it possible to account for the influence of the inflow effect when calculating the deposition of ultrahighly disperse aerosols; this influence does not exceed 3 to 5% even for particles having a diffusion coefficient $D = 0.068$ cm^2/sec. This conclusion agrees with experimental data on the inflow effect /5, 7/. Its influence is low because the decisive change in flow distribution takes place within a very short distance of the pipe inflow: about 0.1 of the length of the inflow section ($l_{in} = 0.1$ ReR, where R is the pipe radius and Re the Reynolds number).

Several French scientists /6, 7, 9, 10, 12/ recently demonstrated that the addition of atoms of emanation daughter products to aerosol particles suspended in air precedes the interaction of these atoms with various gases, such as oxygen, water vapor, HNO_3, etc., contained in the air. The daughter-product atoms are thus covered with gas molecules, to form molecular complexes of different diffusion coefficients, like small ions, which are then attached to the aerosol. These particles will be referred to here as ultra-highly disperse aerosols of emanation daughter products. The spectrum of distribution of ultrahighly disperse radioactive aerosols by diffusion coefficients extends from that of "free" atoms (c. 10^{-1} cm^2/sec) to a minimum of c. 10^{-2} cm^2/sec /6, 7, 9, 10, 12/.

It has been stressed /3/ that the spectrum of radioactive aerosols formed by the addition of emanation daughter products to natural aerosols covers mainly the particle radius range of 10^{-6} to $5 \cdot 10^{-5}$ cm and the corresponding range of diffusion coefficients $1.35 \cdot 10^{-4}$ to $2.74 \cdot 10^{-7}$ cm^2/sec. In the distribution curve of the diffusion coefficient, the ultrahighly disperse aerosols should thus be distinguished by a discontinuity in the spectrum of natural radioactive aerosols. The presence of this discontinuity, as demonstrated by calculations from formulas in /8/, makes it possible to use diffusion batteries as selective samplers of ultrahighly disperse aerosols. If the characteristics of the battery and the rate at which the investigated air is pumped through it are selected correspondingly, the deposition of radioactive aerosols in it will be negligible compared to the deposition of ultrahighly disperse particles. The experimentally measurable coefficient of battery deposition can then be expressed in the form

$$K_e = \frac{A_1'}{A_1 + A_2},$$

where A_1 is the activity of the ultrahighly disperse particles, A_2 is the activity of particles larger than 10^{-6} cm pumped through the battery, and A_1' is the activity of those ultrahighly disperse particles that settle in the battery.

The deposition coefficient of ultrahighly disperse particles in the battery is $K_\tau = \frac{A_1'}{A_1}$ and the relative amount of ultrahighly disperse particles is $f = \frac{A_1}{A_1 + A_2}$. Hence

$$f = \frac{K_e}{K_\tau}. \qquad (1)$$

Since the shape of the spectrum of ultrahighly disperse radioactive aerosol distribution with respect to the diffusion coefficient is unknown, K_τ cannot be calculated theoretically. For its experimental determination, a Ra^{226} source of 10^{-6} curie activity was placed in dust-removed air in a 1-m^3

2KA-NZh chamber. The air was free of dust, so only ultrahighly disperse radioactive aerosols of radon daughter products could form in it. The air from the chamber was pumped simultaneously at a constant rate through two identical 1-cm-long diffusion batteries composed of 75 cylindrical channels. The coefficient of deposition of the ultrahighly disperse aerosols in the battery was determined from the difference in activity between two LFS-1 filters positioned at the entrance to one and the outflow section of the other battery. The measurements were conducted by the spectrometric method /1/ on a USA-2 setup, on RaA alone. The results for different pumping rates Q are shown in Figure 1. The curve was used for calculating the diffusion coefficient of ultrahighly disperse aerosols from the formulas of Gormey and Kennedy. The results are given in Figure 2. According to the method described in /11/, the minimum diffusion coefficient in the spectrum of ultrahighly disperse aerosols can be found by extrapolating the curve in Figure 2 to $Q=0$, which yields $D_{min}=2.3 \cdot 10^{-2}$ cm^2/sec, in good agreement with the data in /6, 7, 9, 10, 12/.

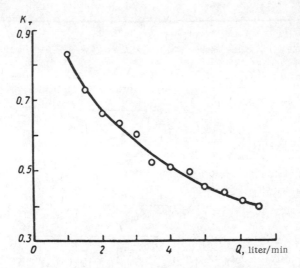

FIGURE 1. Coefficient of deposition K_T of ultrahighly disperse radioactive aerosols in the battery at different pumping rates Q.

To check the assumption that the ultrahighly disperse radioactive aerosols on the distribution curve of diffusion coefficients are distinguished from the natural radioactive aerosols by a break, and thus only ultrahighly disperse particles deposit selectively in the battery, we conducted a series of experiments similar to the preceding, except that dust-loaded air from the laboratory premises was pumped into the chamber. The K_e value was measured at pumping rates of 1 to 7 liter/min through the battery. The values so found were used for determining f from formula (1) at corresponding K_T values from Figure 1. Measurements at different rates yielded similar results: the proportion of ultrahighly disperse aerosols of RaA was c. 40% of the overall RaA activity. This proved that only ultrahighly disperse particles selectively deposit in the battery; were it not so, the f value determined from formula (1) for low rates would be far higher than that for high rates, due to deposition of aerosols to which ultrahighly disperse RaA aerosols attach themselves.

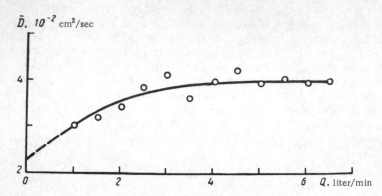

FIGURE 2. "Apparent" mean diffusion coefficient $\overline{D}$ vs. pumping rate Q.

The error δ in determining f from formula (1) is

$$\delta = \sqrt{\left(\frac{\Delta K_e}{K_e}\right)^2 + \left(\frac{\Delta K_\tau}{K_\tau}\right)^2} \,. \tag{2}$$

Since K_e depends on the difference in activity between the inflow filter (A_{in}) and the outflow filter (A_{out}),

$$K_e = \frac{A_{in} - A_{out}}{A_{in}} \tag{3}$$

and

$$\frac{\Delta K_e}{K_e} = \frac{A_{out}}{A_{in} - A_{out}} \sqrt{\left(\frac{\Delta A_{in}}{A_{in}}\right)^2 + \left(\frac{\Delta A_{out}}{A_{out}}\right)^2} \,. \tag{4}$$

But (3) and (1) imply that $A_{in} - A_{out} = K_e A_{in} = K_\tau f A_{in}$ and $A_{вых} = (1 - K_\tau f) A_{in}$. Consequently,

$$\frac{\Delta K_e}{K_e} = \frac{1 - K_\tau f}{K_\tau f} \sqrt{\left(\frac{\Delta A_{in}}{A_{in}}\right)^2 + \left(\frac{\Delta A_{out}}{A_{out}}\right)^2} = \gamma \sqrt{(\delta_1)^2 + (\delta_2)^2} \,, \tag{5}$$

where

$$\gamma = \frac{1 - K_\tau f}{K_\tau f} \,, \qquad \delta_1 = \frac{\Delta A_{in}}{A_{in}} \,, \qquad \delta_2 = \frac{\Delta A_{out}}{A_{out}} \,.$$

Table 1 lists values of $\Delta K_e/K_e$ in relation to f and $\sqrt{(\delta_1)^2 + (\delta_2)^2}$ at a pumping rate $Q = 1$ liter/min, i.e., $K_\tau = 0.829$ (Figure 1).

TABLE 1. Error, %, in the coefficient of aerosol deposition in the battery

f	γ	$\dfrac{\Delta K_e}{K_e} = \gamma \sqrt{\delta_1^2 + \delta_2^2}$ for			
		$\sqrt{\delta_1^2 + \delta_2^2} = 20$	$\sqrt{\delta_1^2 + \delta_2^2} = 10$	$\sqrt{\delta_1^2 + \delta_2^2} = 5$	$\sqrt{\delta_1^2 + \delta_2^2} = 1$
1.00	0.21	4.2	2.1	1.0	0.21
0.80	0.51	10.2	5.1	2.6	0.51
0.50	1.41	28.2	14.1	7.0	1.41
0.40	2.01	40.2	20.1	10.0	2.01
0.25	3.83	76.6	38.3	19.1	3.83
0.20	5.02	—	50.2	25.1	5.02
0.10	11.0	—	—	55.0	11.0
0.05	23.1	—	—	—	23.1
0.02	59.2	—	—	—	59.2

Thus, the error in determining f depends on the total activity of the aerodisperse system, determined by errors δ_1 and δ_2, as well as on the proportion of ultrahighly disperse particles f, determined by the factor γ.

The errors in measuring filter activities depend mainly on the statistical error of measurement and on the error in measuring the air pumping rate, $\dfrac{\Delta Q}{Q}$, i. e.,

$$\sqrt{(\delta_1)^2 + (\delta_2)^2} = \sqrt{\left(\frac{1}{\sqrt{A_{in}}}\right)^2 + \left(\frac{\Delta Q_{in}}{Q_{in}}\right)^2 + \left(\frac{1}{\sqrt{A_{out}}}\right)^2 + \left(\frac{\Delta Q_{out}}{Q_{out}}\right)^2}. \quad (6)$$

The errors in the K_τ values given in Figure 1 depend mainly on the variation in the very spectrum of ultrahighly disperse aerosols due to fluctuations in humidity, temperature and other air characteristics. The K_τ values given in Figure 1 were obtained by averaging a great number of measurements obtained in the summer, fall and winter of 1968. The scatter of these measurements never exceeded $\Delta K_\tau = 0.07$ at any pumping rate, i. e., the maximum error in the determination of K_τ did not exceed the values given in Table 2.

In our measurements, the pumping rate was measured to within $\dfrac{\Delta Q}{Q} \leqslant 2\%$.

TABLE 2. Errors in the coefficient of deposition of ultrahighly disperse aerosols in the battery

Q, liter/min	1.0	2.0	3.0	4.0	5.0	6.0
K_τ	0.828	0.672	0.577	0.510	0.455	0.413
$\dfrac{\Delta K_\tau}{K_\tau}$, %	8.4	10.4	12.1	13.7	15.4	16.9

At a pumping rate $Q = 1$ liter/min the statistical error in measuring filter activities did not exceed 6 to 7%. Thus, the total measurement error calculated from the formula

$$\delta = \sqrt{\gamma^2(\delta_1^2 + \delta_2^2) + \left(\frac{\Delta K_\tau}{K_\tau}\right)^2}\qquad(7)$$

at $Q = 1$ liter/min was c. 35 to 45% when $f \approx 0.4$.

The method described facilitates reliable measurements of the proportion of ultrahighly disperse radioactive aerosols of emanation daughter products, if this proportion is not below $f > 10$ to 20%.

No method has yet been developed for measuring the concentrations of ultrahighly disperse radioactive aerosols. The one described apparently applied to the measurement of the highly disperse fractions of long-lived radioactive aerosols.

BIBLIOGRAPHY

1. Labushkin, V.G. and L.S.Ruzer. O metode opredeleniya kontsentratsii korotkozhivushchikh dochernikh produktov radona v vozdukhe po α- i β-izlucheniyam (Determining the Concentrations of Short-Lived Radon Daughter Products in the Air by the α- and β-Radiations).— Atomnaya Energiya, Vol. 19, No. 1. 1965.

2. Lekhtmakher, S.O., N.M.Polev, L.S.Ruzer, and S.A.Stoyanova. Konvektivnaya diffuziya v predelakh vkhodnogo uchastka otbornoi trubki (Convective Diffusion Within the Inflow Section of the Sampling Pipe).— In: Materialy Vos'moi vsesoyuznoi mezhvuzovskoi konferentsii po voprosam ispareniya, goreniya i gazovoi dinamiki dispersnykh sistem (Proceedings of the 8th All-Union Gas Conference of Schools of Higher Learning on Problems Relating to the Evaporation, Combustion, and Gas Dynamics of Disperse Systems). Odessa. 1968.

3. Polev, N.M. and L.S.Ruzer. Metod izmereniya kontsentratsii "svobodnykh" atomov dochernikh produktov emanatsii v vozdukhe s pomoshch'yu diffuzionnykh batarei (Method for Measuring the Concentration of "Free" Atoms of Emanation Daughter Products in the Air with the Aid of Diffusion Batteries).— Atomnaya Energiya, Vol. 25, No. 3. 1968.

4. Fuchs, N.A. The Mechanics of Aerosols.— Oxford, Pergamon Press. 1964.

5. Fuchs, N.A. and A.G.Sutugin. Vysokodispersnye aerozoli (Highly Disperse Aerosols).— Kolloidnyi Zhurnal, Vol. 26, No. 1. 1964.

6. Bricard, J., F.Billard, D.Blank, M.Cabane, J.Fontan, and F.Perrin. Ionisation des gaz. Structure détaillée du spectre mobilité des petits ions radioactifs dans l'air.— C.r. Acad. Sci. Paris, Series B, Vol. 263, pp. 761—764. 26 September 1966.

7. Fontan, J., D.Blanc, M.Z.Huertas, A.M.Marty, and F.Neyme. Mesure du coefficient de diffusion de particules radioactives neutres ultrafines.— Journée d'électronique de Toulouse, Colloque international sur l'électronique nucléaire et la radioprotection. 4—8 March 1968.

8. Gormley, P.G. and M.Kennedy. Diffusion from a Stream Flowing Through a Cylindrical Tube.— Proc. Roy. Irish Acad., Vol. 52, Section A, No. 12. 1949.

9. Madelaine, G. Comportement des descendents du radon et du thoron en atmosphère dépoussiérée.— Tellus, Vol. 18, p. 2. 1966.

10. Perrin, F. et al. Radioactivité atmosphérique. Etude de la mobilité des ions radioactifs formés sur les atomes provenant de la désintégration du thoron dans l'air et différents gaz.— C.r. Acad. Sci. Paris, Series B, Vol. 262, pp. 1315—1317. 9 May 1966.

11. Pollak, L.W. and A.L.Metnieks. On the Determination of Diffusion Coefficients of Heterogeneous Aerosols by the Dynamic Method.— Geofisica pura e applicata, Vol. 37, pp. 183—190. 1957.

12. Pradel, J. Les atmosphériques dans les mines d'uranium.— Symposium sur la mesure des doses d'irradiation radiologique, Session No. 5, Stockholm. 12—16 June 1967.

UDC 539.163:546.296

SEPARATE DETERMINATION OF Rn, RaA, RaB AND RaC
CONCENTRATIONS IN AIR FROM THE α -ACTIVITY
DECAY CURVE OF A FILTER

V. N. Bakulin and B. G. Starikov

The relationships between radon and its decay products are of interest when studying turbulent agitation and contaminant washout processes in the lower troposphere. An examination of the different methods of separate determination of the concentrations of radon daughter products shows that only some of them yield satisfactory results at low atmospheric concentrations of radon.

An analytical analog has been developed of the graphical method of separate determination of Po^{218}, Pb^{214} and Bi^{214} concentrations from the curve of filter α-activity decay; the analog is as accurate as the least squares method for three unknowns, but the calculations are incomparably simpler.

A comparison of these methods for known proportions of the radon decay products proved the adequacy of the proposed method.

The existence of standard proportions between the short-lived radon decay products under natural conditions was demonstrated; they make it possible to determine the concentration of each of them from the α-decay curve within 11 to 60 min from the end of filtration.

The relation between radon and its decay products (the extent to which the equilibrium in the radon series has been disturbed) is increasingly preoccupying scientists, as it allows one to determine the coefficient of radioactive aerosol washout from the atmosphere by precipitation /14/ and cloud droplets /13/, the variation of the turbulence coefficient in time /2/, and the moments at which new portions of "fresh" radon penetrate the given volume /8/. Besides, neglecting the disturbance of equilibrium in the radon series can lead to substantial errors in the measurement of concentrations of natural radioactive substances in the air by the filtration method /1/.

The relations between short-lived radon decay products are usually determined from the curve of filter α-activity decay by one of the following methods:

1) the least squares method for the three unknown concentrations of RaA, RaB, and RaC /15/;

2) Malakhov's graphical method /9, 18/;

3) the three-point method /16, 17/;

4) the method of visual comparison of the decay curve with theoretical curves /4/;

5) the twin-reading method /6, 10/.

Other, less widespread, methods are:

6) the method of α-spectrometry /12/ or α-radiography /5/;

7) the ion-chamber method /11/;

8) the scintillation-chamber method /7/;

9) the method of combined α- and β-spectrometry and the coincidence method /12/.

Not all of them apply to the measurement of atmospheric concentrations of radon decay products. Methods 4, 5, 7 and 8 are only used at high concentrations of radon daughter products in the air of mine galleries or unventilated premises. The sensitivity of method 6 is still low and does not permit separate determination of the concentration of Pb^{214} (RaB) and Bi^{214} (RaC) in atmospheric air. In addition to the usual errors, methods 2 and 4 are affected by a certain ambiguity owing to the subjective evaluation of the agreement between statistical and theoretical curves. Method 3 yields satisfactory results at high concentrations only. The most accurate are methods 9 and 1, but the former is technically complicated and the latter involves complicated calculations. To simplify the calculations while preserving the accuracy, we developed an analytical analog of the graphical method 2.

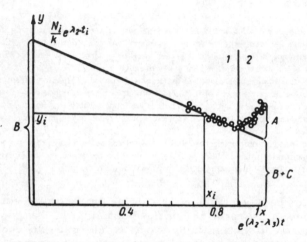

FIGURE 1. Determination of A, B and C from the curve of filter α-activity decay.

The decay of a mixture of short-lived radon decay products on the filter can be represented as

$$A e^{-\lambda_1 t} + B e^{-\lambda_2 t} + C e^{-\lambda_3 t} = \frac{N_t}{k},$$

where λ_1, λ_2, λ_3 are the decay constants of RaA, RaB, RaC, respectively; A, B and C are constants depending on the RaA, RaB and RaC contents on the filter and the moment $(t=0)$ at which filter activation ends; k is the counting efficiency of the setup; N_t is the number of disintegrations per unit time on the filter.

If both sides of the equation are multiplied by $e^{\lambda_2 t}$, we obtain

$$A e^{(\lambda_2 - \lambda_1) t} + B + C e^{(\lambda_2 - \lambda_3) t} = \frac{N_t}{k} e^{\lambda_2 t}, \qquad (1)$$

represented graphically in Figure 1 in terms of the coordinates

$$x = e^{(\lambda_2 - \lambda_3)t} \text{ and } y = \frac{N_t}{k} e^{\lambda_3 t}. \tag{2}$$

The experimental points usually fall near the ideal curve. Considering section 1 in Figure 1 (at $t \geqslant 11$ min) as a straight line, one can find the values of B and C by the least squares method:

$$B' = \frac{\sum y_i \sum x_i^2 - \sum x_i \sum (x_i y_i)}{n \sum x_i^2 - (\sum x_i)^2}, \tag{3}$$

$$C' = \frac{n \sum (x_i y_i) - \sum x_i \sum y_i}{n \sum x_i^2 - (\sum x_i)^2}, \tag{4}$$

where y_i and x_i are values defined in (2) corresponding to time t_i, and n is the number of experimental points in section 1 of Figure 1.

The value of A is also determined by the least squares method in section 2 of Figure 1 $(0 \leqslant t \leqslant 11$ min) from the formula

$$A' = \frac{\sum y_i - C' \sum x_i - n B'}{\sum e^{(\lambda_2 - \lambda_1)t_i}}.$$

Since section 1 is actually not linear, these values of A', B' and C' should be corrected:

$$A = 1.08 A'; \quad B = B' + 0.169 A'; \quad C = C' - 0.25 A'. \tag{5}$$

From these values of A, B and C, the concentrations of RaA, RaB and RaC in the air can be calculated using well-known formulas /3/.

In our tests, the filter counting started 2 to 3 min after the end of filtration, and ended after 57 minutes. The last of the 30 to 32 points taken on the decay curve were averaged over periods of 2 to 3 min in order to obtain the same statistical frequency.

The data obtained were processed simultaneously by three methods: method 1, modernized method 2 described above, and the three-point method. Filter activities measured 3, 11.5 and 44 min after filtration were used in the last case. The accuracy of these methods was determined by the deviations from the means for each pair (a separate mean for each method) of results of determining the Po^{218} (RaA), Pb^{214} (RaB) and Bi^{214} (RaC) concentrations on two filters through which the air samples had been passed simultaneously at the same pumping rate. The arithmetic-mean error in determining the concentrations of these isotopes is given in Table 1 for an initial filter activity of 100 to 200 counts per min. The errors were smaller at higher filter activities.

It can be seen that methods 1 and 2 are practically equivalent in accuracy and yield similar results. Nevertheless, in the manual processing of the measurements, method 2 is to be preferred as less laborious. The processing of one series takes 20 min on a desk "Vilnius" or "Vyatka" computer. This time can be at least halved by using multiregister devices.

TABLE 1. Arithmetic-mean errors, %, in determining the concentrations of the different isotopes in the radon series by comparative methods

Method of calculation	Isotope		
	Po^{218} (RaA)	Pb^{214} (RaB)	Bi^{214} (RaC)
Least squares method	26	6.2	8.9
Analytical analog of Malakhov's method	27	7.4	10.6
Three-point method.	50	12	17

The three-point method is very unreliable for determining the Po^{218} (RaA concentration, and often even yields negative values. It can only be used if the initial filter activity exceeds 1000 counts per min.

All these three methods can be used if the filter activation time does not exceed 30 min, otherwise determination of the Po^{218} (RaA) concentration becomes more difficult.

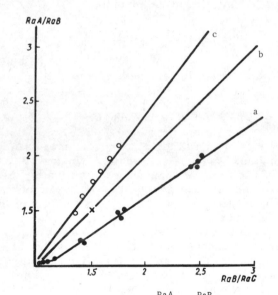

FIGURE 2. Relationship between ratios $\dfrac{RaA}{RaB}$ and $\dfrac{RaB}{RaC}$ and conditions for "fresh" radon inflow for different kinds of radon accumulation (a, b and c).

These three methods for the separate determination of the concentrations of radon decay products in air were also used when the relationships between them were known. Depending on the conditions of fresh radon inflow and the time of accumulation of the decay products, or "growth" τ (min), three main types of relationship between the ratios of concentrations in activity units $m = \lambda_1 q_1 / \lambda_2 q_2$ and $n = \lambda_2 q_2 / \lambda_3 q_3$ can be established for mixtures of these isotopes; these relationships turned out to be almost linear (Figure 2) and can be expressed approximately by simple formulas:

a) accumulation of decay products q_i [atoms/cm^3] in a finite volume after an amount q_0 [atoms/cm^3] of pure radon has been introduced at time $t = 0$:

$$q_i = q_0 \prod_{k=0}^{i-1} \lambda_k \sum_{n=0}^{i} \frac{e^{-\lambda_n \tau}}{\prod_{\substack{k=0 \\ k \neq n}}^{i} (\lambda_k - \lambda_n)}, \tag{6}$$

$$m \simeq 0.7\, n + 0.25;$$

b) accumulation of decay products in a finite volume with uninterrupted radon inflow at rate q_0' [atoms/cm^3·sec] (unventilated premises):

$$q_i = q_0' \prod_{k=0}^{i-1} \lambda_k \sum_{n=0}^{i} \frac{1 - e^{-\lambda_n \tau}}{\lambda_n \prod_{\substack{k=0 \\ k \neq n}}^{i} (\lambda_k - \lambda_n)}, \tag{7}$$

$$m \simeq n;$$

c) accumulation of decay products in the ground layer of the atmosphere with constant emanation E [atoms/cm^2·sec] of radon in the presence of turbulent diffusion /5, 13, 14/:

$$q_i - \frac{E}{VD} \prod_{k=0}^{i-1} \lambda_k \sum_{n=0}^{i} \frac{\mathrm{erf}(\sqrt{\lambda_n \tau})}{\sqrt{\lambda_n} \prod_{\substack{k=0 \\ k \neq n}}^{i} (\lambda_k - \lambda_n)}, \tag{8}$$

$$m = 1.15\, n - 0.05.$$

In all the accumulation cases, the radon concentrations $C_0 = \lambda_0 q_0$ may be considered as equal to the Po^{218} concentration $C_1 = \lambda_1 q_1$ in units of activity to within 10% for $\tau > 30$ min.

An experimental check of the relationships between the Rn decay products for accumulation types a and b, the radon ages being known, confirmed the existence of standard relationships between them which correspond to the calculated ones.

A check of the relationships between the decay products for accumulation type c showed that quantity m under conditions of nocturnal inversion corresponds to the theoretical relationship (8). In this period the radon and its decay products accumulate in the ground layer of the atmosphere against a background of their negligibly small diurnal concentrations. The experimental points for each type of accumulation are presented in Figure 2.

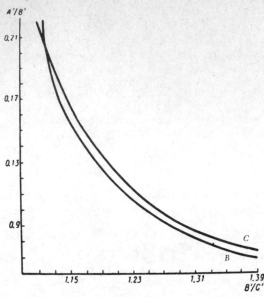

FIGURE 3. Relationship between $\dfrac{A'}{B'}$ and $\dfrac{B'}{C'}$ for the determination of A' (time of air sampling on the filter, 20 min) (b and c are accumulation types).

All this demonstrates the existence of standard relationships in the radon series. In such cases, the Po^{218}, Pb^{214} and Bi^{214} concentrations can be determined by plotting the α-decay curve starting from the 11th or 13th minute, calculating B' and C' which can be determined most accurately from formulas (3) and (4), then finding A' (Figure 3), and halving the volume calculated by method 2.

BIBLIOGRAPHY

1. Bakulin, V. N. and V. P. Matulyavichus. Uchet nekotorykh nestatsionarnykh protsessov pri izmerenii estestvennoi radioaktivnosti vozdukha s pomoshch'yu registratorov (Accounting for Some Nonsteady Processes in Recording Natural Air Radioactivity). — In this collection.
2. Bakulin, V. N., E. E. Sen'ko, B. G. Starikov, and V. A. Trufakin. Ispol'zovanie estestvennykh radioaktivnykh veshchestv dlya issledovaniya protsessov turbulentnogo obmena i samoochishcheniya atmosfery po prizemnym izmereniyam (Utilization of Natural Radioactive Substances in the Study of Turbulent Exchange and Atmospheric Scavenging by Means of Ground Measurements). — In this collection.
3. Baranov, V. I. and L. V. Gorbushina. Voprosy bezopasnosti v uranovykh rudnikakh (Safety Problems in Uranium Mines). — Moskva, Atomizdat. 1962.
4. Gracheva, E. G. O fizicheskikh svoistvakh radioelementov, nakhodyashchikhsya v atmosfere (Physical Properties of Radioactive Chemical Elements in the Atmosphere). — Trudy Radievogo Instituta, Vol. 4. 1937.

5. Labushkin,V.G. and L.S.Ruzer. O metodike opredeleniya kontsentratsii korotkozhivushchikh dochernykh produktov radona v vozdukhe po α- i β-izlucheniyu (Determining the Concentrations of Short-Lived Radon Daughter Products in the Air by the α- and β-Radiation). — Atomnaya Energiya, Vol. 19, No. 1. 1965.

6. Kapitanov,A.P.,A.S.Serdyukova, and A.P.Korenkov. Ekspressnyi metod opredeleniya kontsentratsii radiya i sootnoshenii mezhdu produktami raspada radona v vozdukhe (Rapid Method for Determining the Radium Concentration and the Relationships Between the Radon Decay Products in Air). — Izv. VUZ. Geologiya i Razvedka, No. 11, Issue 10. 1961.

7. Kartashev,N.P. and G.A.Popov. Ob opredelenii kontsentratsii aerozolei korotkozhivushchikh produktov raspada radona (Determining the Concentration of Aerosols of Short-Lived Radon Decay Products). — Atomnaya Energiya, Vol. 12, No. 4. 1962.

8. Malakhov,S.G. and V.N.Bakulin. Vliyanie kolebanii ekskhalyatsii radona i torona na izmenenie kontsentratsii etikh emanatsii i ikh dochernikh produktov v atmosfere (Effect of Radon and Thoron Emanation Fluctuations on the Variation in the Concentration of These Emanations and their Daughter Products in the Atmosphere). — Izv. AN SSSR, Fizika Atmosfery i Okeana, Vol. 3, No. 7. 1967.

9. Malakhov,S.G. and B.G.Starikov. Grafiko-matematicheskii sposob analiza radioaktivnogo raspada smesi RaA, RaB i RaC (Graphical-Mathematical Method of Analyzing the Radioactive Decay of an RaA, RaB and RaC Mixture). — Gigiena i Sanitariya, No. 5. 1966.

10. Markov,K.P. et al. — Trudy SNIIP, No. 2. 1965.

11. Ruzer,L.S. Opredelenie pogloshchennykh doz pri popadanii emanatsii i ikh dochernikh produktov v organizm (Determining the Doses Absorbed during the Penetration of Emanation and its Daughter Products into the Human Body). — Atomnaya Energiya, Vol. 8, No. 6. 1960.

12. Ruzer,L.S. Radioaktivnye aerozoli (Radioactive Aerosols). — Moskva, Standarty. 1968.

13. Styro,B.I.,E.Yu.Vebra, and K.K.Shopauskas. K voprosu ob opredelenii parametrov udaleniya estestvennykh radionuklidov po profil'yu radioaktivnykh kapel' v oblakakh (Determination of the Removal Parameters of Natural Radionuclides from the Distribution of Radioactive Droplets in Clouds). — Vilnius, "Mintis." 1968.

14. Styro,B.I. and B.K.Vebrene. Radioactivity Distribution in Raindrops. — In: Atmospheric Scavenging of Radioisotopes. Israel Program for Scientific Translations, Jerusalem. 1970.

15. Shchepot'eva,E.S. Opredelenie soderzhaniya RaA, RaB, RaC, ThB i ThC po metodu analiza krivoi aktivnogo naleta (Determining the RaA, RaB, RaC, ThB and ThC Contents by Analyzing the Active-Deposit Curve). — Trudy Radievogo Instituta, Vol. 3, pp. 64—100. 1937.

16. Holladay,J. et al. The Radon Problem in Uranium Mines [Russian translation, 1961].

17. Tsivoglou,E.C., H.E.Ayer, and D.A.Helsday. Occurrence of Nonequilibrium Atmospheric Mixtures of Radon and its Daughters. — Nucleonics. Vol. 11, No. 9. 1953.

18. Malakhov,S.G.,V.N.Bakulin, G.V.Dmitrieva, L.V.Kirichenko, T.J.Ssissigina, and B.G.Starikov. Diurnal Variations of Radon and Thoron Decay Product Concentrations in the Surface Layer of the Atmosphere and their Washout by Precipitation. — Tellus, Vol. 18, No. 2—3. 1966.

UDC 621.039.55

NEW METHODS OF MEASURING Rn^{220} (THORON) EXHALATION AND SOME RESULTS

B. I. Styro, T. N. Nedvetskaite, and E. E. Sen'ko

Two new methods are proposed for the measurement of Rn^{220} exhalation. One uses a Pearson collector combined with a decay chamber for radioactive emanations. In the other, the Pearson collector is replaced by an accumulation chamber connected to three auxiliary decay chambers through which the air flows in from the surrounding space with already decaying Rn^{220}. At the same time, these chambers serve for equalizing the pressure in the accumulator. After passing through the decay chamber, the Rn^{220} and Rn^{222} daughter products formed there were trapped on an LFS-1 filter which, after 6 hours of Rn^{222} daughter products decay, was brought into contact with an A-2 nuclear emulsion. The setups were calibrated with Th^{232} salt which was in equilibrium with the decay products. Since the calibration coefficient at low sampling rates fluctuated between 2 and 5%, the air penetrating the decay chamber was ionized by corona discharge, which increased up to fifteenfold the filter's aerosol-trapping efficiency. The use of corona discharge and nuclear emulsions helped considerably in raising the lower sensitivity limit of Rn^{220} exhalation measurement (10^{-17} to 10^{-18} curie/cm^2·sec depending on sampling duration). The error of Rn^{220} exhalation measurement by these two methods does not exceed 20%.

Data are provided on the diurnal variation in Rn^{220} exhalation and mean exhalation values for various states of the earth's surface.

Rn^{220} is assessed in /7, 9/ from the Th^{232} content in the earth's crust. Several studies have been published in which exhalation is measured directly /2, 4, 10/ or evaluated from the Rn^{220} content in the ground layer of the atmosphere /1, 5, 8/. Summary data on Rn^{220} exhalation and determination techniques are given in Table 1.

TABLE 1. Summary of Rn^{220} measurement and evaluation

Point of observation	Method of measurement or evaluation	Mean exhalation, 10^{-16} curie/cm^3·sec	Source
Kuchino	Throughflow ion chamber combined with accumulation chamber	7	/2/
Wellington, New Zealand	Activation of a negatively-charged wire in the accumulation chamber	13	/10/
Toulouse	Large-volume ion chamber combined with accumulation chamber	35	/4/
Berlin	Evaluation from the concentration at ground level	17.2	/8/
Sokkoro	" "	21	/5/
Aachen	" "	11 — 17	/1, 6/

It can be seen that Rn^{220} exhalation is measured mainly with ion chambers, whose lower sensitivity limit is about $4 \cdot 10^{-17}$ curie/cm^2·sec. Apart from the generally known shortcomings due to their operation, great difficulties are created by the penetration of atmospheric air into the volume of the ion chamber.

The present paper presents two new methods for measuring Rn^{220} exhalation. One involves the use of a Pearson collector in combination with a decay chamber for radioactive emanations (Figure 1). Air that entrains the exhaled Rn^{220} circulates in a closed system. During its stay in the collector and the decay chamber, most of the Rn^{220} disintegrates and the filter retains Pb^{212}. Silica gel absorbs the nondisintegrated Rn^{220}.

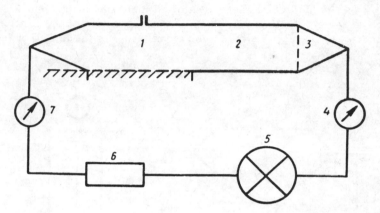

FIGURE 1. Diagram of setup with decay chamber for measuring thoron exhalation:

1) Pearson collector; 2) decay chamber; 3) filter; 4, 7) flow meters; 5) blower; 6) silica gel.

The calculations were conducted on the assumption that Rn^{220} turns at once into Pb^{212} and its exhalation is homogeneous throughout the investigated surface and remains unchanged during one sampling. The number of Pb^{212} atoms deposited on the filter in unit time can be expressed by the equation

$$n = E \frac{a\omega}{S} \frac{\lambda_0}{\lambda_2 - \lambda_0} \left[\frac{\exp\left(-\lambda_2 \frac{S}{\omega} l_2\right) - \exp\left(-\lambda_2 \frac{S}{\omega} l_1\right)}{\lambda_2} - \frac{\exp\left(\lambda_0 \frac{S}{\omega} l_2\right) - \exp\left(-\lambda_0 \frac{S}{\omega} l_1\right)}{\lambda_0} \right], \quad (1)$$

where E is the Rn^{220} exhalation; λ_0 and λ_2 are the Rn^{220} and Pb^{212} decay constants, respectively; a is the chamber width; ω is the rate of air pumping; S is the area of the chamber cross section; l_1 is the collector length; l_2 is the total length of collector and chamber. This equation can be used to compute E.

A variant of this method of measuring Rn^{220} exhalation is the following (Figure 2). Air is continuously recirculated through a Pearson collector (1) placed on the ground, a drier (2) and a 7.5-liter ion chamber (3), which prevents penetration of atmospheric air in the volume of the chamber. The Rn^{220} exhalation is then calculated from the formula

$$E = \frac{\lambda_0 \, S j \, l}{\omega \, v_2 \left[1 - \exp\left(-\lambda_0 \frac{S l}{\omega} \right) \right] \left[\exp\left(-\lambda_0 \frac{v_1}{\omega} \right) - \exp\left(\lambda_0 \frac{v_1 + v_2}{\omega} \right) \right]}, \quad (2)$$

where j is the ion chamber coefficient of calibration on Rn^{220}; l is the speed of motion of the electrometer pointer; v_1 is the volume of the suction equipment; v_2 is the volume of the ion chamber; l is the length of the Pearson collector.

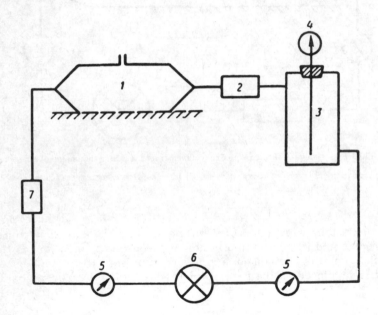

FIGURE 2. Diagram of setup with ion chamber for measuring thoron exhalation:

1) Pearson collector; 2, 7) driers; 3) ion chamber; 4) ionization current recorder; 5) flow meter; 6) blower.

The advantage of this variant is that it facilitates a fairly simple and rapid determination of Rn^{220} exhalation. Its main shortcoming is that it cannot be used during atmospheric precipitation and at night when air humidity is high.

The two variants yield similar results within the limits of measurement accuracy.

According to the second method (Figure 3), the air from under the lower disk (6) of accumulation chamber (1) into which the Rn^{220} atoms are exhaled is filtered through a series of FPP-15—1.7 and FPP-15—2 filters to reach decay chamber (4). When passing through the decay chamber, almost all the Rn^{220} atoms and some Rn^{222} atoms disintegrate; then, during the second filtration of the air through the LFS-14 filter, the Pb^{212} atoms and the Rn^{222} decay products are deposited on the filter.

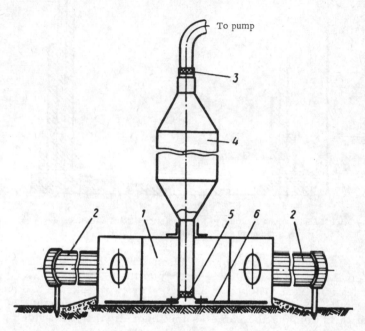

FIGURE 3. Diagram of setup with accumulation chamber and decay chamber for measuring thoron exhalation:

1) accumulation chamber; 2,4) decay chambers; 3,5) filters; 6) lower disk of the accumulation chamber.

The accumulation chamber is connected to three auxiliary decay chambers (2), (4) through which air from the surrounding space, containing already disintegrated Rn^{220}, penetrates without distorting the measurement of Rn^{220} exhalation. At the same time, these chambers equalize the pressure in the accumulation chamber.

By this method, the exhalation can be calculated from the formula

$$E = \frac{2\lambda_0 h n}{\omega \eta \left[1 - \exp\left(-\frac{2\pi h \lambda_0}{\omega} R^2 \right) \right]}, \qquad (3)$$

289

where R is the radius of the disk of the accumulation chamber, and h is the distance between the lower disk of the accumulation chamber and the ground surface.

In both methods, the decay chamber can be replaced by an ion chamber.

After the cessation of activation and the elapse of 6 hours, during which the Rn^{222} daughter products disintegrate, the filters are brought into contact with a nuclear emulsion, type A-2. Radioactivity can also be measured with low-background radiometers.

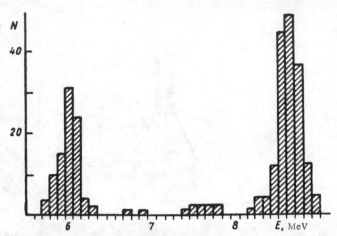

FIGURE 4. Alpha spectrum of filter radiation 6 hours after the end of filtration (N is the number of α-tracks).

Figure 4 is a control histogram obtained by exhalation measurement with nuclear emulsion, type A-2. The energy of the α-particles was determined with the aid of a calibration curve /3/. The two peaks (c. 6.0 and 8.7 MeV) can be identified with Bi^{212} and Po^{212}. The ratio of the number of Bi^{212} to Po^{212} tracks is roughly the same as the theoretical figure, which proves that we have actually measured the Rn^{220} exhalation.

The setups were calibrated with a Th^{232} salt, which was in equilibrium with the decay products.

Since the calibration coefficient η of the setups at low sampling rates fluctuated between 2 and 5% (most probably owing to the high diffusion coefficient of Rn^{220} decay daughter products in the dust-free air and their deposition on the chamber walls), we carried out a series of experiments to achieve better conditions for the test. For this purpose, vapors of volatile substances (such as acetone, alcohol, etc.) were introduced into the chamber. In addition, the air was ionized through corona discharges.

Numerous tests made it clear that the simplest and safest way of augmenting coefficient η was to ionize the air penetrating the chamber by means of corona discharges.

Table 2 provides a few data on coefficient η for three filtration rates and different experimental conditions for c. 15-liter chambers.

TABLE 2. Calibration coefficient η in relation to the volumetric filtration rate under different experimental conditions

Airflow rate, liter/min	η_1, %	η_2, %
0.5	3 ± 1.5	49 ± 8
1	13 ± 10	84 ± 5
3	63 ± 8	95 + 3

Note: η_1) without ionization through corona discharges; η_2) with ionization of the airflow through corona discharges.

The data in Table 2 prove that efficiency is best improved at low air pumping rates, when coefficient η increases up to fifteenfold. At high filtration rates the coefficient η increases only by half to reach 95%. Evidently, the ionization of the air that penetrates the chamber contributes to the formation of molecular complexes, the diffusion coefficients of which are considerably lower than those of Rn^{220} decay daughter products in dust-free air.

The use of corona discharges and nuclear emulsions helped much in raising the lower sensitivity limit in Rn^{220} exhalation measurements; this limit varies between 10^{-17} and 10^{-18} curie/cm^2·sec according to sampling duration.

TABLE 3. Diurnal fluctuations in Rn^{220} exhalation, 10^{-16} curie/cm^2·sec (averaged data)

Point of measurement	Time of day, hr			
	0 − 3	3 − 6	6 − 9	9 − 12
A	30.9 ± 5.2	28.2 ± 5.4	25.1 ± 4.8	28.7 ± 5.0
B	86.2 ± 15.4	76.1 ± 13.8	70.7 ± 1.25	77.2 ± 14.2
	12 − 15	15 − 18	18 − 21	21 − 24
A	27.5 ± 5.2	32.8 ± 6.1	34.2 ± 6.5	29.3 ± 7.2
B	102.3 ± 16.0	139.4 ± 18.6	139.6 ± 18.1	102.3 ± 20.4

When nuclear emulsions were used, the radiometric error of measurement was insignificant, as the number of α-signal tracks exceeds the background by a factor of tens or hundreds. In calculating the errors we were, however, unable to take into account the errors due to possible air indraft, microfluctuations in meteorological factors, and so on. The precision of Rn^{220} exhalation measurement by these two methods is at least 20%.

As an illustration, Table 3 gives data on the diurnal variation in Rn^{220} exhalation (method 1). The ground surface at point A was smooth and lacked grass cover, and was loose to a depth of 20 cm at point B.

TABLE 4. Mean Rn^{220} exhalation in relation to the state of the soil surface

State of the soil surface	Exhalation, 10^{-16} curie/cm^2·sec	Number of measurements
Dry	33 ± 5.0	35
Moist after prolonged precipitation	20 ± 3.0	10
Frozen	8 ± 1.2	10
Covered by a 5-cm-thick layer of fresh snow..	0.1 ± 0.15	10

It can be seen that the diurnal variation in exhalation is the same in both cases, but exhalation from the surface of the loosened soil is two- to threefold that at point A. The maximum occurs during the evening hours, possibly due to convection flows produced in the soil by intense cooling of its surface.

Table 4 gives the mean Rn^{220} exhalation during daytime for different states of the soil surface, as obtained by the second method. Exhalation was measured on a flat terrain without grass cover.

The second method permits the measurement of Rn^{220} exhalation from the snow surface, for its sensitivity is high. Exhalation values down to $0.1 \cdot 10^{-16}$ curie/cm^2·sec are perfectly reliable, in our opinion.

We think these methods are very promising and, with additional improvements, can be used to solve many problems, both physical and practical.

BIBLIOGRAPHY

1. Belekhova, I.G. and I.L.Karol'. K teorii rasprostraneniya radioaktivnykh emanatsii v prizemnom sloe atmosfery (Concerning the Theory of Radioactive Emanation Propagation in the Ground Layer of the Atmosphere). — Fizika Atmosfery i Okeana, Vol.3, No.7. 1967.
2. Gracheva, E.G. Soderzhanie Th v atmosfere (Th Content in the Atmosphere). — Trudy Radievogo Instituta, Vol.4. 1938.
3. Segre, E.(editor). Experimental Nuclear Physics, Vol.1. New York, Wiley. 1953.
4. Blanc, D., J. Fontan, and D. Guedalia. Sur la mesure du flux de thoron sortant du sol. — C.r. Acad. Sci., Ser. A and B. Vol. 264, No.6. 1967.
5. Crozier, W.D. and N. Biles. Measurements of Rn-220 (Thoron) in the Atmosphere Below 50 Centimeters. — J. Geophys. Res., Vol.71, No.20. 1966.
6. Israel, G.W. Thoron Rn-220 Measurements in the Atmosphere and Their Application in Meteorology. — Tellus, Vol. 17, No.3. 1965.
7. Israel, H. Zur Vergleichbarkeit von Radioaktivitäts-Messungen, Atomkernenergie, Vol.6, No.5. 1961.
8. Jacobi, W. Der Thoron-Gehalt der bodennahen Luftschicht. — Atomkernenergie, Vol. 10, No. 11 — 12. 1965.
9. Jacobi, W. and K. Andre. The Vertical Distribution of Rn-222, Rn-220 and their Decay Products in the Atmosphere. — J. Geophys. Res., Vol. 68, No.13. 1963.
10. Rossen, R. Note on Some Observations of Radon and Thoron Exhalation from the Ground. — New Zealand J. Sci. Technol., B., Vol. 38, No.6. 1957.

UDC 539.107.5

A SIMPLE TWO-DIMENSIONAL ANALYZER OF BETA-GAMMA COINCIDENCES IN THE STUDY OF RADIO-ACTIVE FALLOUT SAMPLES

E. F. Kovnatskii, E. I. Roslyi, and A. N. Silant'ev

The paper describes a two-dimensional analyzer of beta-gamma coincidences, based on two commercial AI-100 analyzers. The setup facilitates the recording of coincidence spectra during the measurement, on a punch tape on which are recorded, at the end of the measurent, the beta and gamma spectra picked up by a single-crystal spectrometer.

A functional circuit of the setup and a diagram of the control unit are also given.

The single-crystal gamma spectrometer, widely used in the isotope analysis of samples of radioactive contamination of the environment and of atmospheric precipitation, is sometimes inadequate for the measurement of samples possessing a complex isotope composition /4/.

The use of radiochemical methods for separating the different isotopes extends the duration of sample preparation for measurement, is laborious, and its end result is affected by an error of measurement /2/.

The problem can be solved by using the method of gamma-gamma or beta-gamma coincidences with simultaneous recording of the beta and gamma spectra of the sample, both in the coincidence regime and with a single-crystal spectrometer. In this case it is advisable to use two-dimensional amplitude analyzers /1, 3/.

We have developed a setup which makes possible such measurements. It consists of beta and gamma spectrometers operating in the coincidence regime, two AI-100 analyzers, control devices, and devices for recording the information on punch tape.

The low intensity of sample radiation permits the use of a puncher (PL-80 with a resolving time of 1/12 sec) as memory for coincidences.

In the presence of coincidences, the number of the channel from the beta and gamma analyzers is immediately recorded on the punch tape during the measurement. The amount of numbers on the punch tape is also an indication as to the number of pulses in the analyzer channel during the measurement of coincidence spectra.

After exposure, the pulse spectra measured in the regime of the single-crystal spectrometer are now also recorded already channel by channel.

Figure 1 is a block diagram of the setup. Sample (1) to be measured is placed between the detectors (2), (3) of the beta and gamma spectrometers. From the anodes of the photomultipliers, the pulses reach analyzers (6), (7). The pulses from the diodes of the photomultipliers are fed to coincidence circuit (4), which triggers the control flip-flop (5), so opening the OR gate (8), (9), through which the pulse trains corresponding to the amplitudes of the measured signals are fed to the recorder units (RU) (10), (11). The automatic punching unit (APU) (12) successively interrogates RU (10), (11) and issues the channel number code to the puncher. The data output units (14) ensure the output of information from the memory of the analyzers after measurement through APU (12) to the tape of puncher (13). The cycle of operation of the setup is organized by the control unit (Figure 2), which performs the following functions:

1. Establishing the fact of beta-gamma coincidence.
2. Shaping the pulse that permits transmission of the pulse train.
3. Inhibiting the recording of coincidences during processing and punching of data.

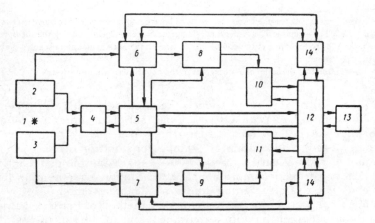

FIGURE 1. Block diagram of the setup for beta-gamma coincidences.

The control unit is comprised of the following functional subassemblies:

1. Coincidence circuit. Control circuit of the coincidence circuit.
2. Beta-channel train transmitter. Control trigger of the beta-channel train transmitter.
3. Gamma-channel train transmitter. Control trigger of the gamma-channel train transmitter.
4. Time-delay univibrator.

The coincidence circuit is built around a 31301A tunnel diode D5. The working point of the diode is selected with the aid of a variable resistor R_{18}. Resistors R_{13} and R_{14} are chosen so that diode D5 only operates at the arrival of two coincidence pulses from the radiation transducers. The coincidence circuit is controlled through transistors T_7 and T_8, which realize a logical operation "I" and trigger T_{g_2}, which controls transistor T_8. During data processing, trigger T_{g_2} inhibits the transmission of coincidence signals and blocks transistor T_8. The trigger is switched to blocking by pulses that block the input of the beta and gamma analyzers, with the aid of diodes D7 and D8 of the collection circuit, and maintained so until an unblocking signal (trailing edge of the "recording" signal) arrives through diode D9.

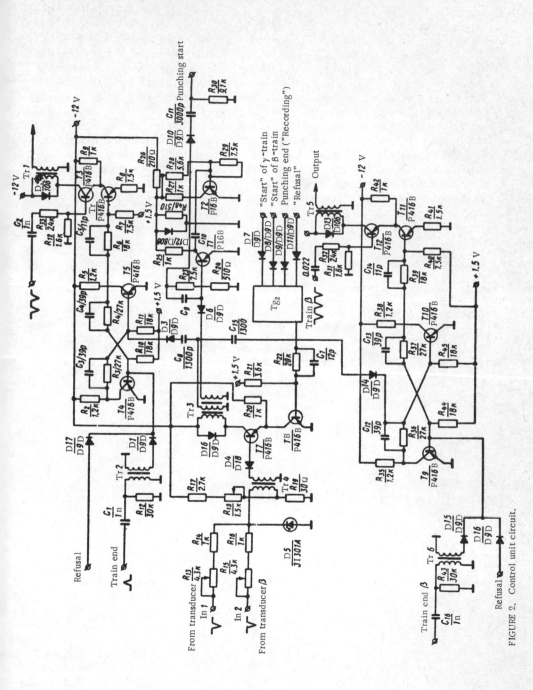

FIGURE 2. Control unit circuit.

The gamma-channel train transmitter is built around transformer Tr_1 and transistors T_3 and T_6. It is controlled by trigger Tg_1, which is built around transistors T_4 and T_5, supplying the resolving potential to the base of transistor T_6.

Suppose the situation of trigger Tg_1 in which transistor T_6 is blocked is "one" and that in which T_6 is open is "zero." Trigger Tg_1 is switched to state "one" by a positive pulse arriving from the circuit of the gamma-channel train to the input of RU (10), and to state "zero" by a positive "train end" signal arriving from the pulse analyzer. The beta-channel train transmitter operates similarly.

The time-delay univibrator is built around transistors T_1, T_2 and intended for delaying the start of punching by the time of beta- and gamma-channel train recording in RU (10) and RU (11). The delay is $T=$ is $200\mu/\sec$ and, if necessary, can be adjusted within wide limits. The end-of-punch signal ("recording") is processed up to the end of the punching. Trigger Tg_2 switches back to its initial state. The analyzer circuit is ready to receive the next coincidence event.

BIBLIOGRAPHY

1. Zigban, K. (editor). Al'fa-beta i gamma-spektroskopiya (Alpha-Beta and Gamma Spectroscopy), No. 1. — Moskva, Atomizdat. 1969.
2. Bowen, H. J. M. and D. Gibbons. Radioactivation Analysis. — Oxford Univ. Press. 1963.
3. Motalin, L. A. et al. Mnogokanal'nye analizatory yadernoi fiziki (Multichannel Analyzers in Nuclear Physics). — Moskva, Atomizdat. 1967.
4. Silant'ev, A. N. and T. V. Polyakova. Massovyi gamma-spektral'nyi analiz radioaktivnykh vypadenii (Mass Gamma-Spectral Analysis of Radioactive Fallout). — Trudy IPG, No. 8. 1967.

UDC 621.039.55

SPECTROMETRIC METHOD OF MEASURING THE CONCENTRATION OF NATURAL RADIOACTIVE AEROSOLS

V. G. Labushkin, V. I. Popov, and L. S. Ruzer

This paper discusses a spectrometric method of determining the concentration of natural atmospheric radioactive aerosols formed by radon and thoron decay daughter products.

The determination of radon daughter product concentrations is accompanied by measurement of the α- and β-activity of the disperse phase of aerosols deposited on a fine-fibered LFS-1 (AFA — RSP-10, 20) filter by means of scintillation spectrometric detection units.

For a simultaneous measurement of the concentration of daughter products of both radon and thoron, one can use a spectrometric unit for the detection of α-radiation, composed of a 0.3 to 0.4 mm thick CsI (TI) crystal of 63 mm diameter and a FEU-52 photomultiplier.

It is demonstrated that the adoption of these spectroscopic methods considerably reduces the error and, in addition, facilitates determination of the self-absorption of α-radiation in the aerosol sample and the dust content of the air.

The paper also reports on an investigation of the spectrometric unit for the detection of α-radiation from a wide-area (over 100-cm^2) aerosol sample. The unit consists of a CsI (TI) crystal and a FEU-49 photomultiplier. The topography of the photocathode sensitivity was plotted with the aid of a Pu-239 spectrometric point source. The apparatus used for measuring the concentration of natural radioactive aerosols by spectrometric methods is described.

The main components of natural atmospheric radioactivity are the daughter products of radon and thoron decay. The main radon concentration in atmospheric air is 10^{-10} to 10^{-9} curie/m^3, and that of thoron 10^{-12} to 10^{-11} curie/m^3 /5/.

Table 1 provides the basic data on the decay of radon, thoron and their daughter products. Notably, the energy of α-particles of RaA and RaC' (6.00 and 7.68 MeV, respectively) and the peak energies of the β-particles of RaB and RaC (0.65 and 3.17 MeV, respectively) differ significantly from each other. This facilitates the separate measurement of the activity of each isotope. Characteristic of radon daughter products is the presence of two isotopes (RaC and RaC') at radioactive equilibrium.

There are three alpha-radiating isotopes ThA, ThC and ThC' and three beta-radiating isotopes ThB, ThC and ThC'' in the thoron decay series. Thoron A has a short half-life (0.16 sec), and practically does not accumulate in the atmosphere. The two other α-radiating isotopes (ThC and ThC') have a close quantitative interrelationship: there is 1.97 times as much of the latter.

From among the natural isotopes, ThC' has the highest energy of α-particles (8.78 MeV). This facilitates its separation from a mixture of any radioactive isotopes. The beta-radiating isotope ThB is the longest-lived of the short-lived emanation daughter products.

TABLE 1. Emanations and their daughter products

Element	Symbol	Half-life	Radioactive constant, sec^{-1}	Radiation	Energy, MeV	
					of β-particles	of main lines for γ-radiation (in parentheses, the yield of one disintegration)
1	2	3	4	5	6	7
Radon	86 Em^{222}	3.825 days	$2.097 \cdot 10^{-6}$	α	5.486	—
Radium A	84 Po^{218}	3.05 min	$3.783 \cdot 10^{-3}$	α	5.998	—
Radium B	82 Pb^{214}	26.8 min	$4.310 \cdot 10^{-4}$	β,γ	0.650	0.350(0.435)
						0.294(0.24)
Radium C	83 Bi^{214}	19.7 min	$5.864 \cdot 10^{-4}$	β,γ	1.65(23%)	0.609(0.359)
					3.17(77%)	1.120(0.273)
						1.764(0.22)
Radium C'	84 Po^{214}	$1.6 \cdot 10^{-4}$ sec	$4.23 \cdot 10^{3}$	α	7.68	—
Radium D	82 Pb^{210}	22 years	$9.98 \cdot 10^{-10}$	β	0.027	—
Radium E	82 Bi^{210}	4.99 days	$1.608 \cdot 10^{-6}$	β	1.17	—
Radium F	84 Po^{210}	138.4 days	$5.8 \cdot 10^{-8}$	α	5.298	—
Thoron	86 Em^{220}	54.5 sec	$1.27 \cdot 10^{-2}$	α	6.282	—
Thorium A	84 Po^{216}	0.158 sec	4.387	α	6.774	—
Thorium B	82 Pb^{212}	10.67 hr	$1.816 \cdot 10^{-5}$	β,γ	0.37	0.300(0.344)
						0.238(0.330)
Thorium C	83 Bi^{212}	1.09 hr	$1.766 \cdot 10^{-4}$	α(33.7%)	6.055	0.81(0.104)
					β(66.3%)	2.25	1.81(0.046)
Thorium C'	84 Po^{212}	$2.9 \cdot 10^{-7}$ sec	$2.3 \cdot 10^{6}$	α	8.776	—
Thorium C"	81 Tl^{208}	3.1 min	$3.73 \cdot 10^{-3}$	β,γ	1.792	2.620(0.337)
						0.580(0.275)

The presence of α- and β- radiating isotopes of different energy, genetically related to each other, in the radon decay series produced numerous methods of measuring the concentrations of daughter products. The first method for determining the concentration of radon daughter products was proposed in 1953 /27/; more methods were then developed /3, 11, 15, 16, 23/, most of them modifications of the first. All of them involve counting, i.e., they measure the total α-activity of the aerosol sample at different moments after the end of air filtration, then determine the concentration of each daugher product. These methods are affected by considerable errors, as demonstrated in /19/.

Moreover, the low atmospheric concentration of the radon and thoron daughter products requires the development of special high-sensitivity instruments to permit operative measurements, as the isotopes of natural activity are short-lived.

The systematic errors in the measurement of the concentrations of radon daughter products are due to several factors:

1) the proportions of the daughter product concentrations;
2) the sampling duration;
3) the moment chosen for the activity measurement.

Analysis has shown that the proportion of each daughter product in the overall α-activity of the filter varies considerably in time. In some cases, fairly wide variation in the concentrations of the various products therefore causes little variation in the overall α-activity, which in turn affects the accuracy of concentration measurements. One possibility of improving it is to replace the counting method of measurement by a spectrometric one. *

The method is based on the idea /25/ that the activities of four isotopes in the air sample (two α-radiators RaA and RaC' with energies of 6.0 and 7.68 MeV and two β-radiators RaB and RaC with peak energies of the β-spectra of 0.7 and 3.17 MeV, respectively) are measured simultaneously.

The simultaneous determination of the activity of each isotope separately makes the measurement possible immediately after the end of filtration, which in turn improves the accuracy. In addition, it permits the effect of self-absorption of α-radiation to be taken into account and the dust content of the air to be determined /18/.

The concentration of radon daughter products is determined as follows. After the end of air filtration, the filter with the radon daughter products deposited on it is placed in a setup for the measurement of α- and β-activity, between two detector units, and the pulses are counted over a certain period of time. The activity of α-radiators is measured from the front side of the filter, and that of β-radiators from the rear side. The filters used are spectrometric LFS-1 (AFA—RSP) filters.

The α- and β-detector units must be spectrometric, of sufficient resolution for the energies of the isotopes measured in the aerosol sample.

The pulses from the transducer outputs are fed to the input of the measuring setup, which permits pulse selection by amplitude (one- or multichannel analyzer, differential discriminator with scaling device or ratemeter).

Figure 1 shows the α-radiation spectrum of the radon daughter products RaA and RaC', plotted with the aid of a scintillation spectrometer. It can be seen that the separate determination of the RaA and RaC' contents in the sample causes no difficulty.

The β-radiating RaB and RaC are determined separately as follows. The β-radiation spectrum of the aerosol sample is plotted with the aid of a spectrometric β-transducer. The spectrum of the β-source Cs^{137} is then plotted under the same conditions of measurement; the energy of its conversion electrons (0.624 MeV) is close to the limit energy of the RaB β-spectrum (0.65 MeV). Figure 2 shows the spectra of RaB + RaC and Cs^{137}.

The threshold of the integral discriminator being established on the line of conversion electrons of the Cs^{137} source, the pulses of RaC only are counted with the aid of the scaling device. The separate contents of RaB and RaC in the sample can be determined after measuring the total number of RaB and RaC pulses and the number of pulses corresponding to RaC alone.

---

* We speak of methods for measuring the concentrations of radon daughter products, as the concentrations of thoron daughter products in the atmosphere are usually just tenths of the former and may most frequently be neglected. A method for the simultaneous measurement of the concentrations of radon and thoron daughter products in atmospheric air will be described below.

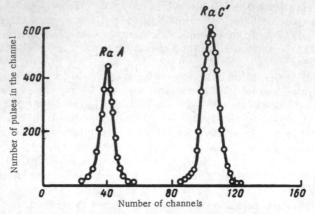

FIGURE 1. Energy spectrum of α-radiation of an RaA- and RaC'-containing aerosol sample.

To determine the concentrations directly in curie/m^3, and adjust the limits of the discriminators during the measurements, standard sources are necessary whose energy spectrum is identical to that of the aerosol sample.

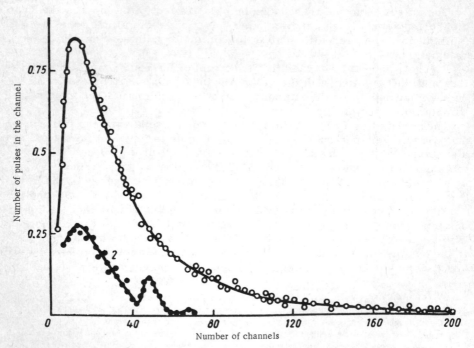

FIGURE 2. Energy spectrum of the β-radiation of an aerosol sample that contains RaB and RaC (1) and Cs^{137} (2).

The first such sources were manufactured in 1963; they contained short-lived products of radon decay in amounts that were practically invariable in time /19/. This was achieved in the following manner. A solution of a salt of radium-226 was placed on a carefully polished support of stainless steel or aluminum, and the source was then subjected to special treatment. The source was finally sealed by coating it with a thin film that contained radon and, consequently, its decay products as well. The film was so thin, that the absorption of α-particles in it was negligible. These sources came to be known as nonemanating Ra^{226} sources. The spectrometric properties of such sources and their certification technique are described elsewhere /1, 2, 7, 12, 17, 19, 21, 22/.

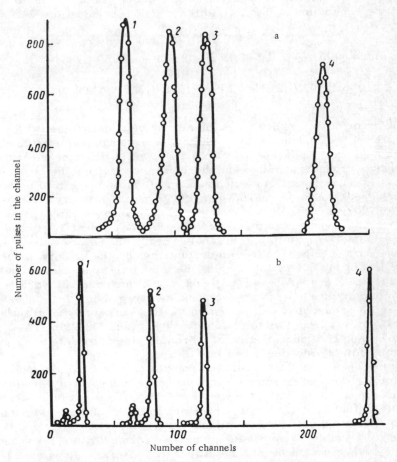

FIGURE 3. Energy spectrum of the α-radiation of a nonemanating Ra^{226} source, plotted with the aid of a scintillation spectrometer (a) and a transistorized one (b):

1) Ra^{226}; 2) Rn^{222}; 3) RaA; 4) RaC'.

Figures 3 and 4 show the α-spectra of a nonemanating Ra^{226} source; they were plotted with the aid of a scintillation α-spectrometer /19/ and a transistorized one /14/.

It can be seen that the determination of the activity of the RaA and RaC' α-radiators, or the adjustment of the discriminator thresholds, which make the separate recording of these products possible, raises no problems.

In some cases, it is not necessary to measure the α- and β-radiation simultaneously, it being sufficient to accurately determine the RaA, RaB and RaC concentrations separately, by spectrometric measurement of only the α-radiation of the aerosol sample. It is enough to measure the RaA activity, and (twice, at different moments) the RaC' activity.

For instance, at a filtration time $Q = 30$ min, filtration rate $v_t = 100$ liter/min and activity measurement times $T_1 = 1$ min and $T_2 = 25$ min*, the formulas for the determination of the RaA, RaB and RaC concentrations will be

$$q_A = 0.044\ N_A\ (1.6)\cdot 10^{-13}\ \text{curie/liter}, \qquad (1)$$

$$q_B = [0.177\ N_{C'}\ (7.12) - 0.066\ N_{C'}\ (25.30) - 0.306\ N_A\ (1.6)]\cdot 10^{-13},$$
$$\text{curie/liter}, \qquad (2)$$

$$q_C = [2.20\ N_{C'}\ (25.30) - 2.46\ N_{C'}\ (7.12) + 3.35\ N_A\ (1.6)]\cdot 10^{-13},$$
$$\text{curie/liter}. \qquad (3)$$

The error of the method based on the use of α-spectrometry in the measurements is much smaller than that of the counting methods.

The method of alpha-spectrometry also applies when the concentrations of daughter products of radon and thoron in the air are to be measured separately. In this case, in which radon and thoron are mixed in the air, the alpha peaks of RaA and ThC daughter products are very close to each other (6.000 and 6.055 MeV, respectively) and cannot be fully resolved even by a transistorized α-spectrometer. But the RaA and ThC activities can be determined separately. In the thoron decay series two radiators, ThC and ThC', are in a well-defined interrelationship: the activity of the former is half that of the latter. Measuring the total activity of the isotopes without resolution of energy (A_{RaA} and A_{ThC}) and $A_{ThC'}$ (which can always be singled out from a mixture of α-active isotopes, its energy being the highest among the naturally α-active ones), we obtain the RaA activity by subtracting half the ThC activity from this total activity of RaA and ThC (since $A_{ThC} = 0.508\ A_{ThC'}$). The concentration of thoron daughter products in air can be determined in the way described in /13/.

Figure 4 presents the α-radiation spectra of an aerosol sample, containing radon and thoron daughter products; the spectra were plotted with the aid of a scintillation α-spectrometer. The separation between ThC (RaA), RaC' and ThC' by the energies in the sample was simple, with a setup composed of two discriminators and two scaling devices /17, 4/.

The first scalar measures the number of pulses $N_{RaA+ThC}$, the second measures $N_{ThC'}$; the windows of the differential discriminators must

---

* T_1 and T_2 indicate the beginning of activity measurement. Its duration is 5 min, i.e., the measurements last from the 1st to the 6th and from the 25th to the 30th min, respectively.

therefore correspond to the first and last α-spectrum peak. Deducting half the reading of the second scaler from the reading of the first, we obtain the number of RaA pulses

$$N_{\text{RaA}} = N_{\text{RaA + ThC}} - 0.5 N_{\text{ThC'}}. \qquad (4)$$

This must be followed by a double measurement of the number of RaC' pulses, in which case the first discriminator is positioned so that the scaler receives pulses from RaC', and ThC' is measured once more.

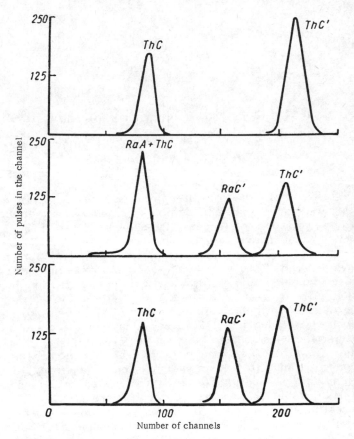

FIGURE 4. Energy spectra of the α-radiation of an aerosol sample containing daughter products of radon and thoron.

The relationship between the measured numbers of pulses and the concentrations of radon and thoron daugher products is then given by

$$N_{\text{RaA}} (\Theta, \ T_1, \ T_2) = v_t \delta q_{\text{RaA}} \int_{T_1}^{T_2} \Phi_{\text{A}} (\Theta, t) dt, \qquad (5)$$

303

$$N_{\text{ThC'}}(\Theta, T_1, T_2) = v_t \delta \left\{ q_{\text{ThB}} \int_{T_1}^{T_2} \Phi_{\text{ThC}}^{\text{ThB}}(\Theta, t)\, dt + \right.$$

$$\left. + q_{\text{ThC}} \int_{T_1}^{T_2} \Phi_{\text{ThC}}^{\text{ThC}}(\Theta, t)\, dt \right\}, \tag{6}$$

$$N_{\text{RaC'}}(\Theta, T_3, T_4) = v_t \delta \left\{ q_{\text{RaA}} \int_{T_3}^{T_4} \Phi_C^A(\Theta, t)\, dt + \right.$$

$$\left. + q_{\text{RaB}} \int_{T_3}^{T_4} \Phi_C^B(\Theta, t)\, dt + q_{\text{RaC}} \int_{T_3}^{T_4} \Phi_C^C(\Theta, t)\, dt \right\}, \tag{7}$$

$$N_{\text{RaC'}}(\Theta, T_5, T_6) = v_t \delta \left\{ q_{\text{RaA}} \int_{T_5}^{T_6} \Phi_C^A(\Theta, t)\, dt + \right.$$

$$\left. + q_{\text{RaB}} \int_{T_5}^{T_6} \Phi_C^B(\Theta, t)\, dt + q_{\text{RaC}} \int_{T_5}^{T_6} \Phi_C^C(\Theta, t)\, dt \right\}, \tag{8}$$

$$N_{\text{ThC'}}(\Theta, T_5, T_6) = v_t \delta \left\{ q_{\text{ThB}} \int_{T_5}^{T_6} \Phi_{\text{ThC}}^{\text{ThB}}(\Theta, t)\, dt + \right.$$

$$\left. + q_{\text{ThC}} \int_{T_5}^{T_6} \Phi_{\text{ThC}}^{\text{ThC}}(\Theta, t)\, dt \right\}, \tag{9}$$

where v_t is the rate of filtration (liter/min); δ is the retention coefficient of the filter; Θ is the filtration time (min); T_1 and T_2 are the moments of beginning and end of measurement of the number of RaC' (ThC') pulses, respectively; T_3 and T_4 are the moments of beginning and end of measurement of the number of RaC' pulses, respectively; T_5 and T_6 are the moments of beginning and end of the second measurement of the number of RaC' (ThC') pulses, respectively; $\Phi_k^i(\Theta, t)$ are functions characterizing the contribution of the ith isotope in the filter activity of the kth isotope of the daughter products of radon and thoron decay.

Functions $\Phi_k^i(\Theta, t)$ depend on the decay constants λ_i and λ_k of the corresponding isotopes and can be found in /17/ or /24/.

Determination of the RaA concentration from equation (5) and its substitution in (7) and (8) yields a system of equations in q_{RaB} and q_{RaC}. The solution of system of equations (6) and (9) in respect to the unknowns q_{ThB} and q_{ThC} results in the ThB and ThC concentrations.

Nonemanating Th[228] sources similar to the nonemanating Ra[226] sources are used for establishing the discrimination thresholds for the measurement of the ThC' activity. The spectrum of the Th[228] source, plotted with the aid of a transistorized spectrometer, is given in Figure 5.

To separately measure the RaA, RaB, RaC, ThB, ThC and ThC' concentrations in air by the described method, one requires spectrometric apparatus of high resolving power. Instruments with scintillation /6, 17/ and transistorized /12, 20, 26/ detector units for radiation transducers have lately found increasing acceptance in the measurement of radioactive aerosols. The resolution of the scintillation α-spectrometer with CsI(Tl) crystal described in /8/ was 3.5% for Pu[239] α-particles of 5.15 MeV (crystal area 3 cm^2). One scintillation spectrometer has a resolution of approximately 5% for a crystal area of 10 cm^2 /20/. The transistorized alpha-spectrometer described in /20/ has a resolution of 1.3% for a detector area of 2 cm^2.

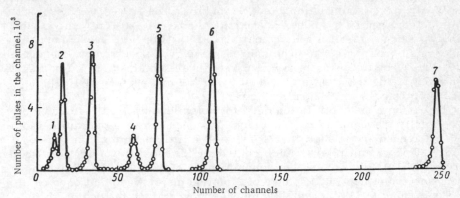

FIGURE 5. Energy spectrum of α-radiation of a nonemanating Th^{228} source, plotted with the aid of a transistorized spectrometer:

1, 2) Th^{228}; 3) Ra^{224}; 4) ThC; 5) Th^{232}; 6) ThA; 7) ThC'.

These spectrometers considerably increase the accuracy of measurement, but measuring the concentrations of natural radioactive aerosols in the atmosphere raises some problems.

1. The low concentrations (c. 10^{-13} to 10^{-15} curie/liter) dictate the use of high-output blowers (100 to 500 liter/min) for pumping large air volumes through the filters.

2. This causes large amounts of inert dust to accumulate on the filters, which increases the self-absorption of α-radiation in the aerosol sample and the filter resistance.

3. Self-absorption in turn blurs the spectra of α-particles and reduces the accuracy of the separate determination of the concentrations of natural radioactive aerosols.

All these factors can be eliminated by using a large-area (c. 100-cm^2) filter, and a spectrometer of high resolving power for recording the radiation of an aerosol sample with the aid of a wide-area (c. 100-cm^2) transducer. No such transducers have been manufactured so far, mainly because resolution drops with increasing detector area.

In order to increase the sensitivity and reduce the systematic error due to self-absorption of α-particles in the aerosol sample, we have studied the possibility of using a photomultiplier with wide photocathode (50 to 180 cm^2). The FEU-52 and FEU-49 tubes have photocathodes with multiple slots and spectral characteristics that correspond to those of the CsI(Tl) crystals used in α-spectrometry.

We found that CsI(Tl, In) crystals, and even a CsI crystal surface-activated with thallium can successfully replace CsI(Tl) crystals in scintillation α-spectrometry. An addition of indium as activator increases the light output by approximately 30% and surface activation facilitates the manufacture of crystals of wide area (200 cm^2 and more).

A transducer consisting of a CsI(TI) crystal of 63 mm diameter and a FEU-52 photomultiplier was developed for determining the spectrometric properties of a scintillation α-spectrometer. The transducer resolution was determined with a nonemanating Ra^{226} source of 10-cm^2 active spot, and a source made of a spectrometric LFS-1 filter with radon daughter products deposited on it. The sources have good spectrometric properties /7, 22/. The following resolving powers were obtained: 3.0% for a surface of about 3 cm^2 of the crystal and filter, 3.5% for a surface of 10 cm^2, 4.2% for 15 cm^2, and 5.2% for 20 cm^2.

In our opinion, scintillation detectors of wide area (c. 100 to 150 cm^2) are totally inadequate for measuring low concentrations of natural radioactive aerosols; we shall therefore dwell a little upon the investigated FEU-49 photomultipliers, which contribute the most in solving the problem.

As in /10/, we studied the nonuniformity of the FEU-49 photocathode. The spectrometric Pu^{239} source of 2 mm diameter was positioned on a 0.4 mm thick CsI(TI) crystal which was moved along the photocathode. The resolution and amplitude at the FEU output was measured at every point chosen. Table 2 gives the results.

TABLE 2. Resolution and amplitude at FEU-49 output in relation to distance from photocathode center

Distance from photocathode center, cm	I		II		III		IV	
	Resolution, %	Amplitude at FEU output, in relative units	Resolution, %	Amplitude at FEU output, in relative units	Resolution, %	Amplitude at FEU output, in relative units	Resolution, %	Amplitude at FEU output, in relative units
7	—	0.47	—	0.46	—	0.46	—	0.63
6	—	0.71	—	0.71	4.4	0.74	—	0.93
5	4.3	0.96	—	0.96	3.8	0.86	—	0.95
4	3.5	1.04	—	1.05	3.9	0.88	—	0.95
3	3.3	1.01	—	1.08	4.3	0.88	—	0.90
2	3.4	1.03	—	1.00	3.9	0.88	—	0.95
1	3.4	1.00	—	0.98	3.2	0.95	—	0.95
0	3.5	1.00	—	1.00	3.5	1.00	—	1.00
−1	3.6	0.96	—	0.95	3.5	1.01	—	0.99
−2	4.0	0.95	—	0.95	3.5	0.97	—	1.01
−3	3.8	0.92	—	0.90	3.6	0.98	—	1.04
−4	3.8	0.95	—	0.95	3.6	0.96	—	1.00
−5	4.1	0.95	—	0.95	3.8	0.97	—	0.91
−6	—	0.86	—	0.93	3.6	0.93	—	0.70
−7	—	—	—	0.63	—	0.74	—	0.46

Note. I, II, III and IV are diametrical directions on the photocathode, at 45° to each other.

The amplitude drops from center to periphery of photocathode, reducing the resolution for wide areas. To keep resolution high, one has to artificially reduce the signal amplitude at the FEU output from the central sections of the photocathode to that of the signal from peripheral sections. One way of achieving this is to place a translucent film, of transparency inversely proportional to the amplitude at the FEU output for the different photocathode sections, between crystal and photocathode. We have already demonstrated / 9, 17 / that translucent films placed between crystal and photocathode do not impair resolution, and often improve it.

Our investigations are continuing, in order to develop a scintillation transducer of large crystal area and high resolving power, capable of accurately measuring the concentrations of natural radioactive aerosols.

For measuring the concentrations of radon and thoron daughter products, the VNIIFTRI has developed a special apparatus: the USA-1 /4/ and USA-2 setups, * which facilitate simultaneous measurement of four isotopes.

Each setup has four scaling channels. Each channel consists of a radiation detection unit, a spectrometric amplifier, a discriminator, and a scaler. The channels count the pulses formed at the output of the corresponding detection units; each channel can cover the entire pulse spectrum, but also a certain section of it, selected by either an integral or a differential discriminator. The linear-transmissivity circuit, which is part of the USA-1 setup, makes it possible with the aid of a multichannel amplitude analyzer to monitor either the entire pulse spectrum from the amplifier output, or that section of it which passes to the counting circuit of any channel. The USA-2 setup has a two-coordinate recorder of the energy spectrum of the pulses fed to the scaling channels; the discrimination threshold of each channel discriminator is established from the resulting spectrogram.

Of the commercial aerosol instruments, the 9063-01 "Korall" with a transducer of a CsI(TI) crystal of 63 mm diameter and FEU-52 photomultiplier may be used for measuring concentrations of natural radioactive aerosols. In this case, its resolving power varies from 12 to 3.5%.

It can thus be said that spectrometric methods and apparatus with scintillation spectrometric α-detectors of large area can contribute very much to solving the problems involved in the measurement of concentrations of natural radioactive aerosols in air.

BIBLIOGRAPHY

1. Albul, V.I., A.P. Ermilov, V.V. Klinov, and V.G. Labushkin. Issledovanie korotkozhivushchikh spektrometricheskikh α-istochnikov, poluchennykh diffuzionnym osazhdeniem dochernikh produktov raspada radona (Study of the Short-Lived Spectrometric α-Sources Obtained by Diffusion Deposition of Radon Decay Daughter Products). — Trudy Institutov Komiteta Standartov, No. 86(146). 1966.

* The USA-2 setup was developed by B. V. Artemov, V. P. Antipenkov, R. V. Khor'kov, A. I. Tsyganov, and L. S. Kuznetsov.

2. Aleksandrov,B.M. et al. Obraztsovye spektrometricheskie istochniki na osnove U^{233}, Pu^{239}, Am^{241}, Cm^{244} Cm^{242}, Th^{228}, Po^{210} (Standard Spectrometric Sources Based on U^{233}, Pu^{239}, Am^{241}, Cm^{244}, Cm^{242}, Th^{228}, Po^{210}). — Tesisy dokladov XVII ezhegodnogo soveshchaniya po yademoi spektroskopii i strukture atomnogo yadra (Summary of Reports to the 17th Annual Conference on Nuclear Spectroscopy and Structure of the Atom Nucleus). "Nauka." 1967.

3. Andreev,S.V. and M.M.Tadzhikov. Razdel'noe opredelenie dochernikh produktov radona i torona pri al'fa-terapii (Separate Determination of Radon and Thoron Daughter Products in Alpha Therapy). — Meditsinskaya radiologiya, Vol. 11, No. 4. 1966.

4. Antipenkov,V.P., B.V.Artemov,L.S.Kuznetsov, V.G.Labushkin,L.S.Ruzer, R.V.Khor'kov, and A.I.Tsyganov. Obraztsovaya ustanovka dlya opredeleniya kontsentratsii dochernikh produktov radona v vozdukhe (Standard Setup for Determining the Concentrations of Daughter Products of Radon in the Atmosphere). — Trudy Institutov Komiteta Standartov, No. 86(146). 1966.

5. Belousova,I.M. and M.M.Shtukkenberg. Estestvennaya radioaktivnost' (Natural Radioactivity). — Moskva, Medgiz. 1961.

6. Bolotin,V.F., V.P.Grigor'ev, and O.A.Chutkin. Statsionarnyi pribor dlya izmereniya kontsentratsii aerozolei dolgozhivushchikh al'fa-aktivnykh izotopov v prisutstvii produktov raspada radona i torona i summarnoi kontsentratsii beta-aktivnykh aerozolei (Stationary Device for Measuring the Concentration of Aerosols of Long-Lived Alpha-Active Isotopes in the Presence of Radon and Thoron Decay Products and the Total Concentration of Beta-Active Aerosols). — In: Sbornik rabot po nekotorym voprosam dozimetrii i radiometrii ioniziruyushchikh izluchenii (Collection of Work on Various Problems of Dosimetry and Radiometry of Ionizing Radiation). Moskva, Gosatomizdat. 1961.

7. Volkova,E.A.,D.M.Ziv,V.G.Labushkin,L.S.Ruzer,E.K.Stepanov, and N.V.Tyutikov. Opredelenie parametrov al'fa-spektrometrov pri pomoshchi istochnikov iz Ra^{226} i RdTh (Determination of the Characteristics of Alpha Spectrometers with the Aid of Sources Made of Ra^{226} and RdTh). — PTE, No. 4. 1966.

8. Gladkova,I.V., B.M.Glukhovskii,R.A.Govorova,V.G.Dobryak,Ya.A.Zakharin, V.G.Labushkin,V.A.Prosyak, and L.S.Ruzer. Uluchshenie razreshayushchei sposobnosti stsintillyatsionnykh al'fa-spektrometrov (Improving the Resolution of Scintillation Alpha-Spectrometers). — Izmeritel'naya Tekhnika, No. 11. 1966.

9. Gladkova,I.V., B.M.Glukhovskii, Ya.A.Zakharin,V.G.Labushkin,V.A.Prosyak, and L.S.Ruzer. Ob uluchshenii razreshayushchei sposobnosti stsintillyatsionnykh al'fa-spektrometrov (Improving the Resolution of Alpha-Spectrometers). — Tezisy dokladov XVII ezhegodnogo soveshchaniya po yadernoi spektroskopii atomnogo yadra (Summary of Reports to the 17th Annual Conference on Nuclear Spectroscopy and Structure of the Atom Nucleus). "Nauka." 1967.

10. Gribanova,V.M.,Yu.P.Pavlov,E.P.Mokhir, and Yu.A.Tsirlin. Zavisimost' stsintillyatsionnykh kharakteristik kristallov ot ikh razmera (Dependence of Scintillation Characteristics of Crystals on their Dimensions). — Atomnaya Energiya, Vol. 24, No. 3. 1968.

11. Gusarov,I.I. and V.K.Lyapidevskii. Uskorennyi sposob opredeleniya zagryaznennosti vozdukha dochernimi produktami radona v lechebnykh uchrezhdeniyakh (Rapid Method for Determining Air Pollution by Radon Daughter Products in Medical Institutions). — Meditsinskaya Radiologiya, Vol. 7, No. 12. 1962.

12. Zhdanova,N.F. and V.G.Labushkin. K voprosu ob otnositel'nykh izmereniyakh soderzhaniya v vozdukhe dochernikh produktov emanatsii (Relative Measurements of Emanation Daughter Product Contents in Air). — Izmeritel'naya Tekhnika, No. 12. 1969.

13. Zhivet'ev,V.M.,V.G.Labushkin, and L.S.Ruzer. Ob izmerenii kontsentratsii dochernikh produktov torona v vozhduke (Measurement of Thoron Daughter Product Concentrations in Air). — Atomnaya Energiya, Vol. 20, No. 6. 1966.

14. Zemskov,B.G.,V.G.Labushkin, and Yu.P.Sel'dyakov. Blok dlya al'fa-spektrometricheskikh izmerenii s poluprovodnikovym detektorom (Unit for Alpha-Spectrometric Measurement with a Semiconductor Detector). — Trudy SNIIP, No. 11(95). 1966.

15. Kapitanov,Yu.T., A.S.Serdyukova, and A.P.Korenkov. Ekspressnyi metod opredeleniya kontsentratsii radiya A i sootnosheniya mezhdu produktami raspada radona v vozdukhe (Rapid Method for Determining the Concentration of Radium A and the Ratios of Radon Decay Products in the Atmosphere). — Izvestiya Vysshikh Uchebnykh Zavedenii, Geologiya i Razvedka, No. 11. 1961.

16. K a r t a s h o v , N. P.   Ekspress-metod opredeleniya kontsentratsii radioaktivnogo aerozol'nogo RaA i skrytoi energii v vozdukhe (Rapid Method for Determining the Concentration of Radioactive Aerosol RaA and the Latent Energy in Air). — Atomnaya Energiya, Vol. 22, No. 5. 1966.

17. L a b u s h k i n , V. G.   Spektrometricheskii metod i apparatura dlya izmereniya kontsentratsii dochernikh produktov emanatsii v vozdukhe (Spectrometric Method and Apparatus for Measuring the Concentration of Emanation Daughter Products in the Atmosphere). — Moskva, Dissertation. 1967.

18. L a b u s h k i n , V. G., N. M. P o l e v , and L. S. R u z e r .   Opredelenie samopogloshcheniya α-izlucheniya v probe pri fil'tratsii vozdukha (Determining the Self-Absorption of α-Radiation in a Sample During Air Filtration). — Atomnaya Energiya, Vol. 19, No. 1. 1965.

19. L a b u s h k i n , V. G. and L. S. R u z e r .   O metode opredeleniya kontsentratsii korotkozhivushchikh dochernikh produktov radona v vozdukhe po α- i β-izlucheniyam (Method for Determining the Concentration of Short-Lived Radon Daughter Products in Air from the α- and β-Radiations). — Atomnaya Energiya, Vol. 19, No. 1. 1965.

20. L a b u s h k i n , V. G., V. I. P o p o v , and L. S. R u z e r .   K voprosu ob opredelenii kontsentratsii dolgozhivushchikh al'fa-aktivnykh aerozolei na fone dochernikh produktov radona i torona (Determining the Concentration of Long-Lived Alpha-Active Aerosols Against the Background of Radon and Thoron Daughter Products). — Izmeritel'naya Tekhnika, No. 12. 1969.

21. L a b u s h k i n , V. G., L. S. R u z e r , E. K. S t e p a n o v , and N. V. T y u t i k o v .   Issledovanie spektra α-izlucheniya neemaniruyushchego istochnika Ra^{226}, nakhodyashchegosya v ravnovesii s dochernimi produktami (Study of the α-Radiation Spectrum of a Nonemanating Ra^{226} Source at Equilibrium with the Daughter Products). — Trudy Institutov Komiteta Sandartov, No. 89(149). 1967.

22. L a b u s h k i n , V. G., L. S. R u z e r , E. K. S t e p a n o v , and N. V. T y u t i k o v .   O spektrometricheskikh kharakteristikakh neemaniruyushchikh istochnikov iz $^{226}_{88}$ Ra and $^{228}_{90}$ Th (Spectrometric Characteristics of Nonemanating $^{226}_{88}$ Ra and $^{228}_{90}$ Th Sources). — Tezisy dokladov XVI ezhedgodnogo soveshchaniya po yadernoi spektroskopii i strukture atomnogo yadra (Summary of Reports to the 16th Annual Conference on Nuclear Spectroscopy and Structure of the Atom Nucleus). "Nauka." 1966.

23. M a r k o v , K. P., N. V. R y a b o v , and K. N. S t a s '.   Ekspress-metod otsenki radiatsionnoi bezopasnosti, svyazannoi s nalichiem v vozdukhe dochernikh produktov radona (Rapid Method for Assessing the Safety from Radiation, Relating to the Presence in Air of Radon Daughter Products). — Atomnaya Energiya, Vol. 12, No. 4. 1962.

24. R u z e r , L. S.   Radioaktivnye aerozoly (Radioactive Aerosols). — Moskva, Izdatel'stvo Komiteta Standartov. 1968.

25. R u z e r , L. S. and V. G. L a b u s h k i n .   Sposob opredeleniya kontsentratsii korotkozhivushchikh dochernikh produktov raspada radona (Method for Determining the Concentration of Short-Lived Daughter Products of Radon Decay). Soviet Patent No. 171478. — Byulleten' Izobretenii, No. 11. 1965.

26. L i n d e k e n , C. L. and K. F. P e t r o c k .   Solid-State Pulse Spectroscopy of Airborne Alpha Radioactivity Samples. — Health Physics, Vol. 12, No. 5. 1966.

27. T s i v o g l o n , E. S. and H. E. A y e r .   Emanation of Radon in Uranium Mines and Control by Ventilation. — Archives of Industrial Hygiene and Occupational Medicine, Vol. 8, No. 2. 1953.

UDC 551.510.7

ISOTOPE ANALYSIS OF RADIOACTIVE FALLOUT AND AEROSOL SAMPLES BY BETA-SPECTROMETRY

A. N. Silant'ev, T. V. Polyakova, F. A. Rabotnova, and I. G. Shkuratova

The paper discusses a method for determining the content of radium-106, praseodymium-144, yttrium-90 and strontium-89 isotopes by beta-spectrometric analysis, involving the use of a scintillation beta-spectrometer with a plastic 20-mm-thick scintillator of 70-mm diameter. Only beta radiation of energies above 630 keV is taken into account when processing spectra.

The measured spectra in the range of 630 keV to 3.5 MeV are subdivided into intervals, so that the following system of equations holds:

$$N_i = a_i^{89} S_{89} + a_i^{90} S_{90} + a_i^{144} S_{144} + a_i^{106} S_{106},$$

$$i = 1, 2, 3, 4$$

where N_i is the number of pulses recorded in interval i, S is the number of pulses recorded in the interval above 630 keV, and a_i is the coefficient of transition from the number of pulses in interval i to the number of pulses recorded in the interval above 630 keV. The transition from the number of pulses recorded to the activity of the isotopes can be expressed by the formula

$$N = A_0 \, \varepsilon\omega \, \frac{1 - e^{-\mu d}}{\mu d},$$

where N is the counting rate in the interval above 630 keV, A_0 is the activity of the preparation, ε is the recording efficiency in the said interval, ω is the solid angle accounting for the angular distribution, d is the layer thickness, and μ is the coefficient of beta-radiation attenuation.

Many radioactive isotopes in fallout and aerosols disintegrate giving off beta particles, the energy of which is high enough for them to escape the preparation and be recorded. Such isotopes are ruthenium-106, praseodymium-144, yttrium-90, and strontium-89, with the end-point energies of the beta spectrum of 3.5, 2.95, 2.25 and 1.46 MeV, respectively. The identification of the other long-lived isotopes from the beta spectra is more difficult, their differences in end-point energy being insufficient for a reliable resolution of the complex spectra into components. Moreover, the other isotopes can often be fairly well identified by means of gamma spectrometric analysis.

The weight and volume of the samples for analysis are usually such as to dictate the consideration of self-absorption in the preparation and of the solid angle variation according to the dimensions of the preparation.

We shall first examine the distortions caused by the dimensions of the preparation in the shape of the beta spectrum. We used a scintillation beta spectrometer made of plastic material, with a diameter of 70 mm and a thickness of 20 mm. The 0.5- to 10-g heavy preparation was placed in a

little polyethylene cup of 45 mm diameter and 10 mm height. The cup with
the preparation was positioned about 3 mm away from the surface of the
detector. Only beta radiation of energies above 650 keV will be discussed,
so that the presence of radioactive isotopes with a soft beta spectrum can
be disregarded. This permits exclusion of the conversion electrons of
cesium-137 from the recording.

Figure 1 shows the radiation spectra of praseodymium-144, from
preparations of various weights. The spectra were normalized so that the
spectrum area for energies above 650 keV should be one unit. No significant differences between spectrum shapes were found with samples weighing
0.74, 4.93, 6.53 and 8.78 grams. Similar results were obtained for the
radiation of yttrium-90. Thus, the variation with sample weight of the shape
of the beta spectra of the isotopes can be ignored in the isotope analysis of
samples within the given weight limits.

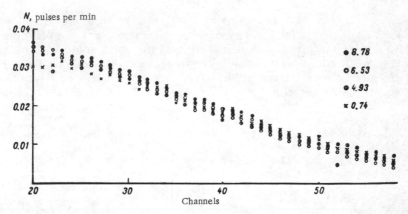

FIGURE 1. Experimental praseodymium-144 spectra from preparations of different weights. The
spectra were normalized in respect of the area unit, and the sample weights are given in grams.

Since the end-point energies differ considerably from each other, the
activities of the said isotopes in the samples can be assessed from the
number of pulses recorded in the different energy intervals of the measured
spectrum. The spectrum range between 630 keV and 3.5 MeV has therefore to be subdivided into several intervals. There should be as many
intervals as there are isotopes to determine. This leads to the following
system of equations:

$$N_i = a_i^{89} S_{89} + a_i^{90} S_{90} + a_i^{144} S_{144} + a_i^{106} S_{106},\qquad(1)$$

$$i = 1,\ 2,\ 3,\ 4,$$

where N_i is the number of pulses recorded in interval i, S is the number
of pulses recorded in the interval above 630 keV and pertaining to the beta
spectrum of the relevant isotope, and a_i are coefficients corresponding

to the transition from the number of pulses recorded in interval i to the number of pulses recorded in the interval above 630 keV. This system of equations can be solved by any method. It has a solution only if coefficients a_i differ significantly from each other. This condition can be satisfied if the limits of the intervals i are suitably chosen. The solution yields the number of pulses recorded in the spectrum of each isotope in the energy interval above 630 keV.

However, in order to proceed from the number of pulses recorded to the activity of the isotopes present in the sample, one must take into account the fraction of the spectrum recorded in the interval above 630 keV, as well as the solid angle covered by the measurements and the self-absorption of beta-particles in the preparation /1/:

$$N = A_0 \, \varepsilon \, \omega \, \frac{1 - e^{-\mu d}}{\mu d}. \qquad (2)$$

Here, N is the recorded counting rate in the energy interval considered (above 630 keV), A_0 is the activity of the preparation, ε is the efficiency of recording in the interval considered, ω is the solid angle accounting for the angular distribution, d is the layer thickness (mg/cm^2), and μ is the coefficient of beta-radiation attenuation. Since we consider not the entire spectrum of beta radiation but only its hard part, the attenuation coefficient will have another value than that given in handbooks. It must be determined experimentally in every case.

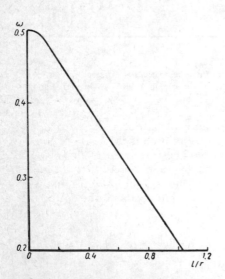

FIGURE 2. Solid angle vs. distance between preparation and detector for cosinusoidal distribution of beta radiation.

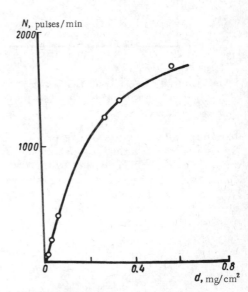

FIGURE 3. Counting rate vs. preparation size.

In assessing the solid angle, one can assume that the angular distribution of the electrons emitted by the preparation is cosinusoidal, since fairly "thick" preparations are used in this case. Figure 2 represents the solid angle as a function of the distance between preparation and crystal for a cosinusoidal distribution of beta radiation and a 0.66 ratio of preparation radius to detector radius /2/. Within permissible limits, the relationship is linear.

Since we are considering fairly hard beta radiation, the distance between preparation and detector can be replaced by the distance between the middle of the preparation thickness and the detector:

$$\omega = \omega_0 \left(1 - a\,\frac{l - \dfrac{h}{2}}{r}\right). \tag{3}$$

Here, ω is the solid angle, ω_0 is a constant of the given setup, l is the distance between crystal and preparation bottom, h is the preparation thickness, r is the detector radius, and a is a constant for the given conditions of measurement (0.6 for the considered geometry of measurement). If the quantities entering the formula are determined experimentally, then and μ are also determined. These two unknowns can be found by measuring several preparations of different thickness of the active layer, but possessing the same specific activity. The ratio of the pulse numbers recorded in the two measurements is

$$\frac{N_1}{N_2} = \frac{\left(1 - a\,\dfrac{l - h_{1/2}}{r}\right)}{\left(1 - a\,\dfrac{l - h_{1/2}}{r}\right)}\,\frac{1 - e^{-\mu\,d_1}}{1 - e^{-\mu\,d_2}}. \tag{4}$$

The solution yields μ. If the specific activity of the salt is known, one can then find $\varepsilon\omega_0$.

As an illustration, consider the results of measuring a salt containing radioactive strontium with yttrium-90. The weights of the preparations were 9.77, 6.01, 4.68, 1.02 and 0.466 grams. The specific activity of the salt was 2.5 disintegrations per minute per milligram for yttrium-90. The corresponding sample thicknesses were 8 mm (0.59 g/cm^2), 4 mm (0.36 g/cm^2), 3 mm (0.28 g/cm^2), 1 mm (0.062 g/cm^2), and 0.5 mm (0.027 g/cm^2). The numbers of pulses recorded per minute were 1670, 1410, 1250, 405 and 190, respectively. The values obtained for μ were 4.4, 4.3, 4.25, 4.4, 4.6, 4.1, 4.45, 4.2, 4.45 (mean value 4.4). The product $\varepsilon\omega_0$ was 0.20. Figure 3 shows the relationship between counting rate and preparation size, and the values obtained by measurement. In the calculations, it was assumed that 1 mm corresponded to 0.08 g/cm^2. The slight deviation of the experimental values from the calculated curve is due to the fact that the bulk density of the preparation differed slightly from the values adopted in the calculations.

BIBLIOGRAPHY

1. Baranov, V. I., A. S. Serdyukova, L. V. Gorbushina, I. M. Nazarov, and Z. N. Efimkina.
       Laboratornye raboty i zadachi po radiometrii (Radiometric Laboratory Work). — Moskva, Atomizdat.
       1966.
2. Gusev, N.G., U.Ya. Margulis, A.N.Marei, N.Yu. Tarasenko, and Yu.M. Shtukkenberg
       (editors).   Dozimetricheskie i radiometricheskie metodiki (Dosimetric and Radiometric Techniques).
       Collected Papers. — Moskva, Atomizdat. 1966.

UDC 539.107.5

RAPID SYSTEM OF AUTOMATIC PUNCH-TAPE OUTPUT
OF INFORMATION FROM THE AI-100—1 ANALYZER

N. F. Mazurin, V. P. Solov'ev, and V. N. Churkin

The paper describes the SAPAR-1m system of automatic punch-tape output of information from a "Raduga" (AI-100—1) multichannel amplitude analyzer of pulses in the code of the "Minsk-2" or "Minsk-22" computer. The block diagram of the system includes an AU-100—1 analyzer, a code-conversion and puncher-control circuit, and a PL-80 tape puncher. In contrast to earlier setups, the code-conversion and puncher-control circuit is transistorized, and thus faster and more reliable.

The top speed of the SAPAR-1m entirely depends on the top speed of the puncher; with the PL-800 puncher, it attains 12 channels per second. Automatic punching of measurement data, combined with machine processing of amplitude spectra on the "Minsk-22" computer, has almost completely eliminated manual operations from gamma-spectrum processing.

Many problems of experimental — mainly nuclear — physics are solved by analyzing amplitude spectra obtained with different spectrometers. The most widespread Soviet analyzer, the AI-100—1, has no automatic punch-tape output of the information accumulated in the analyzer memory, and this often limits the scope of the device and prevents direct processing of data on computers.

The device for punch-tape output of information from the AI-100—1 analyzer is described elsewhere /1/. It uses relays and stepping selectors. With the PL-20 puncher, its top speed is 1.4 channels per second.

In 1965, we developed a faster system of automatic punch-tape output of information from the AI-100—1 analyzer in the code of the "Minsk-2" or "Minsk-22" computer — the SAPAR-1 system with a top speed of 3.5 channels per second.

In contrast to the device described in /1/, the code-conversion and puncher-control unit of the SAPAR system is transistorized, and thus faster and more reliable. On the whole, the top speed of the SAPAR system depends on that of the puncher used; in the considered combination with the PL-80 puncher it is 12 channels per second (SAPAR-1M, 1966). Programming of the SAPAR system is taken care of without any alteration in the AI-100—1 analyzer circuit.

The automatic system of punch-tape output of information from the analyzer consists of the AI-100—1 analyzer, a code-conversion and puncher-control circuit and a PL-80 tape puncher, all connected in series. There is feedback between the last two.

Figure 1 is a block diagram of code conversion and puncher control. It is fully transistorized and consists of 16 input amplifiers with gates AG_1—AG_{16}, seven output gates G_1—G_7 and amplifiers A_1—A_7, eight triggers Tr_1—Tr_8, a diode matrix DM, gates G_8—G_{10}, inverter I, and OR circuits.

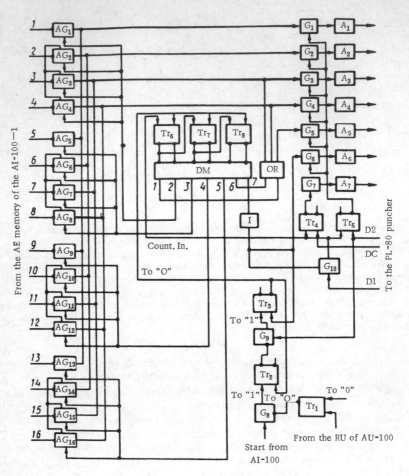

FIGURE 1. Block diagram of code conversion and puncher control.

The main purpose of the circuit is, first, to convert the information contained in the form of a parallel code in the memory of the arithmetic element of the AI-100—1 analyzer, into a sequential code and, second, to punch service marks necessary for direct processing on the "Minsk-2" computer of the tape in addition to the numerical information.

Sixteen outputs from the arithmetic memory of the AI-100—1 are provided in parallel to the little indicating lamps for connecting the analyzer to the code conversion circuit. The punching circuit is controlled directly by the pulse from the cathode of the relaxation-generator thyratron during the automatic selection of channels in the "reading" regime. These pulses are fed to the "1" input of trigger Tr_2 through gate G_8, which in the initial state is opened by a negative potential from the "1" collector of trigger Tr_1 (before information reading, Tr_1 is reset in the initial state through a "general resetting" push-button).

When the triggering pulse arrives at the "1" input of trigger Tr_2 it settles in the "1" state and, through a negative potential from the zero collector, opens gate G_9. The synchronizing pulse D_2 arriving from puncher PL-80 passes on to the input of trigger Tr_3 and toggles it. Through a positive pulse from the "1" output of trigger Tr_3, the distributor P (composed of triggers Tr_6, Tr_7, Tr_8 and diode matrix DM) and trigger Tr_2 settle in the "0" state. Gate G_9 is blocked and no pulses from D_2 reach trigger Tr_3. When distributor P settles in the "0" state, a negative potential appears across output 1 of diode matrix DM and is fed through the OR circuit to the input of gates G_3 and G_4 (code of service combination sign, +10).

At the same time a negative potential from the output of inverter I opens the gates G_{10} and G_6. Since trigger Tr_5 is in the "0" state, the negative potential from the "1" output of trigger Tr_5 maintains the gates G_1—G_6 open. The signals fed to the inputs of gates G_3 and G_4 proceed to amplifiers A_3 and A_4. As a result, the corresponding puncher solenoids are operated and a first line "sign + 10" is punched on the tape. At time 6.5 msec after the pulse from D_2, the pulse from D_1 arrives and is fed through gate G_{10} to the counting input of trigger Tr_6 and to the "1" inputs of triggers Tr_4 and Tr_5. Gates G_1—G_6 are blocked, while gate G_7 opens. Through gate G_7 the negative potential reaches amplifier A_7, which energizes the tape feed solenoid, and the tape moves one line on. The pulses from D_2 and D_3, again following the pulse from D_1, reset the triggers Tr_4 and Tr_5 in the initial state. When the first pulse arrives at the input of trigger Tr_6, distributor P settles in a state in which the negative potential from the output of the second diode matrix DM opens the input gates AG_1—AG_4. The information contained in the older discharge of the first channel of the analyzer AI-100—1 proceeds to the input of gates G_1—G_4, and then, in the way described, it reaches the Sl_1—Sl_4 solenoids of the puncher, and the second line is punched on the tape. All the other discharges of the number and of the service combination "record" are transmitted in a similar manner.

Service instructions

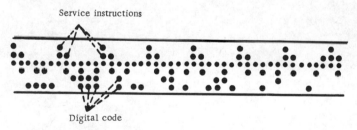

Digital code

FIGURE 2. Punch-tape recording.

When the 6th pulse arrives at the counting input of distributor P, a negative potential appears across the output of the 7th diode matrix DM and, after being inverted by inverter I, blocks the gates G_6 and G_{10} and settles the trigger Tr_3 in the zero state. The punching of the number contained in the first channel of the memory of the AI-100—1 is finished. The circuit awaits the next triggering pulse from the thyratron of the relaxation circuit. The frequency of triggering pulse succession is 10 to 12 Hz.

After the interrogation of the 100 channels, the distributor of the AI-100—1 analyzer issues a pulse to the "1" input of trigger Tr_1; this pulse settles it in the "1" state. As a result, gate G_8 is blocked and blocks the release of the punching circuit. The punching of the information contained in the memory of the AI-100—1 analyzer is thus finished. An example of information recording on punch tape along with additional marks is shown in Figure 2. The discussed automatic system of punch-tape output of information from the AI-100—1 analyzer was tested in 1966—1969 at the Institute of Experimental Meteorology. The code-conversion and puncher-control unit proved to be very reliable.

Combined with machine processing of amplitude spectra on a "Minsk-2" computer, the system of automatic punching of measurement data sharply increased the efficiency of spectrometric work and almost completely excluded manual operations from the processing of instrumental spectra.

The productivity of measuring and computing operations is increased manifold. The advantage is even more substantial with short-term measurements, geophysical investigations from aboard aircraft with the use of analyzers, and so on.

BIBLIOGRAPHY

1. Sokolov, M.P. Sistema vyvoda informatsii, nakoplennoi v zashchishchayushchem ustroistve mnogokanal'nogo analizatora impul'sov ili v schetchike s parallel'nym dvoichno-desyatichnym khodom (Output System for Information Accumulated in the Protecting Device of a Multichannel Analyzer of Pulses or in a Counter with Parallel Binary-Decimal Operation). — In: Trudy 6-i konferentsii po yadernoi radioelektronike (Proc. Conf. on Nuclear Radioelectronics), Vol. 2, p. 102. Moskva, Atomizdat. 1965.

UDC 551.510.72 + 550.378 : 539.16.08

GRAPHOANALYTICAL METHOD FOR DETERMINING CESIUM-137 CONCENTRATION IN SOIL SAMPLES FROM THE GAMMA SPECTRUM

V. N. Churkin

The high-energy part of the amplitude distribution of pulses in the region of the Cs^{137} photopeak of 680 — 740 keV is shown to be fairly well approximated by a Gaussian curve, if the Cs^{137} photopeak in the gamma spectrum of the soil samples is separated from the right-hand base of the curve "parallel to the level of the natural background." This facilitates graphoanalytical determination of the Cs^{137} photopeak area along with calculation of the concentration of this isotope in the soil.

Components due to interfering radiation of natural and artificial isotopes need not be taken into account. The threshold sensitivity for a 50% statistical error of measurement is $2 \cdot 10^{-13}$ curie/g. The method is five to eight times as efficient as known methods. The author assumes that it also applies to measurements in situ, e. g., when Cs^{137} concentration in the soil cover is investigated from aboard aircraft or automobiles.

1. INTRODUCTION

Existing methods of gamma-spectrometric Cs^{137} measurement in soil samples are fairly complicated and laborious /4, 5, 8, 9/. For the most correct application they require a computer, and a complete set of calibrated sources of every isotope present in the soil.

Soil gamma-spectrometry for Cs^{137}, Ru^{106}, Sb^{125}, Mn^{54}, Ce^{144} and the natural radioactive elements Ra, Th and K has recently been conducted at the Institute of Experimental Meteorology according to the following scheme /9/

1. Repeated measurement of all calibrated sources in the given geometry of measurement, for setting up matrices of coefficients.

2. Coefficient matrix inversion on a "Minsk-22" computer according to a standard subprogram.

3. Recording of the soil sample gamma spectrum on a nonlinear energy scale of 0 to 3 MeV. The data output from the analyzer is automatic and presented on a punch tape in the "Minsk-22" computer code. The speed of the data output system is ten channels per second /9/.

4. Solution of a system of linear equations of 8th or 9th order on a computer to determine the isotope concentration A_j in the gamma spectrum of the investigated sample from the formula

$$A_j = \sum_{i=1}^{n} \lambda_{ij} I_i,$$

where λ_{ij} are elements of the inverse matrix of coefficients of the system; I_i is the total counting speed in the reference energy intervals of the investigated isotopes, corrected to account for the natural background and sample weight.

In the analysis of the basic group of long-lived isotopes, the matrix of coefficients of the system is not triangular. When analytical methods of Cs^{137} analysis from the gamma spectrum are used, a complete quantitative analysis is therefore necessary of the entire isotope mixture. The precision of Cs^{137} determination in this case depends in a complicated manner on the statistical fluctuations of the counting rate in the energy intervals, and on the conditionality of the system, the stability of the solution steady operation of apparatus, etc. Calculations show that, for average levels of USSR soil contamination by artificial isotopes in 1963—1967 (Table 1), the relative statistical standard error in Cs^{137} analysis lies between 5 and 10%. Most is due to the error in radium measurement, which in turn is influenced by the gamma radiation of thorium and the high-energy gamma-quanta of Rh^{106}, Pr^{144}, etc. /9/. Thus, strictly speaking, analytical methods of Cs^{137} gamma-spectrometry are not trivial. It would be useful to have a graphoanalytical method for the independent determination of Cs^{137} concentration in soil, based on the unscrambling of the instrumental gamma spectrum only in that energy interval where the Cs^{137} photopeak is recorded.

TABLE 1. Average levels of USSR soil contamination by nuclear test products in 1963 — 1967 on 1 July (mcurie/km^2)

Year	Mn^{54}	$Zr^{95} + Nb^{95}$	$Ru^{106} + Rh^{106}$	Sb^{125}	$Ce^{144} + Pr^{144}$	Cs^{137}
1963	—	460	370	46	570*	86*
1964	—	30	281	63	800*	97*
1965	21	—	140	41	576	108*
1966	8	—	70	21	280	87
1967	5	—	40	15	140	84

* We are now revising these data, to make them more accurate.

From earlier investigations, the pulse amplitude distribution at the photopeak during recording of monoenergetic gamma quanta of a point sourc is known to approximate a Gaussian distribution /3/. The photopeak area is calculated from the height and half-width of the peak, easy to measure for a point source (the "cutoff" method) /2/. If there are loops from high-energy gamma quanta in the region of the independently recorded photopeaks the area of the entire peak can be reestablished sometimes from its vertex ("triangle" method) /10/. The optimum conditions for recording an individual gamma radiation line against a background of uninterrupted distribution of equal interferences depend on the width of the energy interval of measurement, the spectrometric properties of the apparatus, and the intensity ratio of useful to interfering radiations /6/. All these data refer to the recording of an individual line of the gamma radiation of a point sourc

In actual gamma spectra of soil samples (three-dimensional source) the amplitude distribution of pulses at the photopeak differs from the Gauss curve, and the level of interferences in the energy interval of the photopeak and at its margins usually has a complicated form. No information is available to us concerning the graphical interpretation of such gamma spectra. Under such conditions, the main purpose of the graphoanalytical method of interpreting a complicated gamma spectrum is to find ways of calculating the "actual" photopeak area. The present paper discusses the solution to this problem, as illustrated by the separation of the Cs^{137} photopeak area in the gamma spectrum of soil and plant cover samples.

2. FORM OF Cs^{137} PHOTOPEAK IN THE RECORDING OF GAMMA RADIATION FROM A THREE-DIMENSIONAL SOURCE

The gamma spectrogram of soil samples taken and measured in 1964—1968 has a clearcut maximum in the energy interval 600—700 keV. This maximum is formed by photoelectric interaction and Compton scatter of gamma radiation from Cs^{137} (660 keV), Ru^{106} (620 keV), Sb^{125} (600 and 640 keV), Pr^{144} (695 keV), Ra (609 keV), and Th (582 keV). The base of the peak and the "pedestals," i.e., the plateau regions at peak margins, are produced by the gamma radiation of the natural background and by scattering effects in the source material and in the detector of high-energy gamma quanta of the natural and artificial isotopes, producing an uninterrupted distribution. Most pulses in the said energy interval are usually due to gamma radiation of Cs^{137}.

The amplitude distribution of pulses in the photopeak region when recording the monochromatic gamma radiation of a three-dimensional source can be represented, to a first approximation, as a sum of two Gaussian curves:

$$F_\Sigma(E, E_0) = F_1(E, E_0) + F_2(E, E_0') = I_0' e^{-a_1 x_1^2} + Y_0 e^{-a_2 x_2^2}. \quad (1)$$

The first term $F_1(E, E_0)$ characterizes the pulse distribution due to photo-electric interactions and repeated scattering in the crystal of the mono-energetic gamma quanta originating from different points of the three-dimensional source. The second term $F_2(E, E_0')$ is an approximation to the pulse amplitude distribution, which can be identified with the effects of gamma-quanta scatter over small angles in the material of the three-dimensional source and, partly, in the crystal shield. The forms of functions $F_1(E, E_0)$, $F_2(E, E_0')$ and $F_\Sigma(E, E_0)$ are given in Figure 1 (curves 1, 2, 3).

The notation in formula (1) is as follows: I_0' is the maximum ordinate of the normal distribution $F_1(E, E_0)$ with center at E_0=662 keV; $a_1 = \dfrac{1}{2\sigma_1^2} = \dfrac{2.773}{\Delta E_0^2}$ is a parameter characterizing the $F_1(E, E_0)$ distribution; σ_1=0.4246; ΔE_0 is the standard deviation of a normal distribution with center E_0; ΔE_0 is the peak width at half the height, calculated from $F_1(E, E_0)$; $x_1 = E_0 - E$, $x_2 = E_0' - E$ are deviations from the distribution centers E_0 and $E_0' = E_0 - 3\sigma_1$, respectively; $a_2 = \dfrac{1}{2\sigma_2^2} = \dfrac{0.693}{\Delta E_0^2}$ is a parameter characterizing the $F_2(E, E_0')$ distribution;

321

σ^2 is the standard deviation from a normal distribution with center $E_0' = E_0 - 3\,\sigma_1$ $(\sigma_2 = 2\,\sigma_1)$; $Y_0 = v\beta I_0$ is the value of function $F_\Sigma\ (E,\ E_0)$ at the point with abscissa E_0, where v is a correction factor, $\beta = \dfrac{Y_0}{I_0}$ is the reciprocal of the "peak-to-trough" ratio /11/, and I_0 is the maximum value of function $F_\Sigma\ (E,\ E_0)$ (Figure 1).

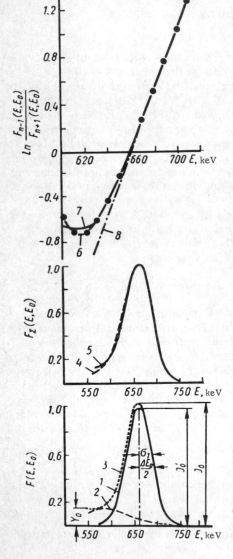

FIGURE 1. Form of the gamma spectrogram of a Cs^{137} source in the energy interval of Cs^{137}:

1) $F_1\ (E,\ E_0)$; 2) $F_2(E,\ E_0')$; 3) $F_\Sigma\ (E,\ E_0)$; 4, 5) normalized calculated (4) and experimental (5) gamma spectra of the three-dimensional source of Cs^{137}; 6, 7) linearization of curves 4 and 5, respectively; 8) linearization of $F_1\ (E,\ E_0)$.

In measurements on a NaI(Tl) crystal measuring 70×50 mm at spectrometer resolution $R = 10\%$ and source thickness 30 mm (uniformly enveloping the crystal), $v = 1.5, \beta = 0.1$, and consequently, $Y \simeq 0.15 I_0$.

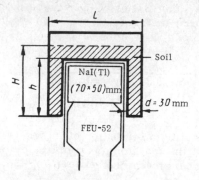

FIGURE 2. Geometry of soil sample measurement.

A comparison of the forms of the calculated spectrum $F_\Sigma (E, E_0)$ with the actual spectrum of a three-dimensional Cs^{137} source shows good agreement between calculated and experimental data (curves 4 and 5 in Figure 1, all values normalized to distribution maximum I_0). This similarity is also evident by linearizing the curves of actual and calculated gamma spectra (curves 6 and 7 in Figure 1). The peaks were linearized according to Zimmerman's formula /12/

$$\ln \frac{F_{n-1} (E, E_0)}{F_{n+1} (E, E_0)} = \frac{2}{\sigma^2} (n - n_0),$$

where $F_{n-1} (E, E_0)$ and $F_{n+1} (E, E_0)$ are the values of function $F_\Sigma (E, E_0)$ in channels $n - 1$ and $n + 1$, while n and n_0 are the numbers of the channels corresponding to energies E and E_0.

The measurement geometry for which the experimental gamma spectra were obtained is shown in Figure 2. The source thickness is 3 cm, its volume approximately 1500 cm^3, and the gamma spectrometer resolution for the 662 keV line 10%.

According to expression (1), the spectrum area S_Σ in the region of the photopeak of a three-dimensional source for monochromatic gamma radiation is

$$S_\Sigma = S_1 + S_2 = I_0 \sigma_1 \sqrt{2\pi} \int\limits_{E_0 - 3\sigma_1}^{E_0 + 3\sigma_1} e^{-\alpha_1 z_1^2} dz +$$

$$+ Y_0 \sigma_2 \sqrt{2\pi} \int\limits_{E_0 - 3\sigma_1}^{E_0 + 3\sigma_1} e^{-\alpha_2 z_2^2} dz, \tag{2}$$

where S_1 is the integral of the distribution function for the curve $F_1 (E, E_0)$, S_2 is the integral of the distribution function for curve $F_2 (E, E_0)$, and

$z_i = \dfrac{E - E_0}{\sigma_i}$. The integral values for normalized Gauss functions are tabulated. The ratio of integral functions S_2/S_1 depends in a complicated manner on the gamma-quanta energy, the source thickness, crystal dimensions, resolution of instruments, etc. We shall calculate S_2/S_1 in % for the measurement conditions considered:

$$\frac{S_2}{S_1} = \frac{Y_0\, \sigma_2\, \sqrt{2\pi}\, 0.4986}{2 I_0\, \sigma_1\, \sqrt{2\pi}\, 0.4986}\, 100\% =$$
$$= \frac{0.15\, I_0\, 2\sigma_1}{2 I_0\, \sigma_1}\, 100\% = 15\%. \tag{3}$$

Let us further examine the distribution of integral functions S_2 to the "left" (S_2^l) and "right" (S_2^r) of the maximum of amplitude distribution E_0 of function $F_2(E, E_0')$, i.e., in the energy regions between $E_0 - 3\sigma_1$ and E_0 and between E_0 and $E_0 + 3\sigma_1$:

$$S_2 = S_2^l + S_2^r = Y_0\, \sigma_2\, \sqrt{2\pi}\left[\int_{E_0-3\sigma_1}^{E_0} e^{-\sigma_2 z_2^2}\, dz + \int_{E_0}^{E_0+3\sigma_1} e^{-\sigma_2 z_2^2}\, dz \right] =$$
$$= Y_0\, \sigma_2\, \sqrt{2\pi}\,(0.4332 + 0.0654) = 0.15\, I_0\, 2\sigma_1\, \sqrt{2\pi}\,(0.4332 + 0.0654). \tag{4}$$

From expressions (3) and (4) it is easy to determine the proportion of scattered radiation in the different parts of the spectrum in the photopeak region, described by the function $F_2\ (E, E_0)$. This approach yields

$$\frac{S_2^l}{S_1} = 13\% \quad \text{and} \quad \frac{S_2^r}{S_1} = 2\%.$$

This reveals important characteristics of the spectrum shape in the region of the photopeak of a three-dimensional Cs^{137} source. For the measurement geometry considered, the proportion of pulses due to gamma-quanta scatter over small angles in the source material and crystal is approximately 15% of the photopeak area described by Gauss curve $F_1(E, E_0)$. Of this, about 13% accounts for the low-energy part, and about 2% for the high-energy part of the photopeak. Such a distribution of components from scattered radiation in the energy interval of the Cs^{137} photopeak causes asymmetry in the region of the Cs^{137} photopeak and peculiarities in the linearization curve of the experimental photopeak for the case of a three-dimensional source:

a) a bend of the linearization curve in the region of energies below $(E_0+\sigma_1)$, where the deviation in the shape of the experimental photopeak from the Gauss curve is at least 1%, the bend being most pronounced to the left of the point with abscissa E_0 (curves 6 and 7 in Figure 1);

b) a change in the sign of the derivative of the linearization curve at the point with abscissa $\sim(E_0 - m\sigma_1)$, where $m = 1.5$ to 2 for our measurement conditions.

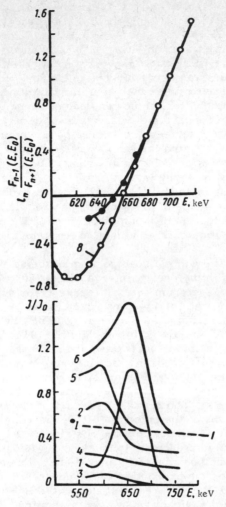

FIGURE 3. Different components of the gamma spectrogram of a soil sample in the Cs^{137} energy interval:

1) gamma spectrum of Cs^{137}; 2) total gamma spectrum of Th, Ra, and K; 3) total gamma spectrum of Rh^{106}, Sb^{125}, and Pr^{144} (1967); 4) natural background; 5) total gamma spectrum of all "interfering" components; 6) total gamma spectrum of all components; 7) linearization of curve 6 for ordinate reading along cutoff line I— I; 8) photopeak linearization of calibrated Cs^{137} source (taken from Figure 1, curve 6).

The shape of the distribution function at the photopeak and its great variability with source thickness, instrument resolution, etc., exclude the possibility of applying classical methods of photopeak processing /1, 6, 7, 10, 12/, widely used in practice with print sources. For the right part of the experimental photopeak the linearization curve (Figure 1, curve 7) closely approximates a straight line (Figure 1, line 8). In this part of the photopeak the parameter σ_1 of the Gaussian curve for function $F_1(E, E_0)$ determines the entire distribution $F_\Sigma (E, E_0)$. Our calculations based on model work with three-dimensional Cs^{137} sources of various thicknesses (0, 1, 3 and 5 cm) showed that the shape of the photopeak is mainly disturbed in its low-energy part, while the high-energy part of the photopeak almost coincides with the Gaussian curve for a wide range of measurement conditions. This predetermines the possibility of plotting the relationships between spectrometer photoefficiency and energy, spectrometer resolution and energy, etc., when recording the gamma radiation of three-dimensional sources. In the given case, these relationships can be used for spectrometric purposes on a par with the similar relationships for point sources.

We have already mentioned that many gamma lines form an uninterrupted distribution in the Cs^{137} energy interval during the measurement of soil samples. By applying formulas (1) and (2) to each gamma line separately, one can determine the shape of the gamma spectrum in the Cs^{137} energy interval for any combination of isotope activities. The shape of this uninterrupted distribution can be calculated from measurements of calibrated sources.

The resolution of the gamma spectrogram of the soil sample into the different components in the energy interval 550—750 keV is shown in Figure 3: the gamma spectrum of Cs^{137} (curve 1) for average levels of soil contamination in 1967; the total gamma spectrum of Th, Ra and K (curve 2) for an $8 \cdot 10^{-4}$ % Th, $8 \cdot 10^{-8}$ % Ra and 2% K content; the total gamma spectrum of Rh^{106}, Sb^{125} and Pr^{144} (curve 3) for the 1967 average contamination levels in Table 1; the gamma spectrum of the natural background (curve 4); the total gamma spectrum of all the "interfering" components without Cs^{137} (curve 5); and the integral gamma spectrum for all components (curve 6). All distributions are reduced to the normalized maximum of amplitude distribution I_0 of the Cs^{137} photopeak. From integral curve 6 of Figure 3 it follows that the shape of the pulse amplitude distribution in the energy interval 550—750 keV ("composite peak") is sharply asymmetric, and the distribution maximum corresponds to 650 keV. Obviously, the shape of the composite peak and the position of its maximum on the energy scale are unstable and depend on the proportion of the different isotopes. *

The contribution of the different isotopes in the Cs^{137} energy interval depends on the level of radioactive soil contamination. For the Soviet Union, the average levels of radioactive contamination of soils are given in Table 1. The soil-cover samples were taken during field trips every summer. The sampling depth was 0 to 10 cm. The isotope analysis was conducted by the gamma-spectrometric method described in /9/.

---

* In practice, the proportion of the concentrations of the different isotopes in the soil sample depends on the sampling technique, other conditions remaining unchanged. In the case considered, it was assumed that the soil sample had been taken from a depth of 0 to 5 cm from an area of 500 cm². The bulk weight of the sample was ~ 1.1 g/cm³, the total weight ~ 1500 g, and the specific Cs^{137} activity in the sample $1.8 \cdot 10^{-12}$ curie/g.

3. GRAPHOANALYTICAL METHOD OF CALCULATING Cs^{137} CONCENTRATION IN SOIL FROM THE GAMMA SPECTRUM

We shall discuss a graphoanalytical method that makes it possible to calculate the Cs^{137} photopeak area in the gamma spectrum described by the integral curve 6 in Figure 3.

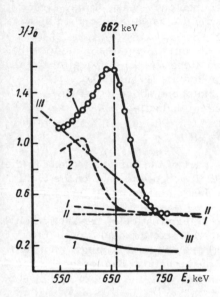

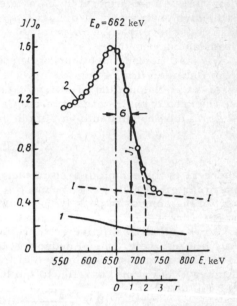

FIGURE 4. Different variants of separation (cutoff) of the Cs^{137} photopeak in the gamma spectrum:

1) level of natural background; 2) total gamma spectrum of all the interfering components; 3) integral gamma spectrum of all components. Line I—I) cutoff "parallel to the level of the natural background," line II—II) cutoff "parallel to the abscissa," line III—III) cutoff along "pedestals." Shaded region [omitted on figure]) spurious increase in Cs^{137} photopeak area (S_{cut}^{t}) when curve 3 is cutoff along line I—I.

Figure 5. Technique of calculating the Cs^{137} photopeak area (s_{cut}^{t}) in the 660—740 keV interval by the graphoanalytical method:

1) natural background; 2) composite peak in the energy interval of Cs^{137}. Line I—I) cutoff "parallel to the level of the natural background," I_{t}) ordinate of Cs^{137} photopeak when at a distance of 1σ from the photopeak center $E_0(r=1)$.

Let us examine the shape of the right part of the composite peak for different variants of its separation ("cutoff") against the background of interferences. The best cutoff variant was chosen in view of three factors: 1) simplicity of Cs^{137} photopeak cutoff method, 2) identity of shape between the (right branch of the) Cs^{137} photopeak after cutoff and the photopeak of the three-dimensional calibrated Cs^{137} source, 3) precision of determination of the actual Cs^{137} photopeak area.

Figure 3 provides data on the linearization of the composite peak for reading the ordinates off the cutoff line I—I. The latter is drawn from the right-hand pedestal of the peak, roughly parallel to the line of the natural background. Figure 3 provides data on the linearization of the gamma spectrogram of a calibrated Cs^{137} source in the energy interval 600—750 keV (curve 8). A comparison of curves 7 and 8 shows that the cutoff of the composite peak "parallel to the natural background," i.e., along line I—I, ensures fairly complete reproduction of pulse distribution in the high energy part of the calibrated-source photopeak. It has already been noted here that the shape of this distribution is well described by a Gaussian curve.

We shall demonstrate that the shape of the curve deviates considerably from Gaussian if the integral curve is read along line II—II, parallel to the abscissa, and along line III—III, along the pedestals (Figure 4).

The area of the right part of the Cs^{137} photopeak above cutoff line I—I (S_{cut}^r) can be calculated by a simple graphical deduction:

$$S_{cut}^r = S_{\Sigma}^r - S_{int}^r, \qquad (5)$$

where S_{Σ}^r is the complete area of the right part of the composite peak in the energy interval 660—740 keV, and S_{int}^r is that part of the area of the right part of the composite peak lying below the I—I cutoff level (Figure 3)("area of interferences").

To evaluate the relative error ε_s in the determination of the area when carrying out the graphical deduction, let us examine the deviation in the calculated area S_{cut}^r from the actual (given) area S_{act}^r when integral curve 3 (Figure 4) is cut off "parallel to the level of the natural background" (line I—I in Figure 4):

$$\varepsilon_s = \frac{S_{cut}^r - S_{act}^r}{S_{act}^r} 100\% = \frac{\Delta S^r}{S_{act}^r} 100\%,$$

where ΔS^r is that part of the area of the interference peak (curve 2 in Figure 4) lying above cutoff line I—I in the energy interval 660—690 keV. The main component of ΔS^r is given by the gamma radiation of radium:

$$S_{act}^r = I_0 \sigma_1 \sqrt{2\pi} \int_{E_r}^{E_0 + 3\sigma_1} e^{-a_1 z_1^2} dz + Y_0 \sigma_2 \sqrt{2\pi} \int_{E_0}^{E_0 + 3\sigma_1} e^{-a_2 z_2^2} dz.$$

For the considered case of separation, the area S_{cut}^r exceeds the actual area S_{act}^r by $\varepsilon_s = +3\%$. By analogy with the previous calculations, the error in the determination of the actual area S_{act}^r for a cutoff "parallel to the abscissa" (line II—II in Figure 4) and "along pedestals" (lines III—III in Figure 4) is +10% and −25%, respectively.

Thus, the cutoff line I—I "parallel to the level of the natural background" ensures maximum precision of the graphical calculation of the actual Cs^{137} photopeak area in the composite gamma spectrum of the soil sample.

In addition to the graphical calculation, the area of the high-energy part of the Cs^{137} photopeak (S_{cut}^r) in the composite gamma spectrum can be conveniently determined by a graphoanalytical method based on the properties of the Gaussian curve. It can be demonstrated that area S_{cut}^r in this case is determined by

$$S_{cut}^r = \sigma_1 \sqrt{\frac{\pi}{2}} I_r \exp\left(\frac{r^2}{2}\right),$$ (6)

where σ_1 is the standard deviation calculated from measurements on a calibrated Cs^{137} source in the right part of the photopeak, and I_r is the counting rate over the cutoff line at the point with abscissa
$r = \dfrac{E - E_0}{\sigma_1}$ (Figure 5).

A special problem is raised by the selection of deviation r and by the technique of calculating the ordinate I_r, for which values the photopeak area S_{cut}^r is measured with the highest degree of accuracy. An analysis of the characteristics of the composite peak in the energy interval 660—740 keV, within a wide range of variations in Ra, Th and K concentrations in the soil up to their highest values, shows that the S_{cut}^r area is best calculated at a distance $r=1$ from the center $E_0 = 662$ keV. To smooth the statistical fluctuations in the counting rate we have to develop an averaged value ("arithmetic mean") of the counting rate $\bar{I}_1$ for $r=1$. The analytical value $\bar{I}$ of the ordinate is

$$\bar{I}_1 = \frac{1}{N} \sum_i^N \zeta_i I_i,$$ (7)

where N is the number of ordinates (channels) in the smoothing zone, $\zeta_i = \exp\left(\dfrac{r_i^2}{2} - \dfrac{1}{2}\right)$ is a factor for reducing the different ordinates to the established distance $r=1$, and $r_i = \dfrac{E_i - E_0}{\sigma_1}$. In practice, ordinate $\bar{I}_1$ is not calculated from formula (7), but read off from the cutoff line to the straight line which determines the gamma spectrum in the deviation range $0.7 \leqslant r \leqslant 1.3$ (part of the Gaussian curve in the region of the point of inflection) (Figure 5). In accordance with the properties of a normal distribution, the straight line averaging the gamma spectrum in the zone where the statistical fluctuations are smoothed ($0.7 \leqslant r \leqslant 1.3$) should intersect the cutoff line I—I at a distance $r=2$. If this last condition is not met during the measurements, this indicates that the Cs^{137} peak has shifted owing to unstable operation of the apparatus.

In the particular case when the resolution of the gamma spectrometer is $R=10\%$ ($\sigma_1 = 2.8$ channels at an energy scale tuning of 10 keV/channel), formula (6) simplifies to

$$S_{cut}^r = 5.8 \, \bar{I}_1.$$ (8)

The sought Cs^{137} concentration in the soil (A_{Cs}) is given by

$$A_{Cs} = \frac{S_{cut}^r}{P_{sam}} \frac{Q}{\eta \gamma},$$ (9)

where η (in pulses per quantum) is the recording efficiency of Cs^{137} gamma quanta in the given geometry of measurement for the adopted method of calculating the photopeak area, $Q = 4.5 \cdot 10^{-13}$ curie/(disintegration/min) is a conversion factor, and P_{sam} is the sample weight. Instead of the calibrating Cs^{137} source, for calibrating the apparatus one can use a three-dimensional radium source (calibration by the 609-keV gamma line). In this case, with a (systematic) error of 10% at most, the Cs^{137} concentration in the soil is

$$A_{Cs} = \frac{S^r_{cut}}{P_{sam}} \frac{Q}{\alpha \, (\eta \gamma)_{Cs}} \, , \qquad (10)$$

where $\alpha = \dfrac{(\eta \gamma)_{Cs}}{(\eta \gamma)_{Ra}}$; under our measurement conditions $\alpha = 1.85 \pm 0.15$.

We stress the fact that the 0.68 quantum yield of the 609-keV gamma line of radium, often adopted in the past /4, 5, 8/, is apparently erroneous. According to the data of our investigations into the relationship between the photoefficiency of the gamma spectrometer and the energy of the gamma quanta (1963), the value should be 0.45 ± 0.04.

The relative statistical error ε in the determination of the Cs^{137} photopeak area by the graphoanalytical method is calculated approximately from the following formulas:

a) if the individual ordinate I (without smoothing of statistical fluctuations) has been found, then

$$\varepsilon = \frac{\sigma_I}{I} = \frac{1}{I} \left[\frac{I + 2 I_{int}}{t} \right]^{\frac{1}{2}} ;$$

b) if the averaged ordinate $\bar{I}_1$ (the statistical fluctuations being smoothed) has been found, then

$$\varepsilon = \frac{Q_I}{\bar{I}_1} = \frac{1}{\bar{I}_1} \left[\frac{1}{N} \sum_i^N \tau_i^2 \frac{I_i + 2 I_{int}}{t} \right]^{\frac{1}{2}} .$$

Here σ_I and $Q_{\bar{I}}$ are the statistical standard errors in the determination of each ordinate I and of the averaged ("arithmetic mean") $\bar{I}_1$; I_{int} is the value of interferences at distance $r \geqslant 3$, and t is the duration of measurement (usually 30 min); the other notation has already been defined. For the average 1967–1968 levels of soil contamination by artificial isotopes (Table 1) and the considered conditions of measurement and soil sampling, the statistical error in one measurement of Cs^{137} concentration in soil is $\varepsilon = 11\%$ for the individual ordinate I (for 1 channel) and 9% for 3 channels. These errors are only 1.1 to 1.3 times as high as the statistical errors in Cs^{137} measurement by the analytical method of gamma-spectra processing by means of inverse matrices /9/.

The accuracy of Cs^{137} photopeak area calculation by the method discussed is highly affected by the unstable operation of apparatus. If the Cs^{137} peak shifts 5 keV continuously in time and the gamma-spectrometer resolution is $R = 10\%$, the error in photopeak area determination is 9%. In practice, the correction for photopeak shift is easily determined from the deviation in the point of intersection between the tangent to the right part of the photopeak and the cutoff line, from the point with abscissa $r=2$ on the cutoff line.

Based on analysis errors at the given level of interference, the minimum (threshold) Cs^{137} concentration in the soil, as determined to within a 50% statistical standard error, is $2 \cdot 10^{-3}$ curie/g. This value is almost only a tenth of the mean Cs^{137} concentration in USSR soils (0 to 5 cm soil layer).

From data on the isotope concentration in soil (Table 1) and the shape of the gamma spectra of artificial isotopes (Figure 3), we calculate the fission-product contributions in the Cs^{137} interval for different times that have elapsed after tests (Table 2).

TABLE 2. Contributions of long-lived fission products in the Cs^{137} energy interval in 1964—1967 (on 1 June), % of the Cs^{137} proportion

Energy interval	Year of soil sampling				Remarks
	1964	1965	1966	1967	
Entire photopeak (580—740 keV)	40	25	15	12*	
High-energy part of photopeak (660—740 keV)	8	4	3	10*	
High-energy part of photopeak (680—700 keV) and the region of $\bar{I}_1$ ordinate calculation	3	2	1	2*	The components were calculated for the gamma-spectrum area above cutoff line I—I (Figure 3)

* Influence of fresh $Zr^{95} + Nb^{95}$ fallout.

The table shows that, in 1964—1967, the long-lived fission products of Pr^{144}, Rh^{106} and Sb^{125} did not contribute more than 1 to 3% to the high-energy part of the Cs^{137}, 680—700 keV photopeak. Thus, the method of Cs^{137} analysis discussed above is applicable one year after a series of heavy nuclear tests (at the present level of soil contamination by Cs^{137}). At earlier dates, the analysis must account for the gamma radiation of $Zr^{95} + Nb^{95}$.

The data in Table 2 also show that Cs^{137} gamma-spectrometric analysis methods based on the consideration of Ra, Th and K contributions in the full Cs^{137} interval, but disregarding the contributions of fission elements in the region of the Cs^{137} photopeak, yield systematically higher Cs^{137} concentrations in soil. In this case, the error can attain tens of percents, depending on the date of sampling and soil-sample measurement.

4. EVALUATION OF $Zr^{95} + Nb^{95}$ INFLUENCE

Let us examine the possibility of applying the graphoanalytical method of gamma-spectrum processing to heavy soil contamination by $Zr^{95} + Nb^{95}$.

We assume the level of $Zr^{95} + Nb^{95}$ contamination at the soil surface in the middle latitudes of the northern hemisphere to be 10 mcurie/km² at most. This is only about 10% of the Cs^{137} content accumulated in the soil in 1966—1968 (Table 1). For the given ratio of radioisotope contamination levels the amplitude of the $Zr^{95} + Nb^{95}$ photopeak in the spectrogram ($E_0 \approx 760$ keV) is about one-eighth of the Cs^{137} photopeak amplitude. As a result, calculations with formulas of forms (1) to (6) show that the Cs^{137} concentration in the soil is reduced by 12%, if the gamma radiation of $Zr^{95} + Nb^{95}$ is neglected. To reduce the influence of $Zr^{95} + Nb^{95}$ on the precision of Cs^{137} measurement the Cs^{137} and $Zr^{95} + Nb^{95}$ photopeaks must be cut off jointly, the cutoff line resting on the $Zr^{95} + Nb^{95}$ photopeak plateau level (800——850 keV). This reduces the error in Cs^{137} determination from 12 to 3—5%.

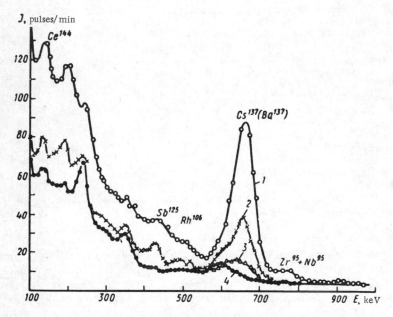

FIGURE 6. Gamma spectra of deep soil samples. Depth ranges:

1) 0—3 mm; 2) 12—15 mm; 3) 40—50 mm; 4) 90—100 mm. Sampling: June 1968. Measurement: July 1968.

Figure 6 represents the gamma spectra of four soil-layer samples, taken from different depths. Sampling and measurement were conducted in June—July 1968. The spectrometer was composed of a transducer with a NaI(Tl) 70 × 50-mm crystal, an FEU-2 photomultiplier, and an AI-100—1 pulse analyzer (system resolution 9% for the 662 keV line). The figure shows that the topsoil (0 to 3 mm) contained considerable amounts of $Zr^{95} + Nb^{95}$. This element was not found in the lower soil layers (the level of interfering radiation was practially the same in the 740—800 keV energy region for the lower soil layers and 800—850 keV for the topsoil).

This shows that the results of the proposed method are not much affected by fresh global $Zr^{95}+Nb^{95}$ fallout, if the density of radioactive soil contamination by these isotopes is approximately 10 to 20 mcurie/km^2. The method can also be used for studying the vertical distribution of Cs^{137} in the soil.

The reliability of the method was checked by comparing the Cs^{137} concentrations in the soil obtained with it, to data of the analytical method of soil gamma spectrometry. The comparison was carried out for deep soil samples, of different Cs^{137} content (Figure 6). The results are tabulated in Table 3.

TABLE 3. Comparison of Cs^{137} concentrations in soil obtained by two methods

Soil layer depth, mm	Cs^{137} content in soil, mcurie/km^2		Divergence of data, %	Statistical error, %
	graphoanalytical method	analytical method with computer		
0 — 3	34	36	− 6	2
12 — 15	8.8	9.1	− 3	5
30 — 33	3.6	3.3	+ 10	20
90 — 100	1.8	2.3	− 22	> 50

N o t e. The concentrations were obtained for sectional layers of $1 \cdot 10^4$ cm^2 area.

The divergence of the results is small, and comparable to the statistical error. The fairly high accuracy of the graphoanalytical method and its economy have earned it wide acceptance in the investigation of soil cover contamination by cesium-137 in 1968.

The use of the complicated analytical method of soil gamma spectrometry in that period was ineffective, because the levels of soil contamination by other isotopes were very low (at the threshold of sensitivity).

5. CONCLUSION

The Cs^{137} analysis method discussed is very simple and does not require the determination of natural or artificial isotope concentrations. All measurements are conducted over one range of the energy scale, and the statistical error at a soil measurement time of 20—30 min is 5 to 15% for the existing levels of soil contamination by Cs^{137}. Processing of the gamma spectrum and calculations take no longer than 30 min. On the whole, the time taken by the analysis of one soil sample for Cs^{137} is 40—50 min. This method is thus five to eight times as rapid as earlier graphoanalytical or analytical methods /4, 5, 8/. It does not require computers. All it takes to calibrate the apparatus is a Cs^{137} or Ra standard (609 keV line, quantum yield 45%) in the given measurement geometry. The presence of $Zr^{95}+Nb^{95}$ traces with a soil-contamination density of approximately

10 to 20 mcurie/km^2 is no hindrance during global fallout of fresh products (i. e., 2 to 3 months after tests). We think the method applies not only to laboratory investigations of soil samples, but also in situ, for instance, to investigations of Cs^{137} concentration in soil from aboard aircraft or automobiles.

The author is much indebted to Sh. D. Fridman for his useful comments made while reviewing the manuscript.

BIBLIOGRAPHY

1. Vartanov, N. A. and P. S. Samoilov. Prakticheskie metody stsintillyatsionnoi gamma-spektrometrii (Practical Methods of Scintillation Gamma Spectrometry). — Moskva, Atomizdat. 1964.

2. Egorov, Yu. A. Stsintillyatsionnye metody spektrometrii i gamma-izlucheniya bystrykh neitronov (Scintillation Spectrometric Methods and Gamma Radiation of Fast Neutrons). — Moskva, Atomizdat. 1963.

3. Zigban, K. Beta i gamma-spektroskopiya (Beta and Gamma Spectroscopy). — Moskva, Atomizdat. 1955.

4. Iokhel'son, S. B. Gamma-spektrometriya radioaktivnykh vypadenii (Gamma Spectrometry of Radioactive Fallout). — In: Sbornik rabot po nekotorym voprosam dozimetrii i radiometrii ioniziruyushchikh izluchenii (Collected Papers on Problems of Ionizing-Radiation Dosimetry and Radiometry). Moskva, Atomizdat. 1961.

5. Iokhel'son, S. B. Gamma-spektrometricheskii analiz prob pochvy (Gamma Spectrometric Analysis of Soil Samples). — In: Sbornik metodik po opredeleniyu radioaktivnosti okruzhayushchei sredy (Collection of Methods of Determining the Radioactivity of the Environment), Parts III, IV, edited by A. N. Silant'ev. Moskva, Gidrometeoizdat. 1967.

6. Kogan, R. M. Primenenie metodov gamma-spektrometrii k izmereniyam radioaktivnykh zagryaznenii mestnosti (Application of Gamma Spectrometric Methods to Local Measurements of Radioactive Contaminants). — In: Sbornik rabot po nekotorym voprosam dozimetrii i radiometrii ioniziruyushchikh izluchenii (Collected Papers on Problems of Ionizing-Radiation Dosimetry and Radiometry). Moskva, Atomizdat. 1960.

7. Stolyarova, E. L. Prikladnaya spektrometriya ioniziruyushchikh izluchenii (Applied Spectrometry of Ionizing Radiation). — Moskva, Atomizdat. 1964.

8. Fedorov, G. A. and I. E. Konstantinov. O metodike opredeleniya Cs^{137} v pochvakh (Technique of Cs^{137} Determination in Soils). — In Sbornik: Voprosy dozimetrii i zashchity ot izluchenii (Collected Papers: Problems of Dosimetry and Protection from Radiation), No. 2. Atomizdat. 1963.

9. Churkin, V. N. Gamma-spektrometriya global'nykh radioaktivnykh zagryaznenii prob pochvy (Gamma Spectrometry of Global Radioactive Contaminants of Soil Samples). — In: Tezisy dokladov simpoziuma po migratsii radioaktivnykh elementov v nazemnykh biogeotsenozakh (Reports of Proc. Symposium on Migration of Radioactive Elements in Land Biogeocenoses). Moskva. 1968.

10. Burras, W. R. Unscrambling Scintillation Spectrometer Data. — JRS Transactions on Nuclear Science, Vol. 5 — 7, No. 2 — 3. 1960.

11. McNeil, K. G. and R. M. Green. Scintillation Spectra from Thick Sources. — Canad. J. Phys., Vol. 39, p. 12. 1961.

12. Zimmerman, W. — Rev. Scient. Instrum., Vol. 32, p. 9. 1961.

UDC 550.35

RADIOCHEMICAL METHOD OF DETERMINING LOW STRONTIUM-90 CONCENTRATION LEVELS IN ENVIRONMENTAL SAMPLES

V. B. Chumichev

A radiochemical method for determining Sr^{90} in 10 liters of seawater is described in detail. It involves a low-background radiometric setup (background of 4 to 6 counts per hour), intended for measuring the β-radiation of the daughter Y^{90}.

The method significantly facilitated the taking and preliminary processing of seawater samples, reduced the consumption of reagents such as soda and hydrochloric acid, eliminated the use of ammonium chloride, and increased the relative yield of strontium. Analysis of the carbonate concentrate became three times as efficient as analysis of the concentrate from a 100-liter sample.

Sr^{90} can be determined in 2-liter seawater samples without a flame photometer. The method was also used to study the sea bottom, at Sr^{90} concentration levels of 10^{-12} curie.

Many investigations relating to the fallout of artificial radioactive products, their accumulation and migration in different objects of the environment, involve numerous radiochemical analyses, among others of Sr^{90}, one of the longest-lived artificial isotopes.

The objects of radiochemical analysis for this isotope are samples of aerosols, atmospheric precipitation, soil, river and seawater, and even biomaterials /3—7/.

The operations are basically the same for all the samples enumerated: sampling, preliminary processing or concentrating, strontium transfer into solution, purification from interfering macroelements and radioactive isotopes. Sr^{90} radioactivity is determined from its daughter Y^{90} by separating the latter from solution with the carrier and measuring the β-radiation either on a 4π counter (background 1.0—3.0 counts per minute at 60—80% efficiency) /5/ or on a low-background setup with an STS-5 counter (background 1.0—3.0 counts/min at 17—20% efficiency) /8/.

To develop a better low-background radiometric setup (background 4—6 counts/hr at 25—50% efficiency) /1/, it should be possible to improve the method of determining Sr^{90} in the said samples, using the same operations.

The method we developed makes it possible either to significantly reduce the amount of material for analysis, which is desirable for almost all kinds of samples, or to determine lower Sr^{90} concentrations than with available methods.

Since our method is most effective in seawater analysis, this is what will be described in detail. The volume of seawater for analysis could thus be reduced from 100 to 10 liters, sometimes to 2 liters only. The initial carbonate concentrating is conducted without addition of ammonium chloride, usually employed for retaining manganese in solution. The reprecipitation of carbonates was also dropped, because the weight of the concentrate obtained did not exceed 50 g. The relative yield of strontium was thus almost doubled: from 40—60% in the analysis of 100-liter samples, to 80-95% now.

Before preliminary concentrating, we no longer introduced into the sample a strontium carrier in addition to the natural strontium of the seawater; it would not increase the strontium yield and could cause additional errors. The yield is therefore determined by flame photometry of the natural strontium, always present in the sample.

When seawater samples are analyzed without separation of calcium and strontium (i. e., using a flame photometer to determine the strontium yield), the available methods preclude the possibility of chromate purification if the sample contains Ba^{140} and La^{140}, owing to the great volume of solution from which yttrium is to be separated. In this case one can either keep the sample for 4 months until Ba^{140} disintegration, or purify Y^{90} of La^{140} (after their separation from Sr^{90} and Ba^{140}), by precipitation of double sulfates of potassium and lanthanum /7/. Retention of the sample for a long time is inconvenient, while the latter operation is fairly laborious and reduces the yttrium yield. With the considerable reduction in sample volume, the method proposed makes possible chromate purification from Be^{140}.

The 10-liter seawater sample is taken from the depth desired with a water sampler, or from the surface with a common bucket, into a polyethylene 12—13-liter bottle. Half a liter of water is taken from the bottle in a glass or polyethylene vial, to determine the content of stable strontium. The water volume in the bottle is brought to the 10-liter mark and 120 g of ash soda added; the bottle content is agitated for 15—20 min until the soda is completely dissolved, and left for 24 hrs.

After settling, the clear part of the solution is carefully decanted with a rubber hose. The sediment of the bottom of the bottle is filtered through a Büchner funnel of 130—180 mm diameter, rinsed with 200 ml distilled water, and transferred into a thermostable beaker.

If the sediment is dry, it is moistened with distilled water and dissolved in a minimum amount of HCl. The solution is diluted to 200 ml, heated to boil, brought to pH $=7$—8 with concentrated NH_4OH, and filtered through an ashless filter. The sediment on the filter is washed with hot distilled water (50 ml). Then, 2 ml of barium chloride solution (10 mg/ml barium) are added to the filtrate, which is then neutralized with a 2N solution of HNO_3 against methyl red, after which two or three drops more of acid are added, and half the volume of a 30% buffer solution of ammonium acetate. The solution is heated almost to boil, and 2 ml of a 10% ammonium chromate solution added while stirring energetically with a glass rod along the beaker walls. After cooling, the deposit is filtered and washed with a 1% ammonium acetate solution. The barium bichromate precipitate is centrifuged.

When the solution is heated almost to boil, the carbonates are precipitated from the weakly-ammoniacal medium by the addition of 120 g of soda. The sample is left to stand for 12 to 24 hours. The deposit is then filtered through a Büchner funnel, transferred to the beaker and dissolved with a minimum amount of concentrated HCl.

Chromate purification is carried out if $Ba^{140} + La^{140}$ are assumed to be present in the samples. Otherwise, the chromate purification and subsequent carbonate precipitation are dropped, and the dissolution of the carbonate concentrate is followed only by double purification on ferric hydroxide, as described below.

The solution is diluted with distilled water to 200—250 ml, 2 ml of ferric chloride (15 mg/ml Fe) are added, the solution is heated to boil and the ferric hydroxide is precipitated by adding NH_4OH without CO_2 at pH = 7—8. The deposit is filtered out, washed with ammonia water without CO_2, and centrifuged. The solution is then acidified with HCl, ferric chloride is added, and the precipitation with ferric hydroxide is repeated as above.

The solution is then acidified with HCl to pH = 3—4, 2 ml of a solution of yttrium chloride or nitrate (10 mg/ml Y) are added, and the solution is left to stand for 16 days for Y^{90} accumulation. After accumulation, the solution is boiled for 20—30 min and the yttrium hydroxide is precipitated by addition of NH_4OH without CO_2 at pH = 7—8, and after coagulation (5—10 min) the deposit is filtered off (the filter consisting of a blue ribbon) and washed with ammonia water without CO_2.

The time of yttrium hydroxide filtration is recorded and then, knowing the starting time of measuring the radioactivity of the sample for counting, one can calculate the correction for Y^{90} decay.

The solution is acidified to pH = 4—5 and the content of stable strontium in it determined on a flame photometer. The initial strontium content being known, one can calculate its yield.

The deposit on the filter is dissolved in a minimum amount of HCl (1:1) (from a pipette into the thermostable beaker to 100 ml), and the filter is washed with 40 ml of distilled water. To the solution are added 2 ml of strontium chloride solution (10 mg/ml Sr), the whole is then boiled for 15—20 min and the yttrium hydroxide is precipitated by addition of NH_4OH without CO_2 at pH = 7—8. The deposit is filtered off into a centrifuge test tube, washed twice with ammonia water without CO_2, and dissolved in a minimum amount of concentrated HNO_3.

The test tube with the solution is warmed on a water bath for 15—20 min, and a saturated solution of oxalic acid added, first drop by drop, to a volume of 10—11 ml; the heating is continued for another 10—15 min. The deposit is filtered off into a centrifuge test tube, washed once with 9—10 ml of distilled water and twice with alcohol (about 3—4 ml).

Three ml of alcohol are added to the deposit, which is then put in suspension and transferred onto a base layer made of ashless filter of 35×35 mm, with a 3—5 mm rim (to remove the alcohol, the base layer is laid on filter paper). The base layer with the deposit is transferred into a porcelain crucible, carbonized on a hot plate and calcined for 40—50 min at 750—800°C in a muffle furnace.

After the cooling of the crucible, the deposit is transferred with a scalpel onto a polyethylene film measuring 35×45 mm, placed on a clock glass, the deposit is leveled out on the film in the shape of a five-kopeck coin with a diameter of 10 mm, and weighed.

The initial amount of yttrium introduced being known as well as its amount at the end of the analysis, one can calculate its yield.

The weighed deposit is then glued onto the film with the aid of 5 or 6 drops of BF-2 glue diluted with alcohol, and held under an IR lamp until dry. A second polyethylene film is then applied onto the deposit and, through a sheet of tracing cloth, the edges are soldered with a soldering iron that has a special bit.

The sample for counting is then cut to the shape of the base layer and counted on a low-background radiometric setup.

Aside from increasing the relative strontium yield, the method described considerably facilitates the sampling and preliminary processing of the samples, and reduces the consumption of reagents such as soda and hydrochloric acid. Ammonium chloride is usually not needed. The analysis of the carbonate concentrates is three times as efficient.

In our opinion, the method for determining Sr^{90} from 2 liter of seawater without using a flame photometer is highly attractive, as the instrument is fairly expensive and can only be operated by highly skilled personnel. The absence of the flame-photometric control over the strontium yield precludes the possibility of using carbonate and oxalate precipitation of alkaline-earth metals. The following variant was therefore checked out: purification on ferric hydroxide, Y^{90} accumulation, Y^{90} separation with the carrier, and the usual subsequent processing.

An analysis of the decay curve of the separated Y^{90} revealed that there was another isotope in the preparation, with a half-life of about 20 days. We put down this pair of natural isotopes as $Th^{234} + Pa^{234}$. The carbonate processing of yttrium made it possible to get rid of these interfering isotopes.

Low-background setups are known to be most effective in the measurement of low radioactivity levels. The method involving a low-background radiometric setup is therefore promising for analyzing soil samples when studying Sr^{90} penetration into the soil, where its content usually drops considerably with increasing depth and the analysis of lower soil horizons is more difficult.

We applied this method to seabed samples: Sr^{90} concentrations as low as $1 \cdot 10^{-12}$ curie could be measured with a statistical error of 10% by radioactivity measurement lasting 5 hours.

For comparison, we can point to the fact that the measurement of such radioactivity levels on a low-background setup with a STS-5 counter (background 1 count/min, efficiency 17%) with the same accuracy would require up to 32 hrs /2/.

When any environmental samples are analyzed by the method described, reagents from large batches must be used and their radioactive impurification must be checked, as it may increase the actual Sr^{90} content in the analyzed samples.

BIBLIOGRAPHY

1. Vakulovskii, S.M. and A.N.Silant'ev. Radiometricheskaya ustanovka dlya opredeleniya
   soderzhaniya strontsiya-90 v morskoi vode (Radiometric Setup for Determining Sr^{90} Content in
   Seawater). — Moskva, Atomizdat. 1968.
2. Dement'ev, V.A. Izmerenie malykh aktivnostei radioaktivnykh preparatov (Measurement of Low
   Activities of Radioactive Preparations). — Moskva, Atomizdat. 1967.
3. Gusev, N.G.(editor). Dozimetricheskie i radiokhimicheskie metodiki (Dosimetric and Radiochemical
   Methods). Collected Papers. Moskva. 1959.
4. Lavrukhina, A.K., T.V.Malysheva, and F.I.Pavlotskaya. Radiokhimicheskii analiz(Radiochemical Analysis). — Moskva, Izd. AN SSSR. 1963.
5. Polevoi, R.M. Izmerenie β-aktivnosti izotopov s aktivnost'yu ot $5 \cdot 10^{-13}$ do $5 \cdot 10^{-7}$ kyuri metodom
   4π schetchika (Measurement of the β -Activity of Isotopes with Activities Between $5 \cdot 10^{-13}$ and
   $5 \cdot 10^{-7}$ Curie by the 4π Counter). — In sbornik: Radioaktivnost' pochv i metody ee opredeleniya
   (Soil Radioactivity and its Determination), edited by I.N. Antipov-Karataev et al. Moskva,
   "Nauka." 1966.
6. Shvedov, V.P. and S.I.Shirokov (editors). Radioaktivnye zagryazneniya vneshnei sredy (Radioactive
   Contamination of the Environment). Collected papers. — Moskva, Gosatomizdat. 1962.
7. Sereda, G.A. et al. (editors). Sbornik metodik po opredeleniyu radioaktivnosti okruzhayushchei sredy
   (Methods for Determining the Radioactivity of the Environment), Parts I and II. — Moskva,
   Gidrometeoizdat. 1966.
8. Silant'ev, A.N.(editor). Sbornik metodik po opredeleniyu radioaktivnosti okruzhayushchei sredy
   (Methods for Determining the Radioactivity of the Environment), Parts III and IV. — Moskva,
   Gidrometeoizdat. 1968.

339

UDC 551.510.7

FALLOUT AND ACCUMULATION OF RADIOACTIVE DECAY PRODUCTS IN 1966–1968 IN THE VICINITY OF LENINGRAD

N. V. Vasil' eva, L. I. Gedeonov, Z. G. Gritchenko, M. I. Zhilkina, and V. M. Flegontov

This paper presents the results of observations of the isotope composition of global radioactive fallout in 1966–1968 in the Leningrad region, the fallout density of radioactive fission products, and the amount of radioactive products deposited on the ground surface at the observation point.

Ce^{141}, Ru^{103}, and Zr^{95} were recorded in 1966–1968 in the ground layer of the atmosphere and in atmospheric precipitation. Longer-lived radionuclides such as Ce^{144} and Ru^{106}, mostly penetrating from the stratospheric source of radioactive contamination, in 1968 contributed much to the overall proportion of total beta activity. The recording of these radionuclides in radioactive fallout samples in 1967 was at the sensitivity limit of the measuring instruments.

The fallout density of Sr^{90} was 1.6 mcurie/km^2 in 1966, 0.8 mcurie/km^2 in 1967, and 1.0 mcurie/km^2 in 1968; that of Cs^{137} was 1.3, 1.7 and 1.9 mcurie/km^2, respectively. Altogether 50.3 mcurie/km^2 Sr^{90} and 96.9 mcurie/km^2 Cs^{137} fell to the ground in 1954–1968 in the vicinity of Leningrad (the figures refer to the moment of fallout).

Based on an analysis of the activity ratio of short-lived radionuclides (Ce^{141}, Zr^{95}) to long-lived ones (Sr^{90}, Ru^{106}, Ce^{137}, Ce^{144}), the global radioactive fallout in the Leningrad district in 1966–1968 is shown to be due almost entirely to 1966–1967 nuclear explosions, while Sr^{90} and Cs^{137} from earlier nuclear tests were present in insignificant amounts only.

At the end of 1968, the accumulated activity of the total beta-radioactive fission products was ~ 0.35 curie/km^2, that of $Ce^{144} + Pr^{144}$ was ~ 13 mcurie/km^2, Ru^{106} ~ 6 mcurie/km^2, $Zr^{95} + Nb^{95}$ ~ 0.55 mcurie/km^2, and that of Ce^{141} was below 0.1 mcurie/km^2. Owing to the low rate of Sr^{90} and Cs^{137} fallout, the accumulated activity of these radionuclides remained at the 1965 level of 42.3 and 82 mcurie/km^2, respectively.

1. GLOBAL FALLOUT OF RADIOACTIVE FISSION PRODUCTS IN THE VICINITY OF LENINGRAD

This paper deals with the results of observations of the fallout density of radioactive products from nuclear explosions onto the ground surface in the vicinity of Leningrad in 1966–1968.

The determined fallout densities of the total fission products and of the separate radionuclides for 1953–1965 have been published earlier /1, 6/. The methods of taking fallout samples, preparing them for analysis, and radiometrically and radiochemically analyzing them are described in /3, 6/.

The monthly fallout densities of the total fission products and of the radionuclides Ce^{141}, Ru^{103}, Zr^{95}, Nb^{95}, Ce^{144}, Ru^{106}, Sr^{90} and Cs^{137} determined in 1966–1968 in the Leningrad district are listed in Table 1. Ce^{141}, Ru^{103}, Zr^{95} and Nb^{95} were recorded there in the ground layer of the atmosphere throughout that period. Another important contribution to the overall proportion of the total beta activity was made by longer-lived radio-nuclides such as Ce^{144} and Ru^{106}, which penetrated mainly from the strato-spheric source of radioactive contamination. In 1967, these radionuclides in fallout samples were recorded at the sensitivity limit of the measuring devices.

TABLE 1. Radioactive fallout of total beta-radioactive fission products and of individual radionuclides in 1966–1968, mcurie/km$^2 \cdot$ month

Sampling date	Precipitation, mm	Total fission products	Ce^{141}	Ru^{103}	Zr^{95}	Nb^{95}	Ce^{144}	Ru^{106}	Cs^{137}	Sr^{90}
1966										
January	40.7	8.1	—	—	—	—	0.12	0.04	0.045	0.04
February	27.6	9.9	—	—	—	—	0.09	0.03	0.016	0.06
March	61.6	2.2	—	—	—	—	0.19	0.06	0.14	0.10
April	55.0	2.6	—	—	—	—	0.25	0.08	0.19	0.20
May	52.5	10.5	0.85	—	1.4	—	0.13	0.04	0.22	0.23
June	31.9	4.1	0.20	—	0.28	—	0.04	0.01	0.08	0.18
July	99.9	11.0	—	—	—	—	0.51	0.19	0.19	0.48
August	77.6	6.2	0.01	—	0.28	—	0.33	0.11	0.19	0.16
September	168.3	3.4	—	—	—	—	0.12	0.04	0.08	0.06
October	61.8	1.2	—	—	—	—	0.04	0.01	0.02	0.04
November	47.2	5.7	0.12	—	0.32	—	0.60	0.20	0.06	0.03
December	41.3	5.4	—	—	0.22	—	0.23	0.08	0.08	0.02
1967										
January	47.0	15.5	0.7	—	0.40	0.36	0.56	0.19	0.30	0.07
February	61.9	10.5	0.7	—	0.60	0.74	0.32	0.10	0.32	0.09
March	67.3	9.4	0.1	—	0.30	0.42	0.21	0.07	0.09	0.09
April	42.2	4.6	—	—	0.20	0.29	0.22	0.07	0.14	0.20
May	80.7	5.7	—	—	0.10	0.15	0.32	0.10	0.27	0.10
June	69.7	3.4	—	—	—	—	0.08	0.03	0.20	0.06
July	16.3	2.3	—	—	—	—	0.05	0.02	0.12	0.03
August	93.3	3.1	—	—	—	—	0.04	0.01	0.06	0.03
September	41.6	2.2	0.1	—	0.10	0.14	0.03	0.01	0.08	0.03
October	210.0	8.2	0.1	—	0.33	0.44	0.09	0.03	0.08	0.05
November	57.6	2.2	—	—	0.20	0.34	0.05	0.02	0.04	0.01
December	57.0	3.4	—	—	0.30	0.54	0.10	0.03	0.04	0.01
1968										
January	23.5	10.6	0.14	0.20	0.25	0.38	0.36	0.20	0.03	0.02
February	56.9	7.4	0.15	0.15	0.16	0.28	0.38	0.12	0.03	0.03
March	55.8	7.8	0.09	0.08	0.24	0.45	0.56	0.22	0.21	0.07
April	48.6	12.6	0.10	0.02	0.48	1.1	1.5	0.50	0.32	0.16
May	49.2	17.2	0.03	0.01	0.40	0.88	1.8	0.60	0.23	0.15
June	31.8	10.8	—	—	0.15	0.32	0.93	0.30	0.18	0.12
July	133.5	17.4	—	—	0.22	0.49	1.8	0.60	0.35	0.15
August	102.4	15.4	—	—	0.10	0.22	1.4	0.45	0.18	0.09
September	80.6	5.6	—	—	0.06	0.14	0.70	0.20	0.14	0.11
October	130.4	6.6	—	—	0.04	0.10	0.60	0.20	0.09	0.06
November	40.0	1.6	—	—	0.02	0.05	0.10	0.05	0.04	0.03
December	37.5	1.8	—	—	0.01	0.02	0.13	0.06	0.06	0.02

TABLE 2. Sr^{90} and Cs^{137} fallout in the Leningrad vicinity in 1954–1968, mcurie/km^2 · month

Year	Sr^{90}		Cs^{137}	
	at the instance of fallout	with allow-ance for decay	at the instance of fallout	with allow-ance for decay
1954–1955	1.08	–	2.2	–
1956	2.6	–	5.2	–
1957	3.4	–	6.8	–
1958	4.7	–	7.2	–
1959	2.6	–	6.3	–
1960	0.8	–	1.7	–
1961	0.67	–	1.42	–
1962	11.5	–	22.0	–
1963	12.1	–	24.2	–
1964	5.4	–	10.8	–
1965	2.1	–	4.2	–
1966	1.6	–	1.3	–
1967	0.8	–	1.7	–
1968	1.0	–	1.9	–
Total	50.3	42.3	96.9	82.1

Table 2 lists data characterizing the annual fallout in the Leningrad area of the radionuclides Sr^{90} and Cs^{137}, which are biologically the most dangerous. In 1966 the fallout density (mcurie/km^2) was 1.6 for Sr^{90} and 1.3 for Cs^{137}; the respective figures in 1967 were 0.77 and 1.7, and in 1968, 1.0 and 1.9. The rate of Sr^{90} and Cs^{137} fallout in 1967 was similar to that in 1960–1961.

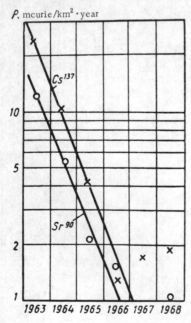

FIGURE 1. Estimated apparent half-life of Cs^{137} from the atmosphere in 1963–1968.

The authors of /4, 5, 7, 8/ noticed a similar trend in the density of radio-active fission-products fallout of those years. On the whole, in 1954–1968, 50.3 mcurie of Sr^{90} and 96.9 mcurie of Cs^{137} per km^2 fell to the ground surface in the Leningrad area (the figures refer to the instant of the fallout).

An estimate of the apparent half-lives of Sr^{90} and Cs^{137} from the earth's atmosphere has been made from data collected in 1963–1967 in the vicinity of Leningrad; it is about 10 months (Figure 1).

An analysis of the activity ratios of short-lived radionuclides (Ce^{141}, Zr^{95}) to long-lived ones (Ce^{144}, Ru^{106}, Sr^{90}, Cs^{137}) showed that the global radio-active contamination in the Leningrad area in 1966–1968 was almost entirely due to the 1966–1967 nuclear explosions, and only insignificant amounts of Sr^{90} and Cs^{137} from earlier nuclear tests were present.

2. ACCUMULATION OF ARTIFICIAL ISOTOPES ON THE SURFACE OF THE EARTH IN THE LENINGRAD AREA IN 1954 — 1968

From the data thus obtained we calculated the accumulation of total beta-radioactive fission products (Figure 2) and individual radionuclides (Figure 3) on the earth's surface in the Leningrad area. The latest results of such calculations were published in /7/ and included data for 1954–1965.

In 1966–1968, the accumulated activity dropped mainly on account of decay of already accumulated radioactive substances with half-life periods of one or more years. The slight increase in the rate of radioactive fallout in mid-1968 (Table 1) could not change this trend, and the accumulated activity of total beta-radioactive fission products dropped to 0.35 curie/km^2 at the end of 1968. Most of it is activity of long-lived radionuclides, such as $Sr^{90} + Y^{90}$ and Cs^{137}.

In 1966–1968, fallout of short-lived radionuclides, such as $Ba^{140} + La^{140}$, Ce^{141} and $Zr^{95} + Nb^{95}$, occurred only immediately after nuclear explosions in the northern hemisphere. The radioactive decay of these substances then started to exceed the rate of radioactive fallout and the level of accumulated activity tended toward zero. The curves in Figure 3 represent the variation in the accumulated activities of Ce^{141} and $Zr^{95} + Nb^{95}$; the trend is parti-cularly clear.

The rate of radioactive fallout of radionuclides with half-lives of less than approximately a year ($Ce^{144} + Pr^{144}$, $Ru^{106} + Rh^{106}$) was lower than the rate of radioactive decay of these nuclides, accumulating on the earth's surface. The accumulated activity dropped from ~ 120 to ~ 13 mcurie/km^2 for $Ce^{144} + Pr^{144}$, and from 41 to ~ 6 mcurie/km^2 for Ru^{106}, between the end of 1966 and the end of 1968.

The drop in the rate of radioactive fallout reflected less on the accumula-tion of long-lived radionuclides such as Sr^{90} and Cs^{137}. Beginning with the end of 1965, the radioactive decay of already accumulated Cs^{137} was ~ 2 mcurie/km^2 on the average, while the annual rate of radioactive fallout was 1.6 mcurie/km^2; for Sr^{90} the figures were ~ 12 and ~ 1.1 mcurie/$km^2 \cdot$ year, respectively. This means that the natural decrease in these radio-nuclides owing to radioactive decay is not compensated for by their supply from the atmosphere; in 1965, the activity of Sr^{90} and Cs^{137} accumulated on the earth's surface started dropping slightly. At the end of 1968, the accumulated activity on the earth's surface was 42.3 mcurie/km^2 for Sr^{90} and 82 mcurie/km^2 for Cs^{137}.

FIGURE 2. Activity accumulation of total fission products in the Leningrad area in 1954–1968.

CONCLUSIONS

1. The isotope constitution of radioactive fallout in the Leningrad area included mainly Zr^{95}, Nb^{95}, Ce^{144}, $Sr^{90} + Y^{90}$, Cs^{137}, etc.

2. The global radioactive contamination in the Leningrad area in 1967–1968 was almost entirely due to nuclear explosions of 1966–1967, and only an insignificant amount of Sr^{90} and Cs^{137} originated from earlier nuclear tests.

3. The apparent half-life periods of Sr^{90} and Cs^{137} from the atmosphere in 1963–1967 were ~ 10 months.

4. The accumulated activity of total beta-radioactive fission products at the end of 1968 was 0.35 curie/km^2, ~ 13 mcurie/km^2 for Ce^{144}, ~ 6 mcurie/km^2 for Ru^{106}, less than 0.1 mcruie/km^2 for Ce^{141}, and ~ 0.55 mcurie/km^2 for $Zr^{95} + Nb^{95}$. Because of the low rate of Sr^{90} and Cs^{137} fallout, the accumulated activity of these radionuclides remained at the 1965 level, being 42.3 and 82 mcurie/km^2, respectively.

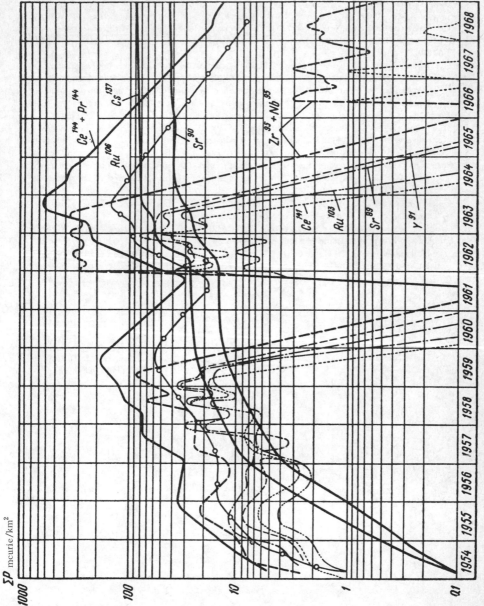

FIGURE 3. Amounts of individual radionuclides deposited on the ground surface in the Leningrad area in 1954–1968.

BIBLIOGRAPHY

1. Gedeonov, L.I. and M.I.Zhalkina. Vypadenie produktov deleniya v okrestnosti Leningrada v 1957–1965 gg. (Fission Products Fallout in the Leningrad Area in 1957–1965).– Moskva, GKIAE, Atomizdat. 1967.

2. Gedeonov, L.I., Z.G.Gritchenko, M.I.Zhilkina, and V.M.Flegontov. Nakoplenie iskusstvennykh izotopov na zemnoi poverkhnosti v raione Leningrada v 1954–1965 gg. (Artificial Isotopes Accumulation on the Earth's Surface in the Leningrad Area in 1954–1965).– Atomnaya Energiya, Vol.23, No.4. 1967.

3. Gritchenko, Z.G., L.I.Gedeonov, and V.M.Flegontov. Ob izmerenii beta-aktivnosti summy produktov deleniya (Beta-Activity Measurement of Total Fission Products).– In Sbornik: Radio-aktivnye izotopy v atmosfere i ikh ispol'zovanie v meteorologii (Radioactive Isotopes in the Atmosphere and their Utilization in Meteorology). Mozkva, Atomizdat. 1965.

4. Zykova, A.S., E.L.Telushkina, G.P.Efremova, G.A.Kuznetsova, V.P.Rublevskii, and V.I.Shushakov. Radioaktivnost' atmosfernogo vozdukha i nekotorykh produktov pitaniya v g. Moskve v 1965 i 1966 gg. (Radioactivity of Atmospheric Air and Some Food Products in Moscow in 1965 and 1966).– Moskva, GKIAE, Atomizdat. 1967.

5. Mukhin, I.E. and L.I.Nagovitsina. Soderzhanie strontsiya-90 v global'nykh vypadeniyakh na territorii Ukrainskoi SSR v 1963–1966 gg. (Sr^{90} Content in Global Fallout on Ukrainian Territory in 1963–1966).– Moskva, GKIAE, Atomizdat. 1967.

6. Shvedov, V.P. and S.I.Shirokov (editors). Radioaktivnye zagryazneniya vneshnei sredy (Radioactive Contaminants of the Environment).– Moskva, Gosatomizdat. 1962.

7. Cambray, R.S., E.M.R.Fisher, W.L.Brooks, and D.H.Peirson. Radioactive Fallout in Air and Rain: Results to the Middle of 1966.– AERE–R-5260. 1966.

8. Hardy, E.P., M.W.Meyer, J.S.Allen, and H.F.Alexander. Strontium-90 on the Earth's Surface.– Nature, Vol.219, p.584. 1968.

UDC 551.510.72

PENETRATION OF RADIOACTIVE FISSION PRODUCTS
FROM 1964–1967 NUCLEAR TESTS INTO THE GROUND
LAYER OF THE ATMOSPHERE IN THE LENINGRAD AREA

L. I. Gedeonov, Z. G. Gritchenko, and V. M. Flegontov

Radioactive fission products formed during tests of nuclear weapons in countries that did not adhere to the Moscow agreement on the prohibition of nuclear tests in the three media were recorded in 1964–1968 in the ground layer of the atmosphere in the Leningrad area.

The following radioactive isotopes were determined with the aid of a scintillation and a Ge(Li) drift gamma spectrometer in radioactive aerosols filtered out of the ground layer of atmospheric air: Ba^{140}, La^{140}, Ce^{141}, Ru^{103}, Zr^{95}, Nb^{95}, Ce^{144}, Ru^{106}, and Cs^{137}. The forming of these radioactive fission products was dated from the activity ratios of the following pairs of radionuclides: Ba^{140}/Ce^{141}, Ce^{141}/Zr^{95}, Ce^{141}/Ce^{144}, Zr^{95}/Ce^{144}, and Ce^{144}/Cs^{137}. These radionuclides turned out to have been released into the atmosphere during the explosions of 14 October 1964, 14 May 1965, 9 May, 27 October and 28 December 1966, 17 June and 24 December 1967.

Atmospheric nuclear tests of increasing power and the depletion of the stratospheric reserve of radioactive fission products from the 1961–1962 test series produced a stable balance in the stratosphere between the long-lived radionuclides from nuclear tests conducted in 1964–1967. The proportion of long-lived fission products from these nuclear explosions therefore began to predominate in 1966 in global radioactive fallout.

Nuclear explosions in the atmosphere are the main source of contamination of the stratosphere with artificial radioactive substances. Once in the stratosphere, these radioactive substances link up with very fine aerosols. Under the influence of various geophysical factors, these aerosols slowly pass from the stratosphere into the troposphere. From the troposphere they are brought to the earth's surface mainly through the washing action of atmospheric precipitation.

Extensive observations of the variation of fission product concentrations in the ground layer of the atmosphere have revealed a direct relationship between the content of radioactive fission products in the lower layers of the atmosphere and their reserves in the stratosphere. Attempts are being made to determine the proportion of global radioactive contamination from nuclear tests conducted in 1964–1967, from observations of the fission product contents in the ground layer of the atmosphere.

Radioactive aerosols in the ground layer of the atmosphere were sampled with the aid of filtering devices using an FPP-15 filter, by a method described in /1/. The air filtration went on continuously. The capacity of the setups was 2.4 to $2.8 \cdot 10^4 \, m^3/day$. After the filter material collected the aerosols it was calcined in a muffle furnace at no more than 500°C. The ash residue went to be measured for total beta activity and for the contents of various gamma-radiating fission products to be determined by the methods described in /2–4/.

The gamma-spectrometric analysis with a scintillation gamma spectrometer (sodium iodide crystal of 40×40 mm, FEU-13 photomultiplier, and 100-channel AI-100 pulse analyzer) is the main common method for determining the contents of the different gamma-radiating radionuclides in the samples. In most cases, however, the determination of the entire constitution of gamma radiators in the sample required several measurements, over an interval of up to several months.

The most promising method of analyzing complex radioactive mixtures made use of a gamma spectrometer with Ge (Li) drift detector combined with a multichannel (4,096-channel) pulse analyzer /5/. The overall resolution of this system is 4.5–5.0 keV; with a detector volume of 8 to 12 cm^3, one measurement with an exposure of 10–20 hours can determine the contents of the various gamma radiators in the sample at their activity levels of $\sim 10^{-10}$ curie. Figure 1 gives the general appearance of a gamma spectrum of an atmospheric aerosol sample.

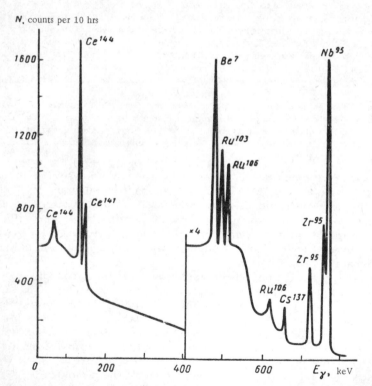

FIGURE 1. Gamma spectrum of an atmospheric aerosol sample taken on 1–5 April 1965 and measured on 20 April 1965 with the aid of a spectrometer with Ge(Li) drift detector.

The final result of the gamma spectrometric analysis makes it possible to determine the contents of the following radionuclides in the radioactive fallout samples: $Ba^{140} + La^{140}$, Ce^{141}, Ru^{103}, Zr^{95}, Nb^{95}, Ce^{144}, Ru^{106}, Cs^{137} and Be^{7}. All these radionuclides measured in one sample provide a clue as to the time of formation and penetration in the lower atmosphere of a mixture of fission products of complex radiochemical constitution. If the fission products arrive in the atmosphere at a rate of one discharge in 6—12 months, one can determine the proportion of long-lived radionuclides from the last few explosions in the global radioactive fallout. A method for such an analysis from measurements of Zr^{95}, Nb^{95}, Ce^{144} and Cs^{137} activity is proposed in /6/.

Global radioactive contaminants from all the nuclear weapon tests conducted in the northern hemisphere in 1964—1967 were recorded in the Leningrad area. There are general features in the distribution of global radioactive contaminants from these explosions. The tropospheric transfer of radioactive fission products at the Leningrad latitude took place after all explosions, except that of 17 June 1967 /7/. Observations of the penetration of "fresh" radioactive fission products permitted one to establish that they move in the troposphere with a mean velocity of 15 m/sec and are recorded in the Leningrad area 14—16 days after the explosion. This rule was broken in the case of the sixth nuclear explosion only, and the radioactive products of that explosion were detected in the Leningrad area after 100 days or more.

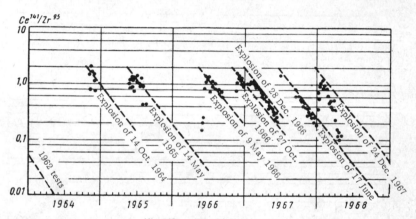

FIGURE 2. Variation of the Ce^{141}/Zr^{95} activity ratio in the ground layer of the atmosphere in 1964—1968.

Short-lived radionuclides, such as Ba^{140}, La^{140}, Ce^{141} and Ru^{103}, were usually ascribed entirely to the very last explosion, just before the samples of radioactive aerosols were taken from the atmosphere. The dating of the time of formation from the variation in the activity ratio of the radionuclide pairs Ce^{141}/Zr^{95}, Ce^{141}/Ce^{144} and Zr^{95}/Ce^{144} made it possible to determine whether the radioactive material originated from a specific nuclear test. Figures 2—4 present the variation of these activity ratios in 1964—1968 (dashed lines indicate the expected variation).

The majority of each radionuclide formed during nuclear weapon tests in 1964—1967 reached the stratosphere. Up to the moment of the seasonal exchange of air masses between stratosphere and troposphere, much of the short-lived radionuclides underwent radioactive decay, and only radioactive fission products with half-life periods of over 100 days reached the lower layers of the atmosphere.

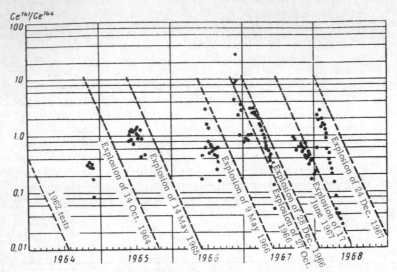

FIGURE 3. Variation of Ce^{141}/Ce^{144} activity ratio in the ground layer of the atmosphere in 1964–1968.

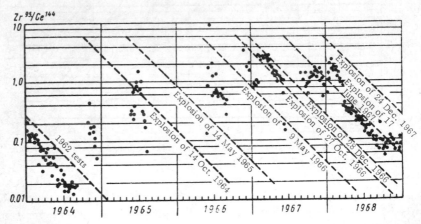

FIGURE 4. Variation of Zr^{95}/Ce^{144} activity ratio in the ground layer of the atmosphere in 1964–1968.

As a result of the increasingly powerful nuclear explosions produced in the atmosphere in 1965–1967, on the one hand, and of the depletion of the stratospheric reserve of radioactive fission products from the test series of 1961–1962, on the other, a stable reserve of long-lived radionuclides was formed in the stratosphere. As of 1966, the proportion of long-lived fission products from 1964—1967 nuclear explosions therefore started to predominate in the global radioactive fallout.   Figure 5 shows the variation of the mean-monthly Ce^{144} and Cs^{137} concentrations in the ground layer of the atmosphere in the Leningrad area from 1959 till 1968.   Figure 6 represents the variation of the Ce^{144}/Cs^{137} activity ratio, which indicates that most of the Ce^{144} and Cs^{137} collected from the air in 1966—1968 originated from nuclear explosions that took place in 1965—1967.

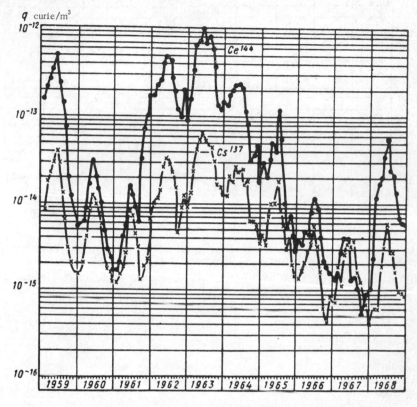

FIGURE 5.   Variation of mean-monthly Ce^{144} and Cs^{137} concentrations in the ground layer of the atmosphere in the Leningrad area between 1959 and 1968.

The latitudinal distribution of radioactive fission products from nuclear weapon tests of 1966—1967 points to a localization of these substances in that hemisphere where they were discharged into the atmosphere /3/.   In the northern hemisphere, the zone of maximum contamination lies between 30 and 50°N, which is the latitudinal belt in which the Gobi Desert test grounds are located, and in which air masses are seasonally exchanged between stratosphere and troposphere.   With surprising stability, maximum concentrations in the ground layer of the atmosphere in the Leningrad area are generally observed in May—July of each year (Figure 5).

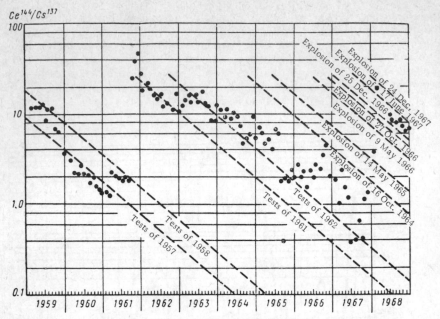

FIGURE 6. Variation of Ce^{144}/Cs^{137} activity ratio in the ground layer of the atmosphere in 1959–1968.

An evaluation of the proportion of long-lived radioactive fission products from nuclear weapon tests yielded 0.06% in 1964, 12% in 1965, 40% in 1966, 50% in 1967, and 95% in 1968, of the overall global radioactive fallout in the Leningrad area in those years.

BIBLIOGRAPHY

1. Shvedov, V.P. and S.I.Shirokov (editors). Radioaktivnye zagryazneniya vneshnei sredy (Radioactive Contaminants of the Environment).— Moskva, Atomizdat. 1962.
2. Radioaktivnye izotopy v atmosfere i ikh ispol'zovanie v meteorologii (Radioactive Isotopes in the Atmosphere and their Utilization in Meteorology).— Moskva, Atomizdat. 1965.
3. Gidrofizicheskie issledovaniya Tikhogo i Atlanticheskogo okeanov v krugosvetnom plavanii NIS "Mikhail Lomonosov" (20-i reis) (Hydrophysical Investigations of the Pacific and Atlantic Oceans During the Round-the-World (20th) Voyage of the R/V "Mikhail Lomonosov").— Sevastopol', Izd. MGI AN USSR. 1967.
4. Silant'ev, A.N. (editor). Sbornik metodik po opredeleniyu radioaktivnosti okruzhayushchei sredy (Methods for Determining the Radioactivity of the Environment).— Moskva, Gidrometeoizdat. 1968.
5. Gritchenko, Z.G., T.P.Makarova, Yu.Ts.Oganesyan, Yu.E.Penionzhkevich, and A.V.Stepanov. γ-izluchenie nekotorykh redkozemel'nykh elementov — produktov deleniya U tyazhelymi ionami (Gamma Radiation of Some Rare Earth Elements — Products of U Fission by Heavy Ions).— Yadernaya Fizika, Vol.10, No.5, p.929. 1969.
6. Gritchenko, Z.G. Fission Product Age Determination from the Variation in Time of the Area of the Total $Zr^{95} + Nb^{95}$ Photopeak.— UN Document A/AC 82/G/L, p.847. 1962.
7. Murayama, N. and H.Fujimoto. Meteorological Analysis of Radioactive Fallout by Four Nuclear Explosions of 1966 to 1967.— Koshocho Kenkyi Jiho, Vol.19, p.575. 1967.

UDC 621.039.55

STUDY OF THE RESISTANCE OF FIBROUS FILTERING
MATERIALS IN RAREFIED AIR

I. V. Petryanov, B. I. Ogorodnikov, and L. A. Zimina

The resistance of fibrous FP filtering materials in a flow of rarefied air is studied. The material resistance Δp was found to decrease with increasing length λ of the mean free path of the gas molecules, because the gas flow glides along the filter fibers, and at normal atmospheric pressure the resistance of almost all FP materials is already lower than its maximum.

For FPP-5, LFS-2 and FPP-15 materials, which consist of ultrafine fibers, the loss of resistance is 10—20%. Higher compaction β leads to a slight additional drop in resistance from the maximum for the given compaction. The resistance of FP materials under gliding flow conditions is shown to be computed by the formula

$$\Delta p = \frac{4\beta \eta vh}{a^2_{\text{hydr}}\left(-0.5 \ln \beta - 0.5 + \dfrac{\lambda}{a_{\text{vis}}}\right)},$$

where η is the air viscosity, v is the linear air velocity, h is the filter thickness, and a_{hydr} and a_{vis} are the hydrodynamic and mean visual fiber radii, respectively.

A correction for gliding is recommended when $\dfrac{\lambda}{a_{\text{vis}}} > 0.005$.

Fibrous FP filtering materials comprise layers of randomly arranged polymeric fibers. The fiber diameter, compaction and resistance are chosen according to the purpose and operation conditions of the filtering materials; undoubtedly, this reflects upon their aerosol trapping efficiency. Calculating the resistance of filters is an important problem, as the pressure drop in the filter determines its thickness, the capacity and cost of the filtering device.

Assuming that all fibers in the filter are positioned perpendicular to the flow and equating the pressure drop Δp in the filter to the sum of hydrodynamic forces acting upon the fiber, Fuks and Stechkina /5/ found that

$$\Delta p = \frac{4\beta \eta vh}{a^2(-0.5 \ln \beta - \varkappa)}, \tag{1}$$

where β is the compaction (the part of the filter volume occupied by fibers), η is the viscosity of the gaseous medium, v is the flow velocity before the filter, h is the filter thickness, a is the fiber radius, and $\varkappa$ is a coefficient (0.5 to 0.75).

Formula (1) is in fair agreement with experimental data, but does not reflect the specific airflow conditions in a filter made of ultrafine fibers, or the flow of rarefied air. Natanson /2/ has demonstrated that, in these cases, airflow gliding over the fiber surface must be taken into account (flow velocity at the fiber surface does not vanish). Pich /6/ has derived an expression for the resistance of fibrous filters, in which gliding is taken into account. When $\beta \ll 1$, which is the case for practically all FP filters, he found that

$$\Delta p = \frac{4\beta\eta vh\,(1 + 2K_n)}{a^2\,[-0.5\ln\beta - 0.75 + K_n\,(-\ln\beta - 0.5)]}, \tag{2}$$

where $K_n = \dfrac{\lambda}{a}$, λ being the length of the mean free path of a molecule of the medium. Formula (2) proved not to correspond to numerous experimental results concerning the dependence of Δp on λ.

At constant compaction and linear airflow velocity, the filter resistance was found to decrease with decreasing pressure, the experimental points in a system of $\dfrac{1}{\Delta p}$, λ coordinates fitting a straight line /4, 7/. A modification of formula (2) by a series expansion in K_n produced an analytical relationship that agrees with experimental results:

$$\Delta p = \frac{4\beta\eta vh}{a^2\,(-0.5\ln\beta - \varkappa)}\ \frac{1}{1 + K_n\,(-0.5\ln\beta - \varkappa)^{-1}} =$$
$$= \frac{4\beta\eta vh}{a^2\,(-0.5\ln\beta - \varkappa + K_n)}. \tag{3}$$

To study the dependence of Δp on λ and β we investigated different specimens of fibrous FP filtering materials, manufactured from chlorinated polyvinyl chloride. The results of 100−150 measurements under an optical microscope were used to determine the mean apparent diameter d_{vis} of the fiber for each specimen. The mean hydrodynamic fiber diameter d_{hydr} was calculated from formula (3) for $\varkappa = 0.5$ and $\beta = 0.03$. It was usually smaller than d_{vis}, because the fiber of FP filters has mostly an elliptical or dumbbell-like cross section /1, 3/. The filters were positioned between plane-parallel grids of a hermetic filter holder. At fixed position of the grids, measured to within 0.05 mm with a slide caliper, the filter resistance was measured as a function of the air pressure in the system. The distance between the two grids was then reduced and the resistance was measured again. About ten series of such measurements were made for each specimen, which corresponded to a compaction variation from 0.015 to 0.07. The highest Knudsen number attained in the experiments was nearly 5. Figure 1 shows the results obtained for specimen No. 55 with a compaction of 0.017 and the finest fiber ($d_{hydr} = 0.65\mu$) of all the investigated specimens. The experimental points approximate well a straight line. Similar results were also obtained for the other specimens. Only the slope angle varied: the coarser the fibers, the milder the slope.

The experimental results showed that the data obtained were more accurate and in agreement with experiment if in formula (3) values of the visual radius are used instead of the hydrodynamic radius in the Knudsen number.

It follows from formula (3) that, if compaction and the airflow velocity and viscosity remain constant, the fibrous filtering materials must have some maximum resistance, attainable at low Knudsen numbers, i.e., in the absence of gliding. For coarse fibers of over 10μ diameter the maximum resistance is reached already at standard atmospheric pressure; for ultra-fine filters (FPP-15, FPP-5, LFS-2) it is only attained at pressures of dozens of atmospheres. The maximum resistance can easily be calculated from the intercept on the ordinate axis in a $\dfrac{1}{\Delta p}$, λ system of coordinates. Table 1 gives the maximum and actual resistances measured under standard conditions at an airflow velocity of 1 cm/sec for all the investigated specimens with a compaction density of 0.03. The actual resistance is smaller with all specimens already at standard pressure; this "fault" is most noticeable (10−20%) for materials with ultrafine fibers.

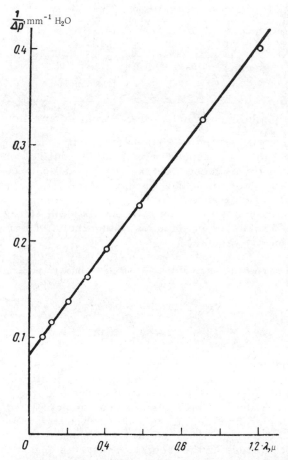

FIGURE 1. Resistance of sample No.55 of 0.017 compaction density vs. length of the mean free path of the gas molecules. Linear velocity of airflow, 1 cm/sec.

TABLE 1. Characteristics of investigated specimens of FP materials

Sample	d_{hydr}, μ	d_{vis}, μ	Specimen resistance at $v = 1\,\text{cm/sec, mm}\ H_2O$		Loss of resistance on account of gliding, %	
			at maximum pressure	at a pressure of 760 mm Hg	from experiment	from formula (3) for $K_n = \dfrac{2\lambda}{d_{\text{vis}}}$
No.55	0.65	0.93	13.7	11.4	16.7	15.2
No.227	0.83	1.16	11.9	10.8	9.7	11.9
No.155	1.21	1.34	7.3	6.7	8.2	10.5
No.8	1.51	1.97	7.8	7.2	7.8	7.6
FPP-15	1.6	1.91	5.5	5.1	7.0	7.9
FPP-25	1.63	1.96	6.4	6.0	6.5	7.6
No.5	2.96	4.12	1.89	1.84	2.4	3.6
FPP-70	3.86	6.1	2.48	2.43	2.0	2.4

The relationship between $\dfrac{1}{\Delta p}$ and λ for different compaction densities β showed that, although according to formula (3) the resistance drop on account of gliding should not depend on compaction, such a dependence exists in practice, however loose. On the basis of the data in Figure 2, Table 2 lists the ratios of resistance at maximum pressure to resistance at 50 mm Hg for different compactions of specimen No. 5. A reduction in compaction by a factor of approximately 3 entails a 10—15% increase in the resistance ratio. For the other samples, with either finer or coarser fibers, this ratio hardly varies.

TABLE 2. Ratio of maximum resistance to resistance at 50 mm Hg for different compaction densities of specimen No.5

Compaction density	0.025	0.03	0.033	0.038	0.044	0.052	0.064
Ratio of resistances	1.38	1.4	1.44	1.48	1.47	1.5	1.52

The study of the resistance of fibrous FP filtering materials in rarefied air showed that filtering materials manufactured from ultrafine fibers should be used in the high layers of the atmosphere and in filtering devices that operate under vacuum. The resistance can be calculated analytically, and a correction for gliding must be included at Knudsen numbers over 0.005.

The authors express their gratitude to I. B. Stechkina and A. A. Kirsh for their assistance in discussing the theoretical aspects of this study.

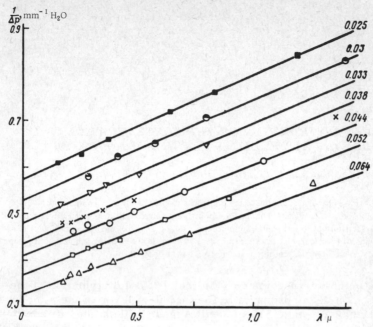

FIGURE 2. Resistance of specimen No.5 vs. length of the mean free path of the gas molecules. Curve numbers indicate compaction densities. Linear airflow velocity, 1 cm/sec.

BIBLIOGRAPHY

1. Glushkov, Yu.M. Soprotivlenie voloknistykh fil'trov v svobodno-molekulyarnom potoke (Resistance of Fibrous Filters in a Free-Molecular Flow).— Izv. AN SSSR, Mekhanika Zhidkosti i Gaza, Vol.4, p.176. 1968.

2. Natanson, G.L. Vliyanie skol'zheniya na effekt kasaniya pri zakhvate amikroskopicheskikh aerozol'nykh chastits tsilindrom iz potoka (Influence of Gliding on the Contact Effect During the Retention of Amicroscopic Aerosol Particles by a Cylinder from the Flow).— Kolloidnyi Zhurnal, Vol.24, p.52. 1962.

3. Petryanov, I.V., V.I.Kozlov, P.I.Basmanov, and B.I.Ogorodnikov. Voloknistye fil'truyushchie materialy FP (Fibrous FP Filtering Materials).— Moskva, "Znanie." 1968.

4. Petryanov, I.V., B.I.Ogorodnikov, and A.S.Suntsov. O nekotorykh svoistvakh voloknistykh fil'trov FP v razrezhennom vozdukhe (Some Properties of FP Fibrous Filters in Rarefied Air).— In sbornik: Radioaktivnye izotopy v atmosfere i ikh ispol'zovanie v meteorologii (Radioactive Isotopes in the Atmosphere and their Utilization in Meteorology). Moskva, Atomizdat. 1965.

5. Fuks, N.A. and I.B.Stechkina. K teorii voloknistykh aerozol'nykh fil'trov (A Contribution to the Theory of Aerosol Filters).— Doklady AN SSSR, Vol.147, p.1144. 1962.

6. Pich, J. Theory of Aerosol Filtration by Fibrous and Membrane Filters.— In: Aerosol Science, p.223, edited by C.N.Davies. New York, Academic Press. 1967.

7. Stern, S.C., H.W.Zeller, and A.J.Schekman. The Aerosol Efficiency and Pressure Drop of a Fibrous Filter at Reduced Pressure.— J. Colloid.Sci., Vol.15, p.546. 1960.

UDC 551.510.71

VERTICAL DISTRIBUTION OF THE CONCENTRATION OF RADON DECAY PRODUCTS IN THE 0–300-m LAYER

L. V. Kirichenko and S. G. Malakhov

Data on the vertical distribution of the concentration of radon decay products in the 0–300-m layer of the atmosphere are provided. The measurements were carried out in August 1961 on the Obninsk altitude tower of the Institute of Experimental Meteorology. During daytime, the concentration of radon decay products remains practically constant throughout the layer. In the evening and at night it drops rapidly with increasing altitude from the ground surface up to a height of 50–75 m.

This brief note reports data on the vertical distribution of the concentration of radon decay products in the 0–300-m layer of the atmosphere. Nine measurements were carried out in August 1961 on the altitude meteorological tower of the Institute of Experimental Meteorology in Obninsk (Kaluga Region). The air was filtered through an FPP-15 filter for 5 min at a time. The α-activity on the filter was measured immediately after each filtration, using a ZnS screen. The counting setup was calibrated with the aid of a Po^{210} preparation. In the concentration calculations, it was assumed that the radon decay products in the air were in radioactive equilibrium.

TABLE 1. Mean distribution of concentration of radon decay products over the vertical, in the atmospheric layer between ground level and 300 m (in 10^{-13} curie/liter)

Time of day	Altitude, m	Concentration	Time of day	Altitude, m	Concentration
2130–2400 hrs	0	1.0	1300–1600 hrs	0	0.33
(one measurement)	25	0.4	(four measurements)	25	0.32
	50	0.14		50	0.23
	75	0.12		100	0.33
	150	0.13		150	0.32
	300	0.13		200	0.32
0900–1100 hrs	0	0.90		250	0.30
(four measurements)	25	0.75		300	0.35
	50	0.70			
	75	0.60			
	150	0.56			
	300	0.60			

Table 1 lists averaged data on the vertical distribution in the evening, during daytime, and in the morning. In the evening (2130–2400 hrs), when the vertical exchange in the ground layer of the atmosphere is more difficult, the concentration of radon decay products drops quite sharply with increasing height. At 300 m altitude, the concentration was almost only one tenth of that at ground level. The main drop occurs over the first 50—75 m above ground level. A gradual drop in concentration with increasing height also occurs in the morning (0900—1100 hrs), but to a much lesser extent. During daytime (1300—1500 hrs), when the vertical turbulent exchange is most intensive, the concentration hardly varies up to 300 m.

TABLE 2. Vertical distribution of the concentration of radon decay products in the atmospheric 0—300-m layer (in 10^{-13} curie/m^3)

Date	Time of day	Altitude, m							Temperature profile
		0	25	50	100	150	200	300	
7 August 1961	1450—1554	0.28	0.30	—	—	0.30	—	0.35	Temperature drop with increasing altitude
9 August 1961	1311—1555	0.3	0.14	0.05	0.15	0.14	0.19	0.20	Inversion in the 40—100-m layer, and temperature drop with increasing altitude above it

Table 2 gives a few examples of individual measurements, along with data on the vertical distribution of temperature. Two daytime measurements are considered. In the first, the concentration remained practically constant with height. This corresponds to the clear continuous drop in air temperature with increasing height, and to the intense vertical exchange. In the second case, there was an elevated temperature inversion in the 40—100-m layer, where the radon concentration was lower than in the layers below and above. This again stresses the important role played by temperature inversion in the vertical distribution of the concentration of radon decay products. The low concentration in the inversion layer was apparently due to the fact that temperature inversion hinders radon penetration from the layers below. The higher concentration above the inversion layer was due to air advection from adjacent areas.

Kirichenko /1/ has shown that, if there is a temperature inversion layer in the troposphere, the radon concentration underneath increases considerably. We were unable to detect this in the 9 August 1961 measurements, because the lower boundary of the inversion layer lay between the measurement levels.

Table 1 shows that, even at 300 m altitude, the daily variation in concentration can be considerable. The very limited measurement statistics make it impossible for us to judge how often such daily variation occurs in the 300-m layer. The maximum concentration of radon decay products at 300 m in the morning is apparently due to a breakdown in the nocturnal temperature inversion near the ground, which drives upward the radon accumulated during the night in the lowest layer of the troposphere. During daytime (1300—1600 hrs), radon is transferred vertically to high altitudes, and its concentration at 300 m therefore becomes lower than in the morning (0900—1100 hrs).

BIBLIOGRAPHY

1. K i r i c h e n k o , L.V. Vertikal'noe raspredelenie produktov raspada radona v svobodnoi atmosfere (Vertical Distribution of Radon Decay Products in the Free Atmosphere).— In sbornik: Voprosy yadernoi meteorologii (Problems of Nuclear Meteorology). Moskva, Gosatomizdat. 1962.

UDC 551.577.7

NATURAL SNOWFLAKE RADIOACTIVITY DUE TO
SHORT-LIVED RADON DECAY PRODUCTS

A. S. Avramenko and K. P. Makhon'ko

The paper discusses snowflake radioactivity due to short-lived products of radon decay. Nuclear photo-plates of the A-2 type were used as indicator. Of the 3,106 snowflakes measured, 1,270 were radioactive. The frequency of the specific radioactivity of snow flakes has two maxima, at $C = 0$ and at $C = 16$ to $32 \cdot 10^3$ a-tracks per gram, and one minimum at $C = 4$ to $8 \cdot 10^3$ a-tracks per gram. The number of nonradio-active snowflakes and the specific snowflake radioactivity decreases with increased snowflake mass. A scheme for the radioactivation of snowflakes in order to examine the patterns obtained is also discussed. The coagulation constant of radioactive aerosols with the cloud elements is assessed from experimental data on the number of nonradioactive snowflakes.

1. METHOD OF MEASUREMENT

The radioactivity of individual snowflakes was determined with the aid of nuclear photoplates of A-2 type, with a 50-μ-thick emulsion layer. A transparent celluloid film served as trapping surface. Warmed up in advance to 60°C, it was placed in the open during snowfall. After the trap-ping of snowflakes, the celluloid film was dusted with potassium perman-ganate, dried, and brought into contact with the nuclear emulsion. The traces of the thawing snowflakes on the celluloid were obtained in the shape of colored round spots. For further precise coincidence between trapping surface and emulsion layer, the latter was perforated along the edges through the celluloid film. After development, these perforations appeared as tiny black dots on the emulsion.

To determine the mass of the falling snowflake from the trace it left on the trapping surface, the latter was calibrated in the laboratory. The data obtained are given in Table 1.

After the plate was exposed, developed, and dried as described in /1/, the initial thickness of the emulsion was restored. For accurate superposition of the snowflake trace on that part of the emulsion layer which was in con-tact with it during exposure, the celluloid film and photoplate were super-posed using the pin marks. The α-tracks on the plate were counted under an MBI-1 microscope, at ×420 magnification.

2. CALCULATION OF OPTIMUM EXPOSURE OF
NUCLEAR PLATES

The measurement of snowflake activity by counting the α-tracks on the autoradiogram is rendered more difficult by the presence in the emulsion of a variable number of background tracks. The background on the emulsion increases in time, while the snowflake radioactivity decreases because of decay. An optimum time of snowflake exposure has therefore to be chosen.

The process of background restoration starts immediately after its removal from the plate. According to /2/, the mean speed a of background formation for Ilford G5 emulsion was 10 α-tracks per cm^2 per day, of which four were due to radioactivity of the emulsion and six to that of glass. The nuclear, type A-2 plates (50-μ thickness) that we used had a background of about 1,000 α-tracks per cm^2 at the end of the fourth month of storage; 75% of the tracks started in the immediate vicinity of the glass support, i.e., they were due to radioactivity of the glass. The corresponding value of a would be ~ 8 α-tracks per cm^2 per day. The agreement of our data with the results in /2/ points to a relatively stable rate of background formation; in our further considerations, quantity a will therefore be regarded as constant in time and equal to $\sim 10^{-4}$ α-tracks/cm$^2 \cdot$ sec.

For measuring the radioactivity of various hydrometeors, they are usually trapped on filter paper, polished steel plates or, as in our case, celluloid film. The trapping surfaces are then dried using different heat sources, and brought into contact with the nuclear emulsion.

Usually, the natural radioactivity of the investigated hydrometeors is practically all due to short-lived Rn decay products /3/, i.e., RaA, RaB, RaC and RaC'. The number of α-particles escaping 1 cm^2 of the sample on the emulsion side is given by

$$n(t) = \frac{1}{2} \int_{\tau_0}^{\tau_0 + t} (\lambda_1 n_1 + \lambda_3 n_3)\, d\tau, \tag{1}$$

where τ_0 is the time elapsed from the moment the sample was taken until it was put into contact with the nuclear emulsion, t is the exposure time, n_1 and n_3 are the numbers of RaA and RaC atoms per 1 cm^2 of hydrometeor trace during time τ measured from the moment the sample was taken, and λ_1 and λ_3 are the decay constants of RaA and RaC. Quantities n_1 and n_3 are given in /3/:

$$n_1 = n_{10}\, e^{-\lambda_1 \tau}, \tag{2}$$

$$n_3 = n_{10} \frac{\lambda_1 \lambda_2}{(\lambda_2 - \lambda_1)(\lambda_3 - \lambda_1)} e^{-\lambda_1 \tau} + \left[n_{10} \frac{\lambda_1 \lambda_2}{(\lambda_1 - \lambda_2)(\lambda_3 - \lambda_2)} + \right.$$

$$\left. + n_{20} \frac{\lambda_2}{\lambda_3 - \lambda_2} \right] e^{-\lambda_2 \tau} + \left[n_{10} \frac{\lambda_1 \lambda_2}{(\lambda_1 - \lambda_3)(\lambda_2 - \lambda_3)} - \right.$$

$$\left. - n_{20} \frac{\lambda_2}{\lambda_3 - \lambda_2} + n_{30} \right] e^{-\lambda_3 \tau}, \tag{3}$$

where n_{10}, n_{20} and n_{30} are the RaA, RaB and RaC concentrations at the moment the sample is taken.

We substitute the values of n_1 and n_3 in equation (1). Integration yields

$$n(t) = \frac{1}{2}\left\{n_{10}\left[1 + \frac{\lambda_3\lambda_2}{(\lambda_2-\lambda_1)(\lambda_3-\lambda_1)}\right][e^{-\lambda_1\tau_0} - e^{-\lambda_1(\tau_0+t)}] + \right.$$

$$+ \left[n_{10}\frac{\lambda_1\lambda_3}{(\lambda_1-\lambda_2)(\lambda_3-\lambda_2)} + n_{20}\frac{\lambda_3}{\lambda_3-\lambda_2}\right][e^{-\lambda_2\tau_0} - e^{-\lambda_2(\tau_0+t)}] +$$

$$+ \left.\left[n_{10}\frac{\lambda_1\lambda_2}{(\lambda_1-\lambda_3)(\lambda_2-\lambda_3)} - n_{20}\frac{\lambda_2}{\lambda_3-\lambda_2} + n_{30}\right][e^{-\lambda_3\tau_0} - e^{-\lambda_3(\tau_0+t)}]\right\}. \quad (4)$$

Further calculations will be made on the assumption that the Rn decay products are at radioactive equilibrium at the moment of sampling, i.e.,

$$\lambda_1 n_{10} = \lambda_2 n_{20} = \lambda_3 n_{30} = A. \quad (5)$$

Equation (4) then assumes the form

$$n(t) = \frac{A}{2}\left\{\frac{1}{\lambda_1}\left[1 + \frac{\lambda_2\lambda_3}{(\lambda_2-\lambda_1)(\lambda_3-\lambda_1)}\right][e^{-\lambda_1\tau_0} - e^{-\lambda_1(\tau_0-t)}] + \right.$$

$$+ \frac{\lambda_1\lambda_3}{\lambda_2(\lambda_1-\lambda_2)(\lambda_3-\lambda_2)}[e^{-\lambda_1\tau_0} - e^{-\lambda_2(\tau_0+t)}] +$$

$$+ \left.\frac{\lambda_1\lambda_2}{\lambda_3(\lambda_1-\lambda_3)(\lambda_2-\lambda_3)}[e^{-\lambda_3\tau_0} - e^{-\lambda_3(\tau_0+t)}]\right\}. \quad (6)$$

Substitution of $\lambda_1 = 3.788\cdot 10^{-3}$ sec^{-1}, $\lambda_2 = 4.31\cdot 10^{-4}$ sec^{-1} and $\lambda_3 = 5.864\cdot 10^{-4}$ sec^{-1} in (6) yields

$$n(t) = \frac{10^3}{2} A\left[\Phi(\tau_0) - \Phi(\tau_0+t)\right], \quad (7)$$

where Φ is the function

$$\Phi(x) = 0.27\, e^{-3.788\cdot 10^{-3}x} + 9.87\, e^{-4.310\cdot 10^{-4}x} - 5.59\, e^{-5.864\cdot 10^{-4}x}. \quad (8)$$

The number of α-tracks produced in the emulsion by the nuclear plate's own radioactivity can be determined from

$$n_\phi(t) = a(t_1 + t), \quad (9)$$

where t_1 is the time elapsed from the moment the background of the nuclear emulsion was photographed until the beginning of exposure.

Based on (7) and (9), the relative share of the background in the overall density of the α-tracks produced in the nuclear emulsion during exposure is

$$\frac{n_\phi(t)}{n_\phi(t) + n(t)} = \left[1 + \frac{10^3}{2}\frac{A}{a}\frac{\Phi(\tau_0) - \Phi(\tau_0+t)}{t_1+t}\right]^{-1}. \quad (10)$$

To use formula (10) one must know the value of A. In view of (5), it can be written as

$$A = C_0 G, \quad (11)$$

TABLE 1. Relation of snowflake mass m to trace diameter d on celluloid surface

d, mm	0.03	0.06	0.1	0.2	0.3	0.4	0.5	0.6	0.7	0.8	0.9	1.0	1.1
m, mg	$2.7 \cdot 10^{-3}$	$3.1 \cdot 10^{-3}$	$3.5 \cdot 10^{-3}$	$5.1 \cdot 10^{-3}$	$8.5 \cdot 10^{-3}$	$1.2 \cdot 10^{-2}$	$1.8 \cdot 10^{-2}$	$2.6 \cdot 10^{-2}$	$4.3 \cdot 10^{-2}$	$6.3 \cdot 10^{-2}$	$9.2 \cdot 10^{-2}$	0.13	0.20
d, mm	1.2	1.3	1.4	1.5	1.6	1.7	1.8	1.9	2.0	2.1	2.2	2.3	2.4
m, mg	0.32	0.47	0.68	1.00	1.19	1.39	1.55	1.72	1.89	2.07	2.27	2.49	2.71
d, mm	2.5	2.6	2.7	2.8	2.9	3.0	3.1	3.2	3.3	3.4	3.5	3.6	3.7
m, mg	2.94	3.18	3.43	3.69	3.95	4.23	4.52	4.81	5.12	5.43	5.76	6.09	6.43

TABLE 2. Values of $n_\phi/(n_\phi + n)$ for celluloid as trapping surface

	minutes								hours														days						
	5	10	15	20	25	30	40	50	1	1.2	1.3	1.5	1.7	3	4	5	6	7	8	9	10	15	20	1	2	3	4	5	6	7
$\tau_0 = 0$, $t_1 = 0$	0.60	0.66	0.69	0.73	0.78	0.81	0.90	0.95	1.0	1.1	1.2	1.3	1.4	2.1	2.8	3.5	4.1	4.8	5.4	6.0	6.7	9.7	12.6	14.7	26	34	41	46	51	57
$\tau_0 = 20$ min, $t_1 = 6$ hrs	20	12	10	8	6	5.5	5	4.5	4.5	4.3	4.2	4.2	4.3	4.9	5.7	6.7	7.5	8.7	9.6	10	11	15	19	24	34	43	50	56	60	65

364

TABLE 3. Values of $n_{\text{ф}}/(n_{\text{ф}}+n)$ for filter paper as trapping surface

	Time, t																													
	minutes								hours																days					
	5	10	15	20	25	30	40	50	1	1.2	1.3	1.5	1.7	3	4	5	6	7	8	9	10	15	20	1	2	3	4	5	6	7
$\tau_0 = 0$, $t_1 = 0$	5.6	6.2	6.4	6.8	7.3	7.5	8.3	8.7	9.2	10.0	10.8	11.4	12.1	18.0	22.4	26.5	30.0	33.5	35.5	39.0	42.0	52.0	59	63	77	83	87	90	91	92
$\tau_0 = 20\,\text{min}$, $t_1 = 2\,\text{hrs}$	72	57	54	45	40	37	33	32	32	31	30	30	31	34	38	42	45	49	51	54	56	66	70	76	84	88	91	92	94	96

where C_0 is the specific water radioactivity of the investigated samples at the moment they are taken, and G is the sensitivity of the trapping support, to be determined as the ratio of droplet mass to area of the spot it leaves /4/. For celluloid, G is $\sim 0.10\,g/cm^2$, and for filter paper $\sim 0.006\,g/cm^2$.

The mean value of C_0 for both rain- and cloud water is $\sim 10^{-11}\,curie/g$ /3/. Substitution of C_0 and G values in (11) yields $A = 2.2\cdot10^{-3}\,\alpha$-tracks per cm^2 per sec for filter paper and $3.7\cdot10^{-2}$ for celluloid film. Table 2 shows the share of background calculated from formula (10) for a trapping surface of celluloid film at $\tau_0 = 0$ and 20 min, and $t_1 = 0$ and 2 hours. For comparison, Table 3 lists similar values for filter paper.

It follows from Table 3 that when filter paper is used for trapping hydro-meteors, the share of background in the density of α-tracks on the plate is already equal to that of the hydrometeor radioactivity after an exposure of about 10 hrs. For celluloid, equality is achieved only after 5 days. There is, however, no point in such extensive exposure when investigating the radioactivity of Rn decay products, because 98% of all the possible α-tracks show up during the first 3 hours of exposure.

In view of all these facts, we chose 1.5 to 4 hrs as the optimum exposure of nuclear plates. The error due to background was 2 to 6%, and τ_0 and t_1 never exceeded 20 min and 2 hrs, respectively.

3. MEASUREMENT RESULTS

We took samples in the winter of 1970—1971 in the Murmansk area. We report here data on the radioactivity of stellate snowflakes only. In all, 3,106 snowflakes were measured. Table 4 gives the frequency of snow-flakes of various masses and their contribution in the overall water content of the investigated snowfalls. Most frequent were snowflakes of 0.01—0.04 mg, and those of 0.1—0.3 mg contributed most water in the snowfalls. Only 1,270 snowflakes were found to be radioactive. The number of α-tracks counted directly on the plate varied between 1 and 25 per second. Table 5 gives data on the number of α-tracks per snowflake for the various masses. Snowflakes with one or two α-tracks are the most frequent (74% of all the radioactive snowflakes). The average number of α-tracks increases from 3 to 15 with increasing snowflake mass.

TABLE 4. Frequency P_N of snowflakes of mass m and their share in the overall water content of snowfalls (P_m)

	\(m\), mg											
	0—0.005	0.005—0.01	0.01—0.02	0.02—0.04	0.04—0.08	0.08—0.16	0.16—0.32	0.32—0.64	0.64—1.28	1.28—2.56	2.56—5.12	> 5.12
P_N, %	0.5	7.3	26.2	26.1	15.5	14.0	6.4	2.2	1.0	0.3	0.2	0.1
P_m, %	0.02	0.6	4.1	8.2	9.7	17.4	15.9	11.2	10.0	5.1	7.7	10.0

TABLE 5. Snowflake distribution by the value of radioactivity in α-tracks

n α-tracks	m, mg												ΣN_r
	0–0.005	0.005–0.01	0.01–0.02	0.02–0.04	0.04–0.08	0.08–0.16	0.16–0.32	0.32–0.64	0.64–1.28	1.28–2.56	2.56–5.12	> 5.12	
1	2	3	4	5	6	7	8	9	10	11	12	13	14
1	−	7	44	65	115	300	60	12	7	−	−	−	610
2	−	3	19	63	99	61	60	17	7	−	−	−	329
3	1	2	11	44	20	15	18	13	5	1	−	−	130
4	−	2	4	21	8	7	9	8	4	1	−	−	64
5	−	1	4	9	3	3	8	5	3	1	−	−	37
6	−	−	2	7	1	2	3	2	3	1	1	2	23
7	−	−	3	5	1	−	2	2	−	2	1	−	16
8	−	1	3	4	1	1	1	−	−	1	−	−	12
9	−	1	1	3	−	−	1	1	1	1	1	−	10
10	−	1	1	2	1	1	1	1	−	−	1	1	10
11	−	−	1	1	2	−	1	1	−	−	−	−	6
12	−	−	−	−	1	1	1	−	−	−	−	−	3
13	−	−	−	1	1	−	1	−	−	−	−	−	3
14	−	−	1	−	−	−	1	−	−	−	1	−	3
15	−	−	1	−	2	−	−	−	−	−	−	−	3
16	−	−	−	−	1	−	−	−	−	−	−	−	1
17	−	−	−	−	−	−	1	−	−	−	−	−	1
18	−	−	1	1	−	−	−	−	−	−	−	−	2
19	−	−	−	−	−	−	1	−	−	−	−	1	2
20	−	−	−	−	−	−	1	−	−	−	1	−	2
21	−	−	−	−	−	1	−	−	−	−	−	−	1
22	−	−	−	−	−	−	−	−	−	−	−	−	−
23	−	−	−	−	−	−	−	−	−	−	−	−	−
24	−	−	−	−	−	−	−	1	−	−	−	−	1
25	−	−	−	−	−	−	−	−	−	−	−	1	1
ΣN_r	1	18	96	226	256	392	170	63	30	8	6	4	1,270
Σn	3	59	285	650	544	573	475	222	94	49	66	60	−
$\Sigma n/\Sigma N_r$	3	3.3	3.0	2.9	2.1	1.5	2.8	3.5	3.1	6.1	11	15	−

N o t e. The numbers of α-tracks were obtained by measurement within an angle of 2π.

Table 6 gives the distribution of snowflakes by specific radioactivity C. To determine the specific radioactivity of the snowflakes, the number of α-tracks counted was multiplied by 2, as the snowflake imprint came into contact with the emulsion on one side only (over an angle of 2π). With increasing C, the frequency P_c first decreases; it starts increasing again when $C \sim 4$ to $8 \cdot 10^3$ α-tracks/g, to reach a clearcut maximum when $C \sim 16$ to $32 \cdot 10^{13}$ α-tracks/g. A similar pattern was found by the authors of /5/, with the maximum at $C \sim 40 \cdot 10^3$ α-tracks/g. The minimum at $C \sim 4$ to $8 \cdot 10^3$ is due to the fact that snowflakes of such activity have mainly a comparatively large mass and their number is small. The presence of a second maximum, as rightly stressed in /5/, indicates that the radio-activation of the snowflakes tends to establish a certain shifting equilibrium between the capture of radioactive atoms and their decay.

367

TABLE 6. Snowflake distribution by specific radioactivity C

C, 10^9 α-tracks/g	0	0—4	4—8	8—16	16—32	32—64	64—128	128—256	256—512	512—1,024	1,024—2,048	2,048—4,096
P_c, %	59.1	1.3	0.4	3.3	12.7	6.9	6.5	5.5	2.8	1.0	0.4	0.1

By measuring the radioactivity of snowflakes over a solid angle of 2π we overestimate the number of nonradioactive snowflakes. We therefore carried out parallel measurements over angles of 2π and 4π, after trapping the snowflakes on a thin filter of thickness $0.5\,\text{mg/cm}^2$, which was then exposed between two emulsion layers. The calculated numbers of non-radioactive snowflakes are given in Table 7, which points to overestimated values by a factor of about 1.2. With this correction, Table 8 gives the proportions of nonradioactive snowflakes of mass m. It can be seen that N/N_0 decreases with increasing snowflake mass. Their relationship is given empirically by

$$-\log\frac{N}{N_0}=7\cdot10^3\,m,\tag{12}$$

where m is given in grams.

We shall try and use this relationship to find some characteristics of radioactivity extraction from the atmosphere by precipitation.

TABLE 7. Number N of nonradioactive snowflakes in measurements over angles of 2 and 4π

Overall number of snowflakes N_0	Over an angle of 2π				Over an angle of 2π		$\dfrac{N_{2\pi}}{N_{4\pi}}$
	side I		side II		N	$\dfrac{N}{N_0}$ %	
	N	$\dfrac{N}{N_0}$ %	N	$\dfrac{N}{N_0}$ %			
320	214	67	218	68	182	57	1.2

In /6/, we demonstrated that the occurrence frequency of nonradioactive cloud elements p_0 is given by

$$p_0=1-\frac{Kn_0}{\lambda},\tag{13}$$

where K is a constant of coagulation of cloud droplets with the radioactive aerosols, n_0 is the concentration of radioactive atoms at cloud level, and λ is the effective decay constant of the short-lived Rn decay products $(\sim 4.7\cdot10^{-4}\ \text{sec}^{-1})$ /6/. According to /7/, hydrometeors grow mainly on account of coagulation with cloud droplets. The mass of one snowflake can therefore be regarded as consisting of m/m_0 cloud droplets of mean mass m_0.

TABLE 8. Relationship between the number N of nonradioactive snowflakes and the specific radioactivity C of snowflakes and their mass m

	m, mg											
	0—0.005	0.005—0.01	0.01—0.02	0.02—0.04	0.04—0.08	0.08—0.16	0.16—0.32	0.32—0.64	0.64—1.28	1.28—2.56	2.56—5.12	> 5.12
N_0	16	227	816	812	483	435	198	70	31	8	6	4
N	15	209	720	586	227	43	28	7	1	0	0	0
N/N_0	80	78	75	61	40	8	12	8	3	0	0	0
n α-tracks	6	118	570	1,300	1,088	1,146	950	444	188	98	132	120
n/N_c α-tracks/ snowflake	0.38	0.52	0.70	1.60	2.26	2.64	4.80	6.34	6.06	12.24	22.00	30.00
C, 10^3 α-tracks/g	83.3	71.9	46.7	53.0	37.5	22.0	20.0	13.2	6.3	6.4	5.7	4.0

According to the compound probability law, the probability that our system of m/m_0 droplets be nonradioactive is

$$\frac{N}{N_0} = \left(1 - \frac{Kn_0}{\lambda}\right)^{\frac{m}{m_0}} \tag{14}$$

or

$$-\log\frac{N}{N_0} = \frac{3Kn_0\log e}{4\pi\rho\lambda\,\bar{r}^3} m , \tag{15}$$

where $\bar{r}$ is the mean cloud droplet radius. By comparing (14) and (15), one can evaluate the coagulation constant of cloud droplets with the radioactive aerosols. Let us therefore calculate n_0. If the RaA atoms concentration in the snowflakes intended for α-radiography is neglected, according to /6/ we shall have

$$n_0 = \frac{2}{3}\frac{q}{\lambda} , \tag{16}$$

where $q \sim 10^{-16}$ curie/cm^3 /3/ is the concentration of short-lived radon decay products in the atmosphere.

For the coagulation constant, substitution of $\lambda = 4.7 \cdot 10^{-4}$ sec^{-1} and $r = 7\mu$ /8/ yields $K = 2.4 \cdot 10^{-6}$ cm^3/sec. This value is similar to those obtained by other methods /9, 10/.

From these data, we derived the relationship between the masses of snow-flakes and their radioactivity. Table 8 gives the relationship between the mean number of α-tracks per snowflake and its mass. It can be described by the empirical formula

$$\frac{n}{N_0} = 7 \cdot 10^2 \, m^{0.61}, \ \alpha \text{ -tracks per snowflake.} \qquad (17)$$

This relationship can reflect in principle two processes leading to radio-activation: snowflake coagulation with radioactive cloud droplets, and coagulation with the radioactive atmospheric aerosols. It permits the conclusion that, if there is also a mechanism of snowflake formation on radioactive crystallization nuclei, it does not appear in this relationship, and thus has secondary importance only. Actually, were it not so, the overall activity of the snowflakes would not depend on their mass.

Table 8 also gives the relationship between the specific radioactivity of the snowflakes and their mass. It can be described by the following empirical formula:

$$C = 7 \cdot 10^2 \, m^{-0.39}, \ \alpha \text{-tracks/g.} \qquad (18)$$

The specific radioactivity of the snowflakes obviously decreases with their increasing size. This can be explained as follows.

Under the effect of vertical ascending currents, the fine water droplets in the cloud are lifted up, and their size increases by condensation of water vapor on them and reciprocal coagulation. In the cloud, this establishes a dynamic distribution of droplets of different sizes over the vertical: fine droplets in the lower part of the cloud, and increasingly larger droplets above. Since the radioactive air masses reach the cloud from below, radio-activation is most intense in the cloud's lower part. During the droplets' rise their specific radioactivity drops as a result of cloud-moisture condensation on them, and the coarse droplets in the upper part of the cloud thus possess lower specific radioactivity than the fine droplets in the lower part of the cloud. The snowflakes grow by capture of cloud droplets: if the snowflakes start falling from higher up, they grow to larger sizes. Thus, the fine snowflakes have grown on account of comparatively fine cloud droplets of the lower part of the cloud and possess higher specific radio-activity than the large snowflakes. This is actually observed in practice.

BIBLIOGRAPHY

1. Styro, B.I. and B.K. Vebrene. O metodike izmereniya radioaktivnosti otdel'nykh chastits osadkov i nekotorye predvaritel'nye rezul'taty takikh issledovanii (Technique of Measuring the Radioactivity of Individual Precipitation Particles and Some Preliminary Results of Such Investigations).— Izv. AN SSSR. Fizika Atmosfery i Okeana, Vol.2, p.10.1966.

2. Freshlin, J.H. and M.C. Walters. Background Tracks in Electron-Sensitive Nuclear Emulsions.— Proc. Phys. Soc., Lond. A, Vol.63, pp.1178—9. 1950.

3. Styro, B.I. Voprosy yadernoi meteorologii (Problems of Nuclear Meteorology).— Vilnius, Izd. AN LitSSR. 1959.

4. Litvinov, I.V. Metodicheskie voprosy izucheniya spektral'nogo raspredeleniya chastits osadkov (Problems of Techniques in the Study of the Spectral Distribution of Precipitation Particles).— Trudy VGI, No.1. 1962.

5. Styro, B.I. and B.K. Vebrene. Radioactivity Distribution in Raindrops.— In: Atmospheric Scavenging of Radioisotopes. Israel Program for Scientific Translation, Jerusalem. 1970

6. Avramenko, A.S. Primenenie stokhasticheskogo podkhoda k voprosu o radioaktivatsii oblachnykh i dozhdevykh kapel' (Application of the Stochastic Approach to the Problem of the Radioactivity of Raindrops and Cloud-Borne Drops).— In this collection.

7. Zamorskii, A.D. Koagulyatsionnyi rost snezhinok (Coagulation Growth of Snowflakes).— Trudy GGO, No.24. 1950.

8. Shishkin, N.S. Oblaka, osadki i grozovoe elektrichestvo (Clouds, Precipitation, and Thunderstorm Electricity).—Leningrad, Gidrometeoizdat. 1964.

9. Styro, B.I., E.Yu. Vebra, and K.K. Shopauskas. Opredelenie nekotorykh parametrov udaleniya estestvennykh radioaktivnykh aerozolei iz vozdukha (Determination of Some Parameters of the Removal of Natural Radioactive Aerosols from the Atmosphere).— Izv. AN SSSR, Fizika Atmosfery i Okeana, Vol.1, p.12. 1965.

10. Makhon'ko, K.P. Elementarnye teoreticheskie predstavleniya o vymyvanii primesi osadkami iz atmosfery (Elementary Theoretical Concepts About Admixture Washout from the Atmosphere by Precipitation).— Trudy IPG, No.8. 1967.

UDC 551.510.71

TRACE ELEMENTS AND NATURAL RADIOACTIVITY IN CLOUD WATER AND ATMOSPHERIC PRECIPITATION IN THE CENTRAL CAUCASUS MOUNTAINS

E. P. Makhon'ko, A. S. Avramenko, and K. P. Makhon'ko

Total concentrations of short-lived radon decay products in precipitation, cloud water and air were measured in summer on the Terskol peak of the Central Caucasus, along with the concentrations of Fe, Pb, Mn, Ni, and Mg. The precipitation samples were taken in polyethylene vessels, the cloud-water samples were taken with the aid of a battery of four parallel cyclones, while the atmospheric aerosol samples were taken by means of a filtering setup with an FPP-15—1.5 filter. The admixture concentrations obtained are similar in the precipitation and the cloud water, as are the corresponding coefficients of admixture concentration (concentration ratios of water to air), i.e., the contamination of precipitation takes place mainly in the cloud. The assessed "lifetimes" of the trace elements in the atmospheric layer subjected to precipitation washout (1.4 days), concentration coefficient ($6 \cdot 10^5$), and rate of "wet precipitation" (1.2 km/day) correspond approximately to the values for natural radioactivity ($2 \cdot 10^5$ and 0.8 km/day), and with literature data for macroelements and nuclear explosion products. This is an indication that the aerosol carriers of these admixtures in the atmosphere have similar properties, mainly similar particle sizes.

Our purpose was to study the contents of trace elements and natural radioactivity in cloud water and precipitation, and to determine some of their washout parameters at high altitudes. The samples were taken in the summers of 1968 and 1969 on the Terskol peak of the Central Caucasus (3,100 m above sea level). The total concentrations of short-lived radon decay products in precipitation, cloud water and air were measured. Also determined were the concentrations of trace elements (iron, lead, manganese, and nickel) and, incidentally, the concentration of magnesium, which was high in the samples.

The atmospheric precipitation samples were taken in a vessel with an overall surface of $7.5\,\text{m}^2$. To avoid sorption of the trace elements, the vessels were lined with acid-treated polyethylene. Cloud water samples were taken with the aid of a battery of four parallel cyclones of the type described in /11/. To avoid sorption of the trapped substances on the cyclone walls, their inner surfaces were covered with a hydrophobic organosilicon liquid. The trace element concentrations in the samples were determined by optical spectral analysis /3, 4/. For this purpose, the cloud water and precipitation samples before analysis were concentrated to a hundredth of their initial volume by evaporation and addition of hydrochloric acid, then applied to the surface of flat carbon electrodes and burnt in an AC arc with a 3.5-amp current for 10 sec. The spectral instrument used was an ISP-28 spectrograph with recording on aerial-photographic plates of 0.85 sensitivity (1300 GOST units) and 1.8—2 contrast. The trace element concentrations were determined by the three-standards method.

The inner standard used was the background of the plate in the vicinity of the lines measured photometrically.

The relative standard error of the method was ±20% at most for a method sensitivity of 10^{-9} to 10^{-10} g per electrode. To determine the admixture-washout parameters one must know the trace-element concentration or the natural radioactivity in the air. Aerosol samples were therefore taken from the same spot where the precipitation was sampled, using a filtering setup with an FPP-15—1.5 filter.

The samples were processed and analyzed according to the method described in /14/. To determine the content of natural radioactivity, the cloud-water samples were evaporated dropwise for 10—15 min on an aluminum target and counted under the end window of an MST-17 counter. The radioactivity of the aerosol samples trapped on the filter was determined without preliminary calcination, with the aid of a cylindrical SBT-10 counter (the filter was wrapped around the counter). In accordance with /6/, to calculate the concentration of natural radioactivity, it was assumed that this radioactivity was due to the short-lived radon decay products at equilibrium, and that their concentrations remained the same as during the sampling. An $Sr^{90} + Y^{90}$ preparation whose beta radiation approached that of Pb^{214} and Bi^{214} was used for calibration.

TABLE 1. Trace-element concentrations in cloud water, μg/liter

Sampling date	Time of day	Iron	Lead	Manganese	Nickel	Magnesium
		1968				
15 July	1702—2032	16	4	66	—	—
22 July	0615—0745	50	8	—	—	—
13 July	1837—2030	12	63	12	—	—
13 July	2034—2145	50	30	—	—	—
31 July	1511—2300	63	6	20	—	—
2 August	1600—2200	22	4	40	—	—
3 August	0013—0230	40	3	56	—	—
6 August	0800—0910	75	5	—	6	—
7 August	1730—1815	29	4	57	—	—
8—9 August	1851—0820	29	3	—	4	—
		1969				
24 July	0015—0245	81	34	35	3	230
28 July	1820—2349	68	41	24	2	110
2 August	1420—1600	60	16	6	4	780
13 August	1820—2300	93	21	38	3	290
9 September	0740—0900	5	2	3	4	590
14 September	1835—2055	70	6	55	—	400
18 September	1900—2253	24	1	31	3	340
Mean value		46	15	34	4	390

Tables 1 and 2 list the concentrations of iron, lead, manganese, nickel, and magnesium in cloud water and precipitation. The concentrations of trace admixtures are similar in precipitation and cloud water. A comparison of the mean concentrations of elements in precipitation, as given in Table 2, with values obtained earlier in different regions of European USSR /13/ and with the mean iron and magnesium concentrations in atmospheric precipitation in Japan, as reported by Sugawara in /12/, showed that the trace elements and magnesium concentrations in precipitation are of the same order of magnitude everywhere, except for iron, whose mean concentration

TABLE 2. Trace-element concentrations in precipitation, µg/liter

Sampling date	Time of day, hr	h, mm	Precipitation	Iron	Lead	Manganese	Nickel	Magnesium
1	2	3	4	5	6	7	8	9
			1968					
6 July	—	2.1	Dew	—	70	6.0	430	—
10—11 July	1730—1030	1.1	Snow	99	40	6.0	20	—
17 July	1658—1705	3.4	Snow	350	60	23	90	—
30 July	1717—2055	0.5	Rain, hail, drizzle	63	5.0	8.0	7.0	—
31 July	1621—2300	4.8	Rain	25	3.0	6.0	3.0	—
1—2 August	0800—1615	0.7	Snow	50	3.0	12	9.0	—
2—3 August	2034—2000	3.1	Soft hail	43	3.0	5.0	6.0	—
6 August	1200—1435	2.0	Hail	20	4.0	14	7.0	—
7—8 August	1900—0600	5.0	Snow	24	3.0	5.0	5.0	—
11 August	1209—1603	1.3	Soft hail, rain	20	3.0	20	9.0	—
			1969					
1 July		3.7	Rain	71	36	30	2.0	240
4 July	1110—1900	1.9	Dew	39	18	17	2.4	200
14 July	0730—1440	4.2	Rain	46	14	17	3.0	220
21 July	1949—2030	3.1	"	110	20	23	2.5	250
22 July	1310—1800	3.4	"	42	22	27	2.0	120
23 July	0207—0900	1.9	Dew	62	36	46	—	310
27 July	0034—0430	0.8	"	86	66	28	5.0	270
29 July	1430—1730	1.1	"	130	47	34	2.5	160
30 July	1800—2400	6.1	Rain	91	41	37	2.0	200
1 August	1240—1600	7.1	"	64	27	21	2.8	410
7 August	1425—1900	8.2	Fine hail, drizzle	26	36	30	2.0	280
14 August	1200—2100	6.7	Drizzle, fine snow	34	4.0	35	4.0	630
21 August	2241—2302	2.1	Rain	150	4.0	22	4.0	760
22 August	0715—1400	4.1	"	160	24	29	3.0	480
3 Sept.	1615—2015	2.2	Hail, cloudburst	78	38	44	3.0	280
6 Sept.	1230—1310	1.8	Hail, rain	42	36	5.0	1.0	330
6 Sept.	2055—2103	—	Hail, 4 mm in diameter	110	8.0	13	1.0	170
6—7 Sept.	2105—0805	3.1	Hail, drizzle, snow	130	15	11	1.0	90
8—9 Sept.	1900—0900	1.2	Dew	17	13.0	5.0	2.8	280
22 Sept.	—	0.6	Snow	24	7.2	2.0	1.0	160
Terskol peak average				65	19	20	4.0	300
European USSR average /13/				38	6.0	11	4.0	—
Japan average /12/				230	—	—	—	360

Note. Being abnormally high, the data for 6 and 17 July 1968 were excluded from the calculation of the mean values.

in precipitation in Japan is approximately ten times greater. In the precipitation sampled on the Terskol peak, the manganese and iron concentrations were twice as high, and that of lead three times as high as the European USSR average; the nickel concentrations coincided.

Peculiarities in the trace-element concentrations in the Terskol peak precipitation are apparently due to local conditions. The slopes of the Elbrus, of which the Terskol peak is a spur, comprise dacitic and andesitic lavas, and discharges of volcanic gases are observed in some places in the firn snowfields and at the eastern summit of the Elbrus; there is no source of industrial pollution of the atmosphere in the whole area. On the other hand, the role of industrial sources in atmospheric pollution around the sampling points in Japan is obviously very high, which explains the high iron concentration in Japan precipitation.

It can be assumed that industrial pollution in Terskol peak precipitation is only possible if winds carry dust over long distances. However, no strong winds blew in that area during the period of investigation; the main source of dust was therefore the underlying surface of the geographic region /7/. If the clouds also form within the area under such conditions, the precipitation must to a certain extent correspond to the composition of the dust raised by the wind from the earth's surface.

TABLE 3. Concentration of elements (in µg/liter) in various types of atmospheric precipitation and in cloud water

Sample type	Year	Iron	n	Lead	n	Manganese	n	Nickel	n	Magnesium	n
Cloud	1968,	40(10—80)	9	13(3—63)	10	42(12—66)	6	5(4—6)	2	—	—
water	1969	57(5—93)	7	17(1—41)	7	27(3—55)	7	3(2—4)	6	390(110—780)	7
Dew	1968	—	—	70	1	—	—	—	—	—	—
	1969	67(17—130)	5	36(13—66)	5	26(5—46)	5	3(2—5)	4	244(160—310)	5
Rain	1969	92(42—160)	8	24(4—41)	8	26(21—37)	8	3(2—4)	8	335(120—760)	8
Rain	1968	40(20—60)	2	5(4—5)	2	11(8—14)	2	7(7—7)	2	—	—
with	17 July	350	1	60	1	23	1	90	1	—	—
hail	1968										
	1969	64(26—105)	5	19(4—38)	5	21(5—44)	5	2(1—3)	5	260(170—330)	5
Snow	1968	60(20—100)	2	22(3—40)	2	13(6—20)	2	15(9—20)	2	—	—
with	1969	82(34—130)	2	10(4—15)	2	23(11—35)	2	3(1—4)	2	345(90—630)	2
rain											
Snow	1968	40(20—50)	3	3(3—3)	3	7(5—12)	3	7(5—9)	3	—	—
	1969	24	1	7	1	2	1	1	1	160	1

Note. 1. Maxima and minima are given in parentheses.
2. n is the number of cases.

Table 3 lists data on the relationship between the type of precipitation and its trace-element concentration. It has already been noted that these concentrations are about the same in cloud water and in precipitation. A similar result was earlier obtained for macroelements /2/. The concentrations are highest in dew, cloud water, and rain, and always lowest in snow fallen on the Terskol peak. According to data in /2/, winter precipitation

375

in European USSR is often more highly mineralized than summer precipitation, i.e., the admixture concentration in the snow was higher, on the average, than in rain. The difference is evidently due to geographic features and local conditions. Near-ground temperature inversions are frequent in winter, and the vertical exchange of air masses is then more difficult. In the absence of strong winds, the main source of trace elements in the mountains is the snow-free valleys. When the air does not rise from the valleys, the snow falling on the mountain top must contain less admixtures. On the other hand, in the flatland, inversions facilitate the accumulation of polluting admixtures in the ground layer of the atmosphere and often leads to additional snow pollution.

We tried to evaluate the removal of admixtures from the atmosphere by precipitation, using different parameters characterizing the intensity of this process. An investigation of the relationship between lead and manganese concentrations in precipitation and the duration of the latter showed that, within the limits of error, the experimental values obey an exponential law of decrease, with a relaxation time of $\tau = 1.4$ days. In fact, τ is the "lifetime" of the trace elements in the atmospheric layer subjected to washout by precipitation. It roughly coincides with the value we found earlier for macroadmixtures in the atmosphere over points far away from industrial centers /9/, as well as for natural radioactivity /5/ and nuclear explosion products /8/. The removal of the admixtures from the atmosphere by precipitation is suitably described by ratio C/q, where C is the concentration of trace elements or natural radioactivity in the precipitation, and q is their concentration in the air. Physically speaking, this magnitude characterizes the washout capacity of the precipitation and provides the coefficients of admixture concentration by precipitation /1, 10/. In addition, the removal of the trace elements and natural radioactivity characterizes the rate of extraction of the admixtures by precipitation or the rate of "wet precipitation" $w = Ch/q$ /10/, where h is the daily amount of precipitation.

Table 4 gives averaged values of the concentration coefficient and wet-precipitation rate for July—August 1968 and September 1969. They hardly differ from each other for the various trace elements. The mean value of the concentration coefficient for all the trace elements is $C/q = 6 \cdot 10^5$, and that of the wet-precipitation rate is $w = 1.2$ km/day.

TABLE 4. Concentration coefficient C/q and wet-precipitation rate w of trace elements from measurements on the Terskol peak

Quantity measured	Period of measurement	Lead	Manganese	Iron	Nickel
C, µg/liter	July—August 1968	8.0	9.5	~40	~2
	September 1969	14.1	13.3	83.5	2.3
$q \; 10^{-2}$, µg/m³	July—August 1968	1.3	1.8	7.5	0.53
	September 1969	2.8	1.7	9.9	0.56
C/q, 10^5	July—August 1968	6.2	5.3	~5	~4
	September 1969	5.1	7.7	8.4	4.2
w, km/day	July—August 1968	1.5	1.3	~1	~1
	September 1969	0.9	1.4	1.5	0.7

Table 5 gives the concentrations of natural radioactivity in air and rains, and concentration coefficients and wet-precipitation rates calculated on the basis of these data. The mean value of the concentration coefficient of short-lived radon decay products is $2 \cdot 10^5$, and the wet-precipitation rate is $0.8 \, \text{km/day}$. The figures obtained are similar to those given above for trace elements and identical to the washout parameters for products of nuclear explosions $(C/q = 2 \cdot 10^5, \quad w = 1.0 \, \text{km/day})$ obtained in /10/.

TABLE 5. Rain washout parameters of short-lived radon decay products

Date of sampling	h, mm	q, 10^{-11}, curie/cm^3	C, 10^{-10} curie/m^3	C/q, 10^5	w, km/day
		1968			
27 July	2.0	8.8	2.7	0.3	0.1
30 July	0.5	1.2	4.0	3.3	0.2
31 July	4.3	3.2	3.6	1.1	0.5
11 August	1.3	2.1	6.7	3.2	0.4
		1969			
14 July	4.2	3.0	5.0	1.7	0.7
21 July	3.1	1.0	4.1	4.1	1.3
22 July	3.4	2.6	4.9	1.9	0.6
30 July	6.1	0.9	3.9	4.3	2.6
1 August	7.1	2.4	4.3	1.8	1.3
21 August	2.1	0.7	3.4	4.9	1.0
22 August	4.1	2.1	2.6	1.2	0.5
16 September	1.7	3.4	0.9	0.3	0.5
Mean value		2.4	3.8	2.3	0.8

TABLE 6. Natural-radioactivity concentration in cloud water

Date of sampling	C^v, 10^{-11} curie/cm^3	q, 10^{-10} curie/m^3	C^v/q, 10^5
	1968		
14 July	5.7	1.3	4.4
22 July	8.5	2.7	1.9
27 July	9.1	8.8	1.0
31 July	8.3	3.2	2.6
	1969		
1 August	3.4	2.4	1.4
14 August	7.6	0.5	15
16 August	12.3	3.4	3.6
Mean value	7.8	3.2	4.3

Thus, we did not find great differences between the rates of removal of trace elements and radioactive admixtures from the atmosphere, which indicates that the properties of the aerosol carriers of these admixtures are identical (mainly, the size of the aerosol particles).

The measured concentrations of short-lived radon decay products $(C°)$ are given in Table 6. A comparison of these data with the natural-radioactivity concentrations of rain water (Table 5) shows very small differences. The clouds that covered the Terskol peak usually gave no precipitation; we therefore could not simultaneously measure the radioactivity of cloud water and precipitation from the same cloud. Nevertheless, based on the data obtained, it can be concluded that the natural radioactivities of cloud water and precipitation are of the same order of magnitude, i. e., the radioactivation of precipitation water takes place to a great extent in the cloud. This is confirmed by the coefficient of radioactivity concentration by the cloud water, given in Table 6. This value is similar to the coefficient of radioactivity concentration by precipitation in general.

The authors wish to thank the administration of the High-Altitude Geophysical Institute for allowing us to conduct our work at its base.

BIBLIOGRAPHY

1. Gedeonov,L.I., Z.G.Gritchenko,F.M.Flegontov, and M.I.Zhilkina. Coefficient of Radioactive-Aerosol Concentration in Atmospheric Precipitation.—In: Atmospheric Scavenging of Radioisotopes. Israel Program for Scientific Translations, Jerusalem. 1970.

2. Drozdova,V.M. et al. Khimicheskii sostav atmosfernykh osadkov na Evropeiskoi territorii SSSR (Chemical Composition of Atmospheric Precipitation over European USSR).—Leningrad, Gidro-meteoizdat. 1964.

3. Zhigalovskaya,T.N., V.V.Egorov,E.P.Makhon'ko,R.I.Pervunina, and A.I.Shilina. Spektral'nyi metod opredeleniya mikroelementov v rechnoi vode (Spectral Method of Determining Trace Elements in River Water).—Trudy IEM, No. 2. 1970.

4. Zhigalovskaya, T.N., R.I.Pervunina, V.V.Egorov, E.P.Makhon'ko, and A.I.Shilina. Metodika obogashcheniya prob i opredelenie mikroelementov v atmosfernykh osadkakh (Method for Enriching the Samples and Determining Trace Elements in Atmospheric Precipitation).— In: Tezisy dokladov k mezhdunarodnomu simpoziumu po meteorologicheskim aspektam zagryazneniya atmosfery (Reports of Proc. Int. Symposium on Meteorological Aspects of Atmospheric Pollution). Leningrad, 23—31 July 1968.

5. Karol',L.I. Otsenka srednei skorosti udaleniya estestvennykh radioaktivnykh aerozolei iz atmosfery oblakami i osadkami (Evaluation of Mean Rate of Removal of Natural Radioactive Aerosols from the Atmosphere by Clouds and Precipitation).—Izv. AN SSSR, Seriya Geofizicheskaya, No. 11. 1963.

6. Malakhov,S.G. and P.G.Chernysheva. O sezonnykh izmeneniyakh kontsentratsii radona i torona v prizemnom sloe atmosfery (Seasonal Variations of Radon and Thoron Concentrations in the Ground Layer of the Atmosphere).—In sbornik: Radioaktivnye izotopy v atmosfere i ikh ispol'zovanie v meteorologii (Radioactive Isotopes in the Atmosphere and their Utilization in Meteorology). Moskva, Atomizdat. 1965.

7. Makhon'ko,K.P. Izuchenie perenosa atmosfernoi pyli (Study of Atmospheric Dust Migration).— Izv. AN SSSR, Seriya Geofizicheskaya, No. 11. 1960.

8. Makhon'ko,K.P. Tropospheric Scavenging Rate of Fission Products, and an Estimate of the Vertical Turbulent Diffusion Coefficient for the Upper Atmosphere.—Atmospheric Scavenging of Radioisotopes. Israel Program for Scientific Translations, Jerusalem. 1970.

9. Makhon'ko, K.P., A.S.Avramenko, and E.P.Makhon'ko. Washout of Radioactive Isotopes and Chemical Compounds from the Atmosphere.—Ibid.

10. Makhon'ko,K.P. and G.V.Dmitrieva. Sposobnost' razlichnykh tipov osadkov k vymyvaniyu produktov deleniya iz atmosfery i kharakteristiki vymyvaniya (Capacity of Different Precipitation Types to Wash Out Fission Products from the Atmosphere, and Washout Characteristics).—Izv. AN SSSR, Fizika Atmosfery i Okeana, Vol. 2, p. 3. 1966.

11. Pudovkina,I.B. Metod zabora prob vody tsiklonnym osaditelem (Water Sampling Method with a Cyclone Precipitator).—In sbornik: Radioaktivnye izotopy v atmosfere i ikh ispol'zovanie v meteorologii (Radioactive Isotopes in the Atmosphere and their Utilization in Meteorology). Moskva, Atomizdat. 1965.

12. Sugawara,K. Migratsiya elementov v gidrosfere i atmosfere (Migration of Elements in Hydrosphere and Atmosphere). In sbornik: Khimiya zemnoi kory (Chemistry of the Earth's Crust), Vol. 2. 1964.

13. Drozdova,V.M. and E.P.Makhon'ko.Content of Trace Elements in Precipitation.—J. Geophys. Res. Oceans and Atm., Vol. 75. 1970.

14. Egorov,V.V., T.N.Zhigalovskaya,and S.G.Malakhov. Microelement Content of Surface Air Above the Continent and the Ocean.—J. Geophys. Res. Oceans and Atm., Vol. 75, 1970.

EXPLANATORY LIST OF RUSSIAN ABBREVIATIONS APPEARING IN THIS BOOK

Abbreviation	Full name (transliterated)	Translation
AN SSSR	Akademiya Nauk SSSR	Academy of Sciences of the USSR
DAN SSSR	Doklady Akademii Nauk SSSR	Reports of the Academy of Sciences of the USSR
GGO	Glavnaya Geofizicheskaya Observatoriya im. A. I. Voeikova	Voeikov Main Geophysical Observatory
IEM	Institut Elektromekhaniki	Institute of Electromechanics
IPG	Institut Prikladnoi Geofiziki	Institute of Applied Geophysics
LGMI	Leningradskii Gidrometeorologicheskii Institut	Leningrad Hydrometeorological Institute
MGI	Morskoi Gidrofizicheskii Institut	Marine Hydrophysical Institute
MGU	Moskovskii Gosudarstvennyi Universitet	Moscow State University
NIIAK	Nauchno-Issledovatel'skii Institut Aeroklimatologii	Scientific Research Institute of Aeroclimatology
PMTF	Prikladnaya Mekhanika i Tekhnicheskaya Fizika	Applied Mechanics and Technical Physics
PTE	Pravila Tekhnicheskoi Ekspluatatsii	Technical Operation Instructions
SNIIP	Soyuznyi Nauchno-Issledovatel'skii Institut Priborostroeniya	All-Union Scientific Research Institute of Instrument Making
TsAO	Tsentral'naya Aerologicheskaya Observatoriya	Central Aerological Observatory
UFAN	Ural'skii Filial Akademii Nauk	Ural Branch of the Academy of Sciences
VGI	Vysokogornyi Geofizicheskii Institut	High Altitude Geophysics Institute
VNIIFTRI	Vsesoyuznyi Nauchno-Issledovatel'skii Institut Fiziko-Tekhnicheskikh i Radiotekhnicheskikh Izmerenii	All-Union Scientific Research Institute of Physicotechnical and Radiotechnical Measurements
VNIIG	Vsesoyuznyi Nauchno-Issledovatel'skii Institut Gidrotekhniki	All-Union Scientific Research Institute of Hydro-Engineering
VUZ	Vysshee Uchebnoe Zavedenie	Institution of Higher Learning